major, sed Cervo volante Faemina nonnihil minor. caput illi adest fere
corneum, antennulis duabus non invenustum, oculi pectusq; hirsutum ex
albo flavescunt primulùm, pedes authrancines habet. venter caudaq; plumas refe-
runt gruinas. Scapulae atq; Elytra albes nigrisq; maculis tam pulchre varie-
gantur: lacerto alligatum vt vestem Damascenam esse Phrygia manu
intertextam facile jurares. Hoc Insectum utriq; lacerto alligatum, Magi
contra Quartanas singulare esse dicunt remedium, nisi non Plinio credendum.
lib. 30. cap. 11. Iconem primùm à Carolo Clusio habuit Pennius: bestiolam
verò ipsam Quicquelbergius posteà transmisit.

De Scarabeis minorib̄
Caput 22.

Scarabei omnes minores vel maculati sunt corpore vel immaculati, illos ἀλλόχροὀς
hos verò μονόχροὀς Graeci appellant. Maculae aliorum ex nigro albicant;
alij flavescunt, alij rubescunt. Albicantium è nigro septem, Flavescentia
tredecim, Rubescentium duodecim, quos hic sua quemq; classe do-
navimus.

　Immaculatorum color corporis idem deprehenditur: atq; inter eos
sex nigricantes, duos Spadiceos, globosum unum ex caerulo nigrum, alterū
ex luteo vidimus. Quidam quoq; nuperrimè à nobis deprehensus est
fuco Puniceo: alter muricis succo inebriatus comparuit. Aurescentes
quinq; habemus; parvulos illos quidem, sed clarè micanteq; auro un-
diq; suffusos. quos etiam ne invidisse nepotibus videamur, sculpi
appingiq; curavimus. Quis verò singulorum usus sit, ubi generali-
ter de Scarabeis diximus, explicatum est.

De Proscarabeo &.
Scarabeo aquatico Cap. 23.

Man and Insects

L. H. NEWMAN

Man and Insects

Insect Allies and Enemies

Nature and Science Library

published for

The American Museum of Natural History

by The Natural History Press / Garden City, New York

68-1308

The Natural History Press, publisher for the
American Museum of Natural History, is a division
of Doubleday & Company, Inc. The Press is
directed by an editorial board made up of
members of the staff of both the Museum and
Doubleday. The Natural History Press has its
editorial offices at The American Museum of
Natural History, Central Park West at 79th Street,
New York 24, New York, and its business offices
at 501 Franklin Avenue, Garden City, New York.

First published in the United States of America in 1966 by
The Natural History Press, Garden City, New York
in association with Aldus Books Limited

Library of Congress Catalog Card No. 65-17947
© Aldus Books Limited, London, 1965

Printed in Italy by Arnoldo Mondadori, Verona

Contents

Introduction

OF ALL the creatures of the animal kingdom, insects are the most numerous. Not only are there more different kinds of insects than of all the other species of animals put together, but their total numbers far exceed those of any other animal that lives on land. True, there are insects that live in and on fresh water for at least part of their lives, but the vast majority of insects are land dwellers.

Indeed, apart from the oceans and the polar regions insects are everywhere. Insects live in swamps, jungles, and deserts. They live in temperate zones, in severe mountain climates, and in the artificial climates of our homes. It is rare for even the cleanest home to be entirely free of insects, though they may never be noticed, because they spend most of their lives out of sight, quietly devouring the furniture, or hiding by day in cracks and crannies, emerging only after the lights are out to see what they can pick up in the kitchen.

Long before man, or for that matter the most primitive mammals, began to roam the earth, insects were well established. They adapted themselves in a fantastic variety of ways to the problems of gaining a livelihood and of perpetuating themselves. Many species were so successful in this that they have remained unchanged for millions of years. They found a satisfactory way of life and stuck to it.

Insects are both a blessing and a curse. They are a blessing because they fertilize our flowers and fruits, many of which depend on insects to carry pollen from one blossom to another. Another useful service that they perform, without which life on earth would be almost impossible, is that they act as scavengers, eating, and sometimes even burying, dead animals. It is no exaggeration to say that without insects the earth would be littered with decaying corpses of animals and birds.

Each of the numerous species of insects has its own precise pattern of development. The examples from left to right are: A dragonfly emerging from its nymph case; two larvae of the swallowtail butterfly; winged and ordinary forms of small black garden ants.

The bigger the crop, the more danger there is of insects spreading rapidly. The 19th-century farm (top) would run less risk of infestation than a huge wheatfield (bottom) of the present day.

Foods are attacked at different stages of production by specific insects. The harvest stored in the granary (above) must be kept free of granary beetles. Below: A bacon beetle and its food source.

On the other hand insects are a curse because they eat the crops that man grows for himself and for his domestic animals. No sooner than one species of insect has done mankind a good turn by fertilizing a crop, another species may happen along to devour it. Furthermore, some of the most deadly diseases known to man are carried by insects, and for that reason, too, we must regard them as a curse and do what we can to suppress them.

But if we take a broad view about insects we will find that, like people, some are good, some bad, and some harmless. Harmless to us, that is. But the things that they do to each other are almost incredible in their ingenuity and ferocity, and as we shall see, we can often make use of their savagery to our own advantage by "setting a thief to catch a thief."

As we have said, insects flourished long before man existed, and some scientists believe that if man were so foolish as to destroy the human race (together with all the mammals) by hydrogen bombs, insects would still survive, and might even become the rulers of the animal kingdom. But in the meantime, and assuming no worldwide disaster, we have to accept the fact that insects are here to stay in such numbers that we have no choice but to come to terms with them. There is no reason why we should not control those insects that are harmful to man and to his crops and animals. Life on earth is a battle for survival, and insects are man's chief competitors. But the interplay of plants, insects, and man is so complex and delicately balanced that we can easily make bad mistakes, and in so doing make matters much worse than they were to begin with. The late Rachel Carson's book, *Silent Spring*, tells in horrifying detail of the consequences of an all-out attack on insect pests, and the chain of consequences that has resulted from drastic action taken without sufficient knowledge.

The world's human population is increasing at an alarming rate; this underlines the threat of insects as competitors. Every acre of farm land and forest must yield its maximum crop if millions are not to go hungry. It is more urgent than ever before that we should understand how insects live, how they breed, what are their good and bad points, and how we can play one insect off against another to our own advantage.

The science of insects is called *entomology*. Many people think that entomologists are slightly eccentric "bug hunters" armed with butterfly nets and little collecting boxes. Perhaps there was something to be said for this point of view a century ago, when the main effort of entomologists was catching and classifying as many insects as possible. The sheer number of different species is so great, running into hundreds of thousands as we now know, that the first essential was to catch, describe, and name as many insects as possible. Then and not till then was it possible for scientists to study and work out the ways of living, eating, and reproduction of insects in terms that could be understood by others. We owe a great debt to the early "bug hunters." Without their labors this book could never have been written.

This is a book about insects that are important to man, either as enemies or as friends. It tells of the effect that insects have on man's life and work; it also tells what man has done and is doing to protect himself and his property from insects, and what can be done to make intelligent use of the insect world for his own advantage.

The book starts with a brief description of what insects are, how they live, feed, and breed. This first section is admittedly pure science; not only does it sketch the fascinating variety of insect life, but it also sets the scene for the more practical sections that follow. A brief Who's Who of insects shows the principal orders, and the way in which they are classified, in an Appendix at the end of the book.

Above: Frontispiece of Insectorium . . . theatrum (1634) by Thomas Moffett. This was one of the most important early illustrated entomological treatises. Below: A selection of the equipment 19th-century entomologists used for catching, storing, and displaying insects.

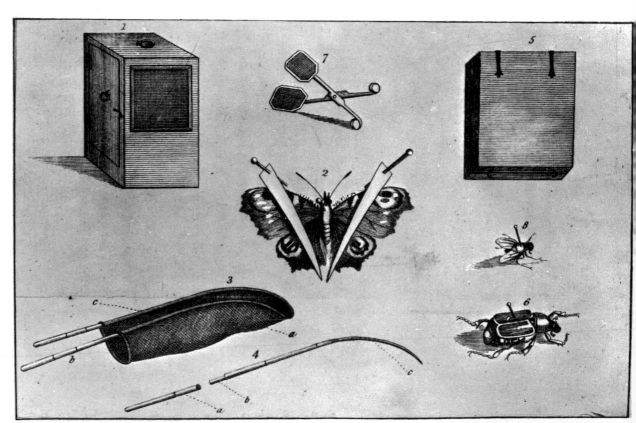

The author demonstrates the proper
way to net a butterfly. He holds the net
sideways and sweeps the insect into it.

Scientists and Insects

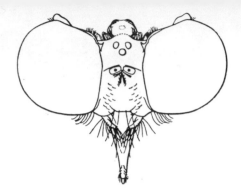

THE entomologist deals with an unusually wide and varied subject. No matter how brilliant he may be, an entomologist has to specialize in some branch of entomology if his studies are to be more than superficial. He must decide early in his career to concentrate on the particular group of insects or aspect of entomology that interests him most. He may work in any one of several branches: on *anatomy* and *classification* (the study of body structure and the grouping of related individuals); on *physiology* (the study of the parts of the body and their functions); on *ecology* (the study of insects in relation to their surroundings); or on insect behavior.

New species of insects are being discovered at the rate of almost ten thousand a year, and it is a huge task merely to describe and classify them.

Much of the anatomy and classification of insects can be studied with dead and preserved specimens. Still there are many problems that can be investigated only by using living insects. Often this work cannot be done in the laboratory but must be done out in the field. An entomologist interested in these problems must therefore know both how to raise insects in captivity and how to find and observe them in the field.

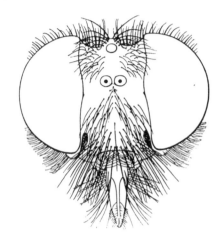

Many people may feel that such detailed study of all kinds of obscure insects is a waste of time. What difference can it make to anybody whether we know that a certain mosquito has some body part one millimeter longer than the same part on another, or that one fly has more hairs on its legs than do flies that live a few miles away? Until a century or so ago even scientists did not always realize the importance of knowing and classifying such small differences. But now that applied entomology has become a practical necessity, it is quite clear that even small differences may help entomologists to distinguish between insects that look almost alike but behave in very different ways. Entomologists can no longer afford to overlook any detail, however insignificant it may seem. Only by exploring and knowing every part of the maze that is the insect world can entomologists be sure of finding the right way to deal with insects.

Today, entomological research is carried on continuously all over the world. Articles and reports of research in many languages are constantly published by scientific societies in countries the world over. To help entomologists keep informed of all the new discoveries, the Entomological Society of America began in 1956 the *Annual Review of Entomology.* Every article in this

Above: Enlarged drawings of the heads of three species of robber flies. Minute structural differences help entomologists to distinguish among closely related insects.

Above right: The author's father and mother inspecting a "sleeve" containing feeding larvae. Below right: The famous French entomologist, Eugene Le Moult.

professional magazine, which runs to more than five hundred pages, gives entomologists a summary of the most recent findings on research of special current interest. Those scientists who want to delve deeper have only to consult the list of books and reports at the end of each article to learn where they can obtain more detailed information. There are international entomological conferences, where scientists from many nations meet to discuss their research. By all such means a constant exchange of information takes place.

This exchange is of great importance to entomologists and saves them a great deal of time. When research workers have some idea of what others are doing and what results have been obtained they can often advance much more rapidly in their own special program. One of the criticisms of some of the great entomologists of the past is that they ignored the work of others and preferred to "plow a lone furrow" rather than to share their experiences with fellow entomologists. When there is a constant exchange of information, as there is today, one worker can pick up where another ends. He does not have to waste time repeating earlier experiments.

Insect physiology is one branch of entomology that more and more scientists are studying with special interest at the present time. Physiology deals with the processes of life and considers problems such as the chemical changes that take place in living bodies and the nature of the electrical impulses that travel along the nerves. These studies have far-reaching applications, because all living things have certain fundamental characteristics in common. Hormones, for example, are chemical substances secreted directly into the blood that trigger off various activities elsewhere in the body. Investigation of hormones in insects is very important. Research in this field may lead to findings that can be applied to higher animals and even to man himself.

Insect poisons, except for that of the honeybee, have never been thoroughly studied in the past. Now a number of entomologists, particularly in the United States, are carrying on research to learn more about these substances. Many physiologists are carrying out special studies of the way in which insects breathe. Others are doing research on reaction of insect nerves to various stimuli. One of the problems currently being studied in Belgium is the production of chemicals called enzymes in the bodies of insects and the effect of such chemicals on development. In Sweden entomologists are conducting extensive tests on the reactions of the eyes of moths to light and darkness. This may be related to problems of human sight—which is why the United

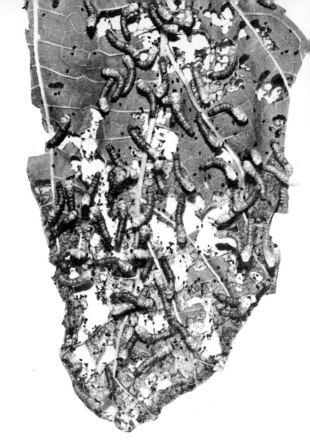

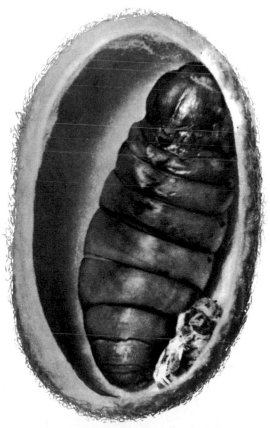

The Entomological Society of London was founded in 1806. Left: Their first journal (1807) and some modern publications from entomological societies of many countries. The miniature is of the 18th-century Swedish naturalist, Karl von Linné—known as Linnaeus, a pioneer in classifying insects and assigning scientific names.

Silk is one of the main industries that make use of applied entomology. Top: Silkworms feeding on mulberry leaves. Above: A silkworm cocoon opened to show the pupa inside.

States Air Force is interested in this project and has helped to finance it.

The study of how best to control insects that spread disease or are agricultural pests is a special branch of entomology of great importance. Scientists working in laboratories and in the field gather the information that manufacturers must have before they can produce efficient insecticides and deterrents. Insects' methods of navigation, their dispersal and migration, their general behavior under natural conditions, the factors that influence their increase and decrease—all are closely linked with methods of crop protection. Entomologists throughout the world are investigating questions of this kind.

Insect nutrition is also being studied. Scientists working in laboratories in the United States have found it possible to raise healthy caterpillars on artificial food substances that can be sterilized and stored. This means that the scientists who need living insects for their research do not have to rely on the seasonal growth of leaves but can raise insects throughout the year. Ways have also been discovered to speed up the breeding of insects. Insects that produce only a single generation a year in the wild now can be made to produce many generations annually. The *diapause,* or resting stage, of insects can now be broken or shortened by various

Spraying cacao trees with a "swing fog" gun at the West African Cacao Research Institute in Ghana. Aldrin, dieldrin, and endrin are some insecticides tested at the Institute.

means so that the whole process of development is speeded up. This is a tremendous help in research programs that might otherwise take many years to complete.

The study of the diseases of insects has wide application, because sometimes there are connections between the diseases of insects and diseases of plants and animals. The ability to infect harmful insects with fatal diseases is of great assistance in the control of pests, particularly in forestry.

A great deal of recent virus research has been done with the aid of insects. Successful experiments have also been made in the treatment of certain human illnesses, such as cancer of the blood, with substances much like those found in the wings of cabbage white butterflies. The basic research on these substances was done by Sir Gowland Hopkins and Professor V. B. Wigglesworth at Cambridge University, England.

The ways insects rid themselves of poisons or react to radiation are other matters that have interested entomologists. Entomological study in these fields so closely linked with biochemistry and physics is, of course, on a very complex level.

Insects have long been used as experimental animals in the study of genetics. They are ideal animals for general studies on inherited characteristics because many species produce generation after generation in a short period of time. And millions of insects, fruit flies especially, are raised for this purpose every year.

Morphology, or the study of different forms, is another branch of entomology. Special attention has been given in England, for example, to the study of what is known as *industrial melanism.* This is a comparatively new phenomenon in which predominately light-colored insect species gradually change to much darker forms in areas affected by industrial smoke.

The senses of insects differ in many respects from those of other animals and offer a wide field for study. Many very interesting experiments have been carried out on insects' sense of smell, hearing, sight and color vision, and their sense of touch.

A great deal of research has been done on the amazing way in which some insects can remain alive and even active when such apparently vital parts as the head have been removed.

How insects communicate with each other in their social communities (such as beehives and anthills) has been studied. So, too, has the relationship between different kinds of insects such as aphids and ants.

These are some of the many subjects studied by entomologists. For more detailed examination, the most important can be roughly divided under different headings, as is done in the following chapters.

Above: Testing a chemical insecticide. Discs are cut from the leaves of bean plants. Adult red spider mites are placed on these discs. The number of mites that die within 12 hours gives a measure of the potency of the chemical.

Above: Testing effects on bean plants of different formulas of pesticide compounds. Plants on the left sprayed with one formula show little chemical deposit on the leaves. Those on the right show a heavy deposit.

Form and Function

BECAUSE there are more species of insects than of all other animal species combined, we can expect to find a great variety of insect forms. But in spite of their variety, all insect species share certain characteristics.

The first feature they have in common is their small size compared with other familiar animals. There were, it is true, some comparatively large insects millions of years ago. One of these, now found only as a fossil, was a creature like a dragonfly with a wingspan of 29 inches. But the insects of the present day are small; even the largest are barely as large as the smallest warm-blooded mammals or birds. Most are quite small, and a great many of them are so tiny as to be barely visible to the unaided eye.

The second main characteristic of insects is that they have no internal skeleton. All active animals need some sort of structural framework in order to maintain their shape and act as an attachment for muscles. As we know, the higher animals have an internal skeleton that serves as an attachment for muscles and protects some of the most important organs. But insects developed along different lines by growing a firm outer skin that acts both as a protection and as an anchor for muscles. Every insect has what we call an external skeleton, or *exoskeleton.*

The exoskeleton consists of three layers. The innermost, called the *endocuticle,* is elastic and flexible. It is made of *chitin* (a fairly hard substance chemically similar to the fibers in wood, with a mixture of protein compounds). The middle layer, or *exocuticle,* is the layer that provides the essential stiffness; it consists of a modified form of chitin called *sclerotin.* The outer layer, or *epicuticle,* is very thin, waxy, and waterproof. It protects the insect against the weather and also prevents loss of water from its body. The epicuticle has no elasticity, but it is folded at the joints to allow for movement.

The hardness of the exoskeleton varies a great deal

The hard, black, waxy outer skin of the rhinoceros beetle (top) protects it from injury and prevents its body fluid from evaporating away. In the Lebanese ant (right) the three main sections of its body—head, thorax, and abdomen—are clearly segmented. Its very narrow jointed waist enables it to move more rapidly than most insects.

from one insect to another. In some beetles, for instance, it is so thick and solid that it can be pierced only with great difficulty by a strong sharp needle. At the other extreme, the exoskeleton of butterflies and gnats is soft and easily damaged.

If this "armor plate" on the bodies of insects were all in one piece, movement would be almost impossible. This brings us to the third main characteristic of insects. Their bodies consist of segments that can slide over each other to a limited extent. The segments themselves are jointed and form separate movable sections. Three main sections can be distinguished in the adult insect: the head; the thorax, a chestlike section that carries the wings and legs; and the abdomen, which may have appendages such as a special egg-laying apparatus called the *ovipositor*.

The comparative size of these separate sections varies and so does the manner in which they are joined. Many of the more highly developed insects, such as bees and wasps, have a very narrow waist between the thorax and

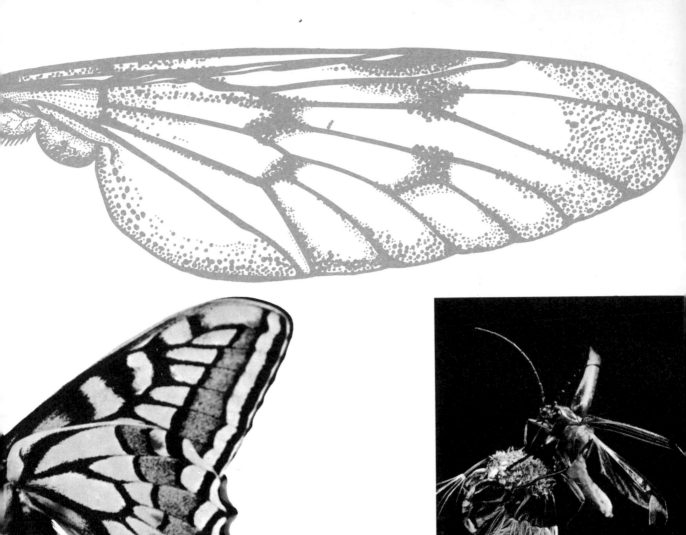

the abdomen. Others, such as flies and beetles, are more or less the same thickness all the way down the body. Ants have a double waist, which gives them great mobility. Some insects, on the other hand, can manage only very slight movement between the thorax and the abdomen. In some insects the head is small and clearly set off from the rest of the body. In others, such as the cricket, the neck is thick and the head as wide as, or even wider than, the thorax.

The wings of insects differ in appearance and in number, depending on their *order*. Order used in this

Top: Drawing of a wing of a dipterous insect (magnified 16 times).

Above: A soldier beetle poised before flight. A pair of tough covers, themselves modified wings, close protectively over its delicate wings when at rest.

Above left: Two of the four wings of a swallowtail butterfly. Tiny pigmented scales cover these wings and form their color pattern.

26

way refers to one of the large groups into which scientists classify living things. Insects of the order Diptera, which includes flies and gnats, have only one pair of wings, which are usually clear and transparent. Other orders of insects have two pairs. These wings may be clear, as in the order of dragonflies; covered with scales, as in the order of butterflies and moths; or consist of one pair of hard wing cases and one pair of skinlike wings, as in the order of beetles. Quite a few insects, even among those belonging to the orders made up of insects that normally have wings, have lost the power of flight. The violet ground beetle, a large and active insect, has its wing cases permanently closed. Several kinds of grasshoppers never develop any wings. And there are many species of moths in which the females are wingless.

Most adult insects have six legs, which are always attached to the thorax and divided into five separate joints. The legs are used for many purposes besides walking. They may have become especially adapted for digging and holding prey, as in the mantids. The legs of some insects have special adaptations for collecting food, such as the pollen "baskets" on the legs of bees. One pair may be greatly enlarged for jumping, or some legs may be almost nonexistent. With certain butterflies, for example, the first pair of legs are merely short, barely visible stumps close under the head. Among aquatic insects the legs have frequently become especially adapted. Often they are flattened and fringed with hairs to serve as paddles or oars.

The size of insects seems to be limited mainly by their system of breathing. They breathe through small openings, known as *spiracles,* along the side of the body. The spiracles are connected with an intricate system of air tubes called the *tracheal tubes.* These tubes are less efficient than lungs and could not supply enough oxygen for the demands of a large body. The respiration of insects has been carefully studied by many eminent entomologists, notably by a Danish scientist, A. Krogh, more than forty years ago and in more recent times by Professor Wigglesworth of Cambridge University.

The tracheal tubes are opened or shut by movements of the spiracles. Normally, when an insect is at rest, the spiracles are closed as much as possible to prevent loss of moisture and are opened only just enough to allow for necessary "ventilation." An insect will often use one or

The powerful pincer-like forelegs of this praying mantis (above) are partially open, ready to seize any edible insect that ventures within range. Each pincer is grooved and armed with sharp spines.

Right: Spiracle and part of trachea (A) of a butterfly larva. Air enters through the spiracle (viewed from the outside, B). The fringed lips (tan) keep out dust and foreign particles. Air intake to the trachea is controlled by the bow (b) at the inner end of the atrium.

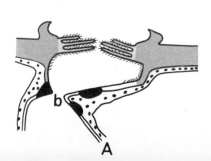

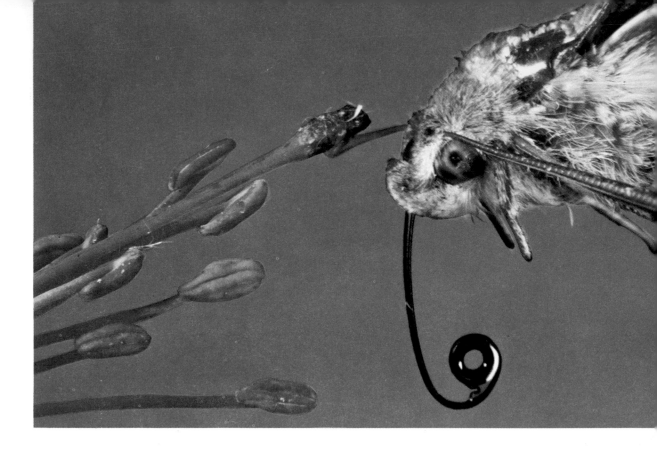

two pairs of spiracles while it is at rest. The others will open when the insect begins to move and thus needs to take in more oxygen and to discharge a greater quantity of carbon dioxide. Small insects cannot inhale in the way the higher animals do and have to rely on the air pressure to force air into the tracheal tubes. The larger and more active insects have a more efficient system. They are able, through various muscular movements, to expel stale air and so allow a fresh supply to enter more quickly.

The heads of insects are generally complicated structures that have developed from six separate body segments fused together. The head carries the mouth parts, the eyes, and also the antennae—special sensory organs, or feelers, that are not found in the higher animals.

The mouth parts of insects are complex and very variable, depending on the kind of food they have to deal with. The mouth parts can be divided roughly into two different types—chewing and biting mouth parts and sucking mouth parts—but there are many variations of each type as well as some that are difficult to classify as either type. There are even insects whose mouths have become useless, so that they cannot feed at all in the adult state.

The jaws of some chewing insects are so powerful that they can bite through lead, zinc, copper, and silver;

The long, tubular proboscis of the hummingbird hawk moth (above) is used for sucking nectar from flowers.

A voracious diving beetle sinking its pincer-like jaws into the tissues of a bloodsucker.

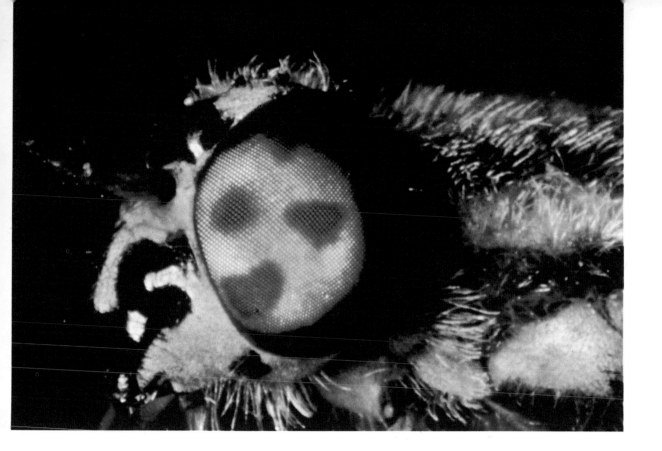

Above: The compound eye of a horse fly. Although composed of thousands of separate lenses, the eye functions as a unit.

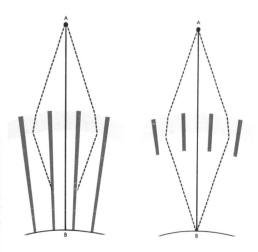

Two diagrams of the compound eye of an insect. In strong light, left, the area B on the retina receives light, through separate lenses, from the object A. Light rays passing through other lenses are refracted into pigment curtains (red) and absorbed. In dull light, right, the curtains are drawn back and the retina receives a stronger, but less refined image through several adjacent lenses.

pulverize solid wood; or dig their way into concrete and mortar. Some large beetles have even been known to damage artillery shells. The mouth of an insect usually has short, jointed organs known as *palps*. These are all that remain of what had been another pair of legs at an earlier stage of insect evolution. Palps are used as sensory organs for examining and tasting the food and also to assist in bringing the food to the mouth. There is a large water beetle that uses its rather long palps almost like hands to push food into its mouth. If the palps are removed the beetle will starve to death.

Many insects have mouth parts adapted both for piercing and sucking, so that they can feed on the blood of mammals and birds or on the sap of plants. Others can suck only liquids that are easy to get to. Houseflies come into this category. Moths and butterflies have jaws that have developed into long tongues that can be extended or rolled up at will. In some moths, in fact, the tongue is longer than the body.

The eyes of insects are quite different from those of other animals. In adult insects, the two main eyes are nearly always compound. That is, they consist of a number of separate six-sided eyes, or *ommatidia*. Each is a complete eye with its own lens. Sometimes there are as many as thirty thousand ommatidia in each compound eye.

Insects that live on the ground and feed on vegetable matter generally have smaller eyes than those that spend much of their time in flight. Insects such as dragonflies, which often catch their prey on the wing, have especially large eyes that enable them to see in all directions at once.

Each separate unit of the compound eye has its own optic nerve, and the image produced by the eye is a composite picture built up, like a mosaic, from innumerable small pieces. It is quite easy to prove that the eyes of the higher insects give a fairly accurate image, because butterflies can be attracted to artificial models resembling their own species and moths have often been observed trying to suck nectar from the flowers printed on wallpaper.

In addition to compound eyes, most insects have several simple eyes, or *ocelli*. In the early stages of their lives ocelli are often the only means of sight. Ocelli cannot give a clear picture of an insect's surroundings, but they are sensitive to light and, in some cases, they

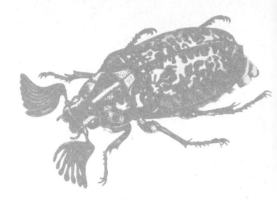

Above: A 19th-century engraving by John Curtis of a Kent cockchafer. Its brushlike antennae contain the receptor organs for the senses of taste, smell, and touch.

The pectinate (comb-like) antennae on the male luna moth can pick up the scent of a female of the species over a distance of up to a mile.

can perceive movement. Their exact function in adult insects has not yet been thoroughly investigated.

Scientists generally agree that many mammals cannot distinguish colors, but a number of insects have well-developed color vision. Many even show a preference for certain colors. This has been tested on bees and butterflies. Given a choice, these insects will first visit flowers of purple or pink in search of nectar. Some insects seem to be unable to distinguish red as a color, but some can see ultraviolet light, which is invisible to humans. For example, moths are strongly attracted to a lamp giving off only ultraviolet rays, which to our eyes does not appear to be shining at all.

Many insects can vary the amount of light that reaches the eye. Their optic nerves are influenced by the brightness of objects. The mercury-vapor moth trap has been a great help in the research on the vision of moths. English scientists, who were among the first to carry out such investigations, discovered many new facts about the reactions of moths to light.

The antennae of insects are very complex sensory organs with many functions. They not only serve as organs of taste, smell, and touch, but also enable the insect to preserve its balance and move in a desired direction. Insects deprived of their antennae are severely handicapped, although some of the functions of the antennae, particularly the sense of taste, also exist in other parts of the body, such as the palps and the feet. Butterflies can recognize even a very weak mixture of sugar in water by wetting their feet. They also find the correct food plant on which to lay their eggs by drumming their feet on a leaf to identify its "flavor."

In many insects, particularly in moths, the antennae of the males are much more developed than those of the females. This enables a male to detect the scent given off by a female who is "calling" for a mate from a distance of as much as a mile. The male can then follow the scent trail to its source unhampered by any other smells that may be met on the way. Such highly selective sensitivity is difficult to understand, because our sense of smell is very poor. But it has been proved again and again by experiments in which moths have collected together using only their sense of smell.

Hearing is not a sense that one usually associates with insects. But it has recently been discovered that certain kinds of moths have a very sharp sense of hearing and can detect sounds far beyond the range of the human ear. A fascinating series of experiments has been carried out by scientists in the United States. They have proved that these moths can hear the supersonic squeaks of bats from a distance of 100 feet or more and respond by acting to avoid being captured.

The swallowtail butterfly has long, slender, sensitive antennae, which are made up of many segments.

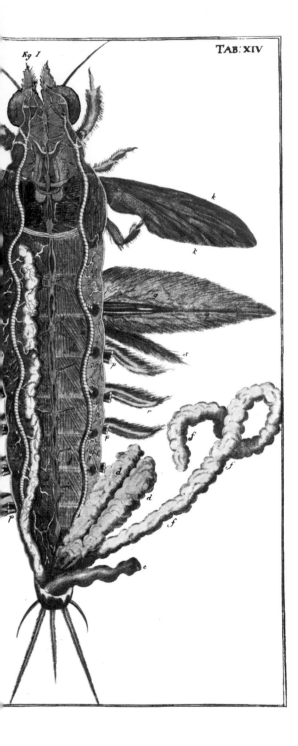

Fig I   TAB: XIV

A drawing by Jan Swammerdam of a dissected mayfly from The Book of Nature; or the History of Insects. This 17th-century entomologist dissected many insects and made detailed drawings of their internal structure.

The "ears," or *tympanic organs,* of moths are in the thorax, close to the region where thorax and abdomen join. Each ear consists of a small air-filled cavity, covered by a thin membrane, which is connected by the tympanic nerve to the central nervous system. Short-horn grasshoppers have a similar hearing organ on the first segment of the abdomen. In longhorn grasshoppers and crickets the hearing organ is situated not on the body but on the front pair of legs — on the joint known as the *tibia,* which corresponds roughly to the shinbone. There are many insects in which no special hearing organs have been found. But these insects seem to pick up sound through their antennae or by the aid of hairs on the body that are sensitive to vibrations in the air. Male midges, for example, can hear and locate the females through their very large feathery antennae.

Because insects live in so many entirely different ways and feed on such an enormous range of foods, the study of insect nutrition is very complicated.

All but a few insects have an alimentary canal in which the food is digested, but the form that this takes differs greatly in different orders. Insects also have salivary glands and produce a number of digestive enzymes, which vary among the different species depending on the type of food they eat. Enzymes are chemical substances that make possible the breakdown of foods within the body. Cockroaches, which feed on many different foods of both animal and vegetable origin, secrete a number of different enzymes. Butterflies, which feed only on nectar, secrete nothing but an enzyme that acts upon sugar.

The digestion of insects, like that of other animals, is assisted by various bacteria and other microscopic organisms. This is especially true in those insects that feed on wood and therefore have to digest cellulose. Like the higher animals, insects need certain vitamins. But insects are apparently able to produce vitamin C in their own bodies without having to absorb it directly from their food.

Many insects are very resistant to cold. Some can even be frozen solid and then become active again when the temperature rises. Why they should have this ability to exist in and recover from a state of suspended animation is still a mystery.

Generally speaking, insects are more active when the weather is warm. Often they are unable to fly until the temperature of their bodies reaches a certain level. This is one reason why some large hawk moths always have a period of "warming up" by vibrating their wings before they actually take flight.

The blood of an insect is not red like that of higher animals. It is either colorless or else slightly green or

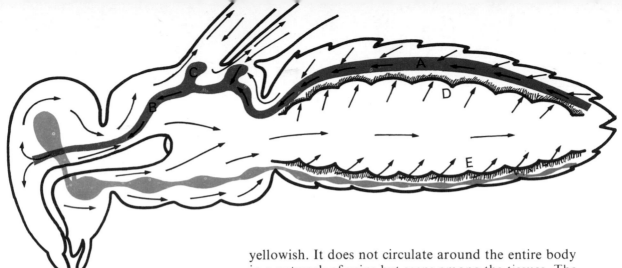

Above: Diagram of the circulatory system of a typical winged insect. Blood is driven forward through the heart (A) to the aorta (B), through the body cavity, and back to the heart again, by the contraction of muscles in the dorsal diaphragm (D). The accessory heart (C) pumps blood to the wings. The ventral diaphragm (E) directs blood to the nerve cord (blue).

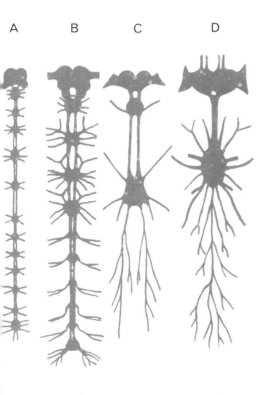

The nerve systems of (A) bristletail, (B) cockroach, (C) water bug, (D) housefly. In the lower insects (A and B) there is a pair of ganglia in every segment. In the higher groups (C and D) fusion of ganglia results in more centralized control.

yellowish. It does not circulate around the entire body in a network of veins but seeps among the tissues. The majority of insects have only a single blood vessel, the *aorta,* running along the back. The rear portion has a pulsating action, comparable to that of a heart. The blood enters the aorta from the body cavity through valves. Then it is pumped forward through the aorta to the head, where it passes through the brain and seeps out again into the body cavity. In some insects there are separate veins to carry blood to the wings, antennae, and legs.

Just as the pulse rate varies in the higher animals, there is a great variation of "heartbeat" in insects. The rate depends on an insect's activity and development. The heartbeat of an adult moth flying fast can be as high as 140 beats a minute. That of a caterpillar is far slower.

Experiments have shown that adrenaline, which accelerates the heartbeat of mammals, also speeds up the heart in insects. Among the chemicals secreted in insect bodies is a secretion very like adrenaline, but very little is yet known as to when and how it is produced.

The nervous system of insects consists of a double strand of nerves, running the length of the body on the underside. In each segment of the body there is a swelling of the nerves, known as a *ganglion.* From this ganglion other nerves branch out to muscles and organs all over the body. A large knot of ganglia—usually called the brain—is in the head. The brain controls the nerves leading to the eyes, the antennae, and the mouth parts. The lesser ganglia in the body can act, to a great extent, independently of the brain.

The fact that insects can remain alive and at least partially active when their heads have been removed has been known for many centuries. Aristotle, the ancient Greek naturalist, observed this in wasps. Recent experiments have shown that the brain inhibits and limits many movements, so that if it is removed the movements become exaggerated and uncontrolled. A headless bee, for example, may go on cleaning itself for hours on end. Experiments with praying mantises have

shown that if the brain is removed the insect moves ceaselessly. If the brain is merely split into two separate sections a mantis can still catch its prey and feed, but it cannot walk. Female insects will often lay their eggs in greater numbers and more rapidly when not controlled by the brain. Research on insects' nervous systems is now carried out mainly by electronic means, which makes for far greater precision than surgical methods.

As far as we know, insects' behavior is almost entirely dependent upon reaction to various stimuli received by their nerves. Healthy, undamaged insects will behave in a way that assures as far as possible the survival of themselves and their offspring. Unlike higher animals, insects of the same species do not vary individually in their behavior. Their actions are usually predictable. Entomologists know that, given certain conditions, insects will react in a certain way; there is very little variation from the standard pattern.

Some insects can, however, be trained to a certain extent. Some water beetles, for example, have been taught to associate certain flavors with the presence of food of an entirely different taste. This seems to indicate that they can profit to a certain degree by experience. Studies of insect behavior are very interesting. However, it is difficult to interpret such research and decide just what it is, in a given instance, that makes an insect behave in the way that it does.

In their tremendous number of species, insects are adapted to live in a variety of ways in a wide range of environments. Take, for example, the aquatic insects that have special adaptations that enable them to carry a supply of air or to breathe by extending a tube to the surface of the water. In the juvenile stages their tracheal tubes are often undeveloped and they breathe with gills. Hunting insects can move at great speed and have good sight and powerful jaws. Vegetarians tend to be more sluggish. Insects like earwigs and bedbugs, which hide in cracks and crevices, tend to be flat. Others, such as the flea that has to move between the hairs on the bodies of animals, are compressed from the sides.

Above: The Indian leaf butterfly, top, which in color, pattern, and shape bears an uncanny resemblance to the surrounding leaves.

Right: The South American mole cricket hides from its enemies by burrowing underground with its powerful forelegs. It uses its knife-sharp pincers for snipping its way through rootlets.

The tiny springtails live in soil where they perform a valuable function in breaking down organic matter. They are so small that by mere walking they could not get very far. Instead they use a powerful leverlike organ under the abdomen to make long leaps. Springtails may be the most widespread of all insects. They can be found all over the world wherever there is some moisture, including the snowfields of high mountains, deep caves, and the sea-washed rocks on the coast where few other insects can exist.

Some of the most interesting animal adaptations are those concerned with camouflage, and in this respect insects are very highly developed. Most insects, except those that have warning colors, have some means of making themselves merge into their surroundings.

Examples of camouflage through *cryptic*, or concealing, coloring, can be found among many different kinds of insects. Moths and butterflies are a particularly

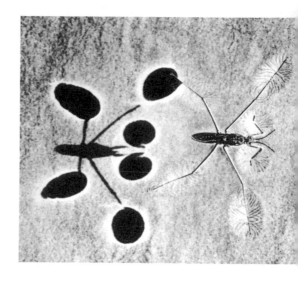

Above: A water strider, which skims across the surface of ponds by holding a bubble of air under each foot. It moves its two middle legs in rowing fashion and steers with its trailing hindlegs.

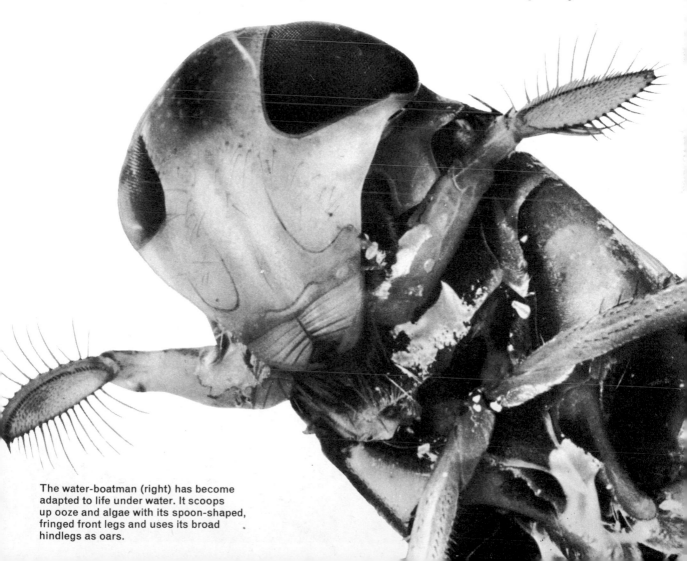

The water-boatman (right) has become adapted to life under water. It scoops up ooze and algae with its spoon-shaped, fringed front legs and uses its broad hindlegs as oars.

good example. Many moths blend perfectly into their background when at rest under natural conditions on lichen-covered tree trunks or furrowed bark. Many butterflies have the undersides of their wings marked and colored in such a way that when they settle and close their wings they hide the colorful upper surface and disappear from view. The common small tortoise-shell butterfly is an example of this; so, to an even greater extent, is the Indian leaf butterfly.

Very often color camouflage is combined with a body shape that resembles natural objects such as twigs, leaves, or flowers. In some instances this resemblance is enhanced by the insect's swaying or rocking, which simulates the movements of plants in a breeze. The leaf insects and stick insects are good examples of this type of camouflage. So are two species of mantids found in Africa, which resemble colorful flowers and move gently to and fro as if shaken by the wind while they wait for prey.

A number of insects protect themselves from enemies by a combination of cryptic coloring and so-called flash colors. Many grasshoppers employ this method and so do several moths. The underwing moths, as their name suggests, have bright colors on the lower surfaces of their wings, which are clearly visible in flight. But the moment the insect settles, the color disappears so that it blends with its background. The combination of a sudden flash of vivid color with an equally sudden disap-

Above: The red underwing moth has bright red "flash color" hindwings. The color shows up in flight but is concealed when the insect closes its wings. This mechanism confuses the moth's enemies.

Right: The huge "eyes" and "mouth" of the spicebush swallowtail scare its enemies away. In fact they are merely patches of color. Its true eyes and mouthparts are very small and are hidden beneath the head.

Below: The head of a short-horned grasshopper, showing its camouflage coloring.

Some butterflies mimic species (called "models") that are well protected against predators. Above are examples of this mimicry: (1) and (2) are models. (3) and (4) are the male and female of a mimetic species; they both look alike. (5) and (6) are members of the same species as (3) and (4) but look different because they have mimicked (1) and (2) respectively. (7) and (8) are the male and female forms of another species, but the female (7) has mimicked (2) and thus bears no resemblance to its own male (8).

pearance tends to confuse pursuers and gives the insect a good chance of escaping.

There are some insects whose bright coloring is never concealed at all and which make no attempt at blending with their surroundings. But they are almost always species that are distasteful to other animals and their colors are in this case a warning signal. A special form of camouflage is shown by insects that resemble not their surroundings but some other larger creature that would normally be feared by their predators. Some of the big silk moths, for example, have wings marked with vivid eyespots that look much like the staring eyes of some fairly large animals. The body of the lantern fly of South America looks strangely like the head of a small alligator.

The ability of an insect species to adapt quite quickly to changing conditions has been studied in great detail in the case of industrial melanism mentioned earlier in this chapter. In England entomologists have done a great deal of work with the peppered moth whose normal coloring in rural areas is a mottled black and white. During the last seventy or eighty years, however, this same species of moth has begun to appear more and more frequently in industrial areas in an almost completely black form. On sooty tree trunks and fences, the black form is far better camouflaged than the original pale form. This interesting phenomenon is often referred to as showing natural selection in action. The black, or *melanic*, moths have more chances of survival than the light-colored ones. They have more chance to breed and pass their own characteristics on to their offspring. Thus they gradually bring about a change in type: the black form gains in numbers while the previously more numerous mottled moths decline.

The caterpillar of a Malayan moth (above) when touched or irritated rears up in this aggressive posture. Its large eyelike marks make it look like a miniature snake.

The bee hawk moth (above) has evolved to resemble a bumblebee. It has transparent wings, feeds on the same nectar source as do the bees, and unlike most hawk moths flies during the day.

From Egg to Adult

ALL animals, including insects, grow and develop during their life. But insects, because of their hard and inelastic skins, cannot grow steadily in the way most other animals do. All but a few of them have to change their skins before they can increase in size.

Skin-casting, or molting, usually occurs many times during the early life of an insect but stops when the adult stage is reached. Only a few insects, such as the silverfish, continue to molt even as adults, after growth has come to an end. The scientific term for molting of the skin is *ecdysis,* and the whole process has been carefully investigated in many different insects.

The number of skin changes varies in different species. Grasshoppers molt five times, cockroaches seven times, the larvae of butterflies and moths molt five to nine times, and the nymphs of the May fly as many as thirty or forty times.

When molting is about to take place, a thin layer of liquid forms between the existing skin and the new one that is developing beneath it. This liquid is really a kind of digestive fluid. It contains enzymes that gradually dissolve the chitin and protein in the endocuticle, but leave the harder exocuticle and epicuticle intact. The dissolved substances are used again in building up the new outer skin. Until molting actually begins, the new skin formed beneath the old one is soft and quite pale in color. It takes on the characteristic color of its species and becomes firm within a few hours after the old skin has been cast off.

When the new skin is ready the insect must, by its own efforts, split its old coat. This is not as difficult as it may sound. All insects still in the molting stage have a weak place somewhere in the skin, usually along the middle line of the thorax. Along this line there is little or no exocuticle, so that when the endocuticle has been dissolved only the very thin epicuticle holds the skin together. A slight increase in blood pressure, brought about when the insect contracts the muscles in its abdomen, is normally enough to rupture the skin. Quite a lot of insects help the process along by swallowing air or water, which distends their bodies.

Once the old skin has been split, the insect must free itself of it. This it does by making contracting and expanding movements until it has pulled itself out. (Because this sometimes proves very difficult, it is quite common to find caterpillars that have been unable to cast their skins completely. They still have rings of old

The three photographs (right) show a buff-tip moth expanding its wings for flight after emerging from the pupa. It does this by swallowing air, which raises the pressure inside the body and forces fluid into the wing veins.

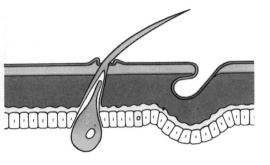

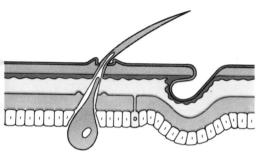

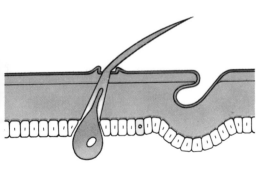

Above: A diagram illustrating the process of ecdysis. Before ecdysis the insect stops feeding and (as in 1) the moulting glands (yellow) secrete a substance that dissolves the endocuticle (dark green) but leaves the exocuticle (blue) and epicuticle (orange) unaffected. Then (as in 2) the epidermal cells begin to form a new endocuticle (light green) separated from the old diminished endocuticle by molting fluid. Internal pressure of the insect then increases, causing the old skin to rupture at the thorax, where there is no tough exocuticle. The insect then discards its old skin by working its way through this split. Within hours a new rigid exocuticle and waxy outer epicuticle have formed. The molting gland becomes dormant again. New hairs, formed by secretion from a gland at the root of each hair, continue to grow throughout ecdysis.

skin like tight girdles around their bodies.) As soon as the skin has been shed, the insect swallows more air or water. It does this in order to increase its size while the new skin is still soft and elastic, because as soon as this skin hardens, any further expansion is impossible. An insect that has just changed its skin apparently becomes much larger. In fact, it has not increased in body weight but only in volume. Not until it begins to feed again does it put on weight.

When an adult butterfly or a dragonfly emerges by casting the skin of the pupa or nymph, it has to expand its wings. This also is done by swallowing air and so forcing the fluid in the body to flow into the veins of the wings and stretch them out. Certain moths and the May flies never feed as adults. They use their stomachs only as an air sac to assist in raising their blood pressure.

In the study of molting, entomologists have found that one of the factors that triggers it off is that the skin becomes too tight for the growing insect. But growth is not the only cause. Some insects will molt even when they are starving. Clothes-moth larvae often do this. They may molt as many as seven or eight times in a few days, without increasing in size at all. This discovery led researchers to look for causes of skin-casting other than growth. It was eventually discovered that molting is also controlled by a hormone contained in the blood.

This hormone, known as the *growth and molting hormone,* is secreted by a gland that begins to act when it receives a signal from the brain.

Once this signal has been received, the hormone will begin its work and molting will take place even if the insect then has its head removed. If no signal has gone out from the brain to stimulate the gland, the decapitated insect will not molt even though it may remain alive for as long as a year. A series of experiments illustrating this has been done with the bloodsucking bug, Rhodnius. It is an easy insect to use because during its period as a nymph it requires only one big meal of blood between each skin change. Other experiments have been made with a Rhodnius that is not able to begin its own molting process because its head has been removed before its brain has triggered the flow of the necessary hormone. The insect can be made to molt by giving it a transfusion of blood from another in which the molting hormone is contained. What it is that triggers the brain into sending its signal to the gland is not yet clear. Physiologists think the stimulus to the brain must come

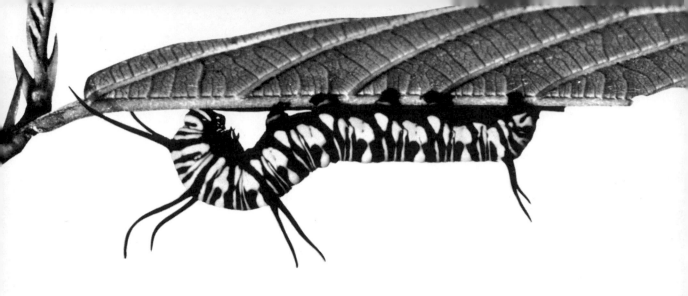

first from the body through the nerve cord because if this cord is cut, molting does not take place.

Along with the growth and molting hormone insects have another very important hormone. It is the *juvenile hormone* secreted by a small gland — called the *corpus allatum* — just behind the brain. The juvenile hormone assures that the insect continues to grow through the correct series of molts until it reaches normal size before becoming an adult. When full development is complete, the juvenile hormone is no longer required and is no longer produced. Then, at the final molt, the adult insect appears instead of yet another juvenile stage.

If the corpus allatum is removed so that no juvenile hormone can be produced, the insect will become a very tiny adult — a dwarf — before it has had time to grow. The very small specimens of butterflies sometimes caught by collectors in the field are probably due to some damage to this important gland.

This theory has been confirmed by Carroll Williams at Harvard University. In laboratory experiments he produced tiny silk moths weighing only a few milligrams. In contrast, it is possible to make a caterpillar that has almost completed its growth to go on growing and molting until it becomes an abnormally large moth when it finally makes its last molt. This is done by transplanting into it the corpus allatum from a young caterpillar.

Apparently, in order to do its job the juvenile hormone must be present in quite large quantities. In butterflies and moths the amount of juvenile hormone present

Above: Three distinct stages in complete metamorphosis. Top: A larva of one butterfly. Middle: The dormant pupal stage of another butterfly. Bottom: The imago (adult butterfly) of the pupa.

controls what is going to happen at each skin change. In normal development, these insects go through three stages of development: larva (or caterpillar), pupa, and adult. For normal development both the growth and molting hormone and the juvenile hormone are necessary in proper balance throughout the body. If this balance is upset, or if the hormones are prevented artificially from reaching certain parts of the body, all kinds of abnormal creatures may develop. Examples are moth larvae that become a pupa at the front end of their bodies but remain a caterpillar at the tail end, or ones that become partially moths while the rest of the body remains in the pupal stage. Very dramatic experiments of this kind have been done by Carroll Williams with the North American Cecropia moth, which, because of its large size, is comparatively easy to work with.

Not all insects develop in the same way. Some, after hatching from the egg, go through a gradual, continuous change in size and development until they reach the adult stage. This kind of development is known as *incomplete metamorphosis*. In contrast to this is *complete metamorphosis,* in which insects pass through three separate stages as do the moths and butterflies discussed above.

The time spent in each of these three stages varies greatly among different orders of insects and sometimes even among different individuals of the same species.

Usually the adult life is rather short compared to the time it takes for the larva to develop, change into a pupa, and emerge as a fully formed insect. The adult life is particularly brief in those insects that cannot feed. For example, adult May flies live for no more than three days under the very best conditions. In contrast, their larval period is very long, lasting for two or three years. But this is by no means a record and seems quite a short time when compared to the life of the cicada, or seventeen-year locust as it is commonly called, which remains for seventeen years as a nymph living underground. Many of the larger beetles such as stag beetles spend three years or so as larvae. Generally when the larvae of an insect rely on foodstuffs poor in nourishment, such as dry wood, they remain longer in the larval stage than when they feed on very rich and nourishing substances. Many flies, which lay their eggs in rotting refuse that has a very high food value, can complete their whole development in only about ten days. This is one of the reasons why flies increase with such astonishing speed in places where the temperature is fairly high and the standard of cleanliness low.

Many insects have a distinct period at some stage of their lives when growth and development stops for a time. This is known as the diapause. When the diapause

Above: Incomplete metamorphosis of silverfish. The photograph shows various instars (the name given to the insect between molts). Each stage is marked by the growth in size of the silverfish and not by any change in its structure.

occurs, the production of the growth and molting hormone stops. Thus all the body's processes slow down almost to a standstill. The insect does not die, but it remains quite inactive and ceases to develop. Although it still needs a small amount of oxygen, it does not feed. During diapause eggs may remain unhatched for many months, larvae may stop feeding and go into hibernation, or insects that have pupated may fail to emerge until conditions improve.

In temperate climates diapause often occurs during the winter, when the temperature is too low for activity and there is no food available. In warmer climates diapause may occur in a time of drought or when special vitamins are lacking in the diet.

Experiments have been made to discover the causes of diapause. Although many factors appear to be involved, it seems that among the important causes is the amount of daylight to which the insect is exposed. This knowledge has made it possible, for example, to breed cabbage white butterflies all through the year by using artificial light to extend the daylight to at least fourteen hours a day. Normally this butterfly spends the winter as a pupa enclosed in its chrysalis. On the other hand, it is possible to breed many generations of some of the moths in succession without a diapause by keeping them warm and dark.

The amount of light influences different insects in different ways. According to the species, it may be either too much or too little light that brings about the diapause. Although the length of daylight is important in the diapause response, other factors are involved. For example, emergence from diapause depends in some cases on a series of temperature changes. In the stag beetle there is a diapause in the adult stage as soon as the beetle has emerged from its underground pupa in the late summer. Instead of making its way to the surface, the newly emerged adult remains quietly hidden for many months and does not start an active life until the following summer.

Insects, such as butterflies and moths, that go into diapause as pupae in the autumn will not emerge again even if they are kept warm and moist. The only way in which they can be made to emerge before their normal time in the spring is by chilling them for a period of some weeks and then placing them in a warm place. The necessary chemical changes that cause the growth and development hormone to be manufactured again will take place only if there is the period of chilling first.

Sometimes, when the diapause occurs during the egg stage, it is possible to interrupt it by treating the eggs with an acid that will soften the shells and allow air to enter. This method has been used to make silkworm

Above: The adult stag beetle stays in a state of arrested development (diapause) in its pupation chamber (bottom) until the weather is warm; then it emerges (top).

Above: The brimstone butterfly
hibernating. This is an adaptation for
survival without feeding during adverse
environmental conditions. Such
conditions probably cause a temporary
lack of the hormone that controls
metabolism.

Insects enter diapause at various stages
of development. Left: Two dormant
pupae of the eyed hawk moth.

eggs hatch soon after they are laid, instead of waiting
for eight months.

Most of the insects that lack a pupal stage and have
only an incomplete metamorphosis develop gradually,
without drastic changes between one stage and the next.
But some, such as dragonflies and May flies, undergo a
dramatic change when the nymphs leave the water in
which they have been living and come to the surface to
allow the fully developed insect to emerge. These nymphs
are fierce-looking creatures, dark and dull in color,
with rather long, jointed bodies and long legs. The
dragonfly nymph has well-developed mouth parts with
a special adaptation of the underlip, called a mask,
which can shoot out suddenly and grip its prey. During

successive skin changes the wings gradually appear as little stumps. In the final stage the organs of the adult develop inside the nymph. When their growth is completed, the dragonfly nymphs crawl out of the water onto stalks of reed or grass. The May fly nymphs simply float to the surface. The nymphs' skins split and the fully winged insects emerge.

As soon as its wings have expanded and become dry and firm, a dragonfly is ready to begin its aerial life. But the May fly undergoes still another molt, and changes from its dull-colored "dun" stage with greenish wings, known as a *subimago,* to a delicately colored insect whose shimmering wings are quite transparent and iridescent. The May flies are the only insects that molt twice in succession like this, after reaching the adult stage. When the final stage emerges, it leaves the skin of the dun completely intact sitting on a leaf, still looking just like a live insect. People who live near rivers where the May fly "rises" in the spring are familiar with these ghost flies, which may remain for days on walls and bridges until they are destroyed by wind and rain.

In insects with a complete metamorphosis, where the juvenile larval stage and the adult stage are separated by a pupal stage, development is different. Here the metamorphosis, which has been studied especially in butterflies and moths, begins toward the end of the larval life. At that point the creature has stopped feeding and is preparing to pupate. The special organs of the caterpillar break down, and a pupa forms inside the caterpillar skin. When the pupa wriggles out of this skin a few days later, it is quite soft. The shell hardens fairly soon and then forms a complete protection for the body; its only openings are the spiracles.

While an insect is in diapause in the pupal stage it is very resistant to outside agents. For example it suffers no harm when exposed to cyanide gas, which instantly kills both caterpillars and adults. It can also survive a dose of diphtheria toxin 1000 times stronger than that which will quickly kill caterpillars or pupae that have begun to develop.

If a pupa goes into diapause immediately after its change from the larval stage, nothing more happens, possibly for several months. But once development does begin again, it goes ahead quickly. Already present in the larva are certain cells that will in time develop into the special organs of the adult. Apart from these, all the tissues break down into a fluid that retains the nourishment accumulated by the larva during its days of feeding. When the diapause ends and growth hormone is once again produced, the fluid inside the pupal shell begins to change. The complete body of the adult then develops from the materials that are already there.

Left: Four stages in the gradual emergence of a dragonfly. The nymph crawls out of the water up a reed, frees itself from the nymphal skin, and emerges as a winged adult dragonfly.

In the Cecropia moth it takes exactly twenty-one days before the moth emerges, if the pupa is kept in a temperature of 25°C. The entire development, from the time when the egg hatches until the adult emerges, takes ten months. Of this time as much as eight months may be spent in diapause.

The development of different insects proceeds at different rates. Beetles usually have a rather short pupal period of not more than a few weeks. Flies often spend only a few days in this stage, and bees and wasps also have a brief period. During the summer months butterflies and moths that produce more than one generation in the year spend only a short time as pupae. During the winter they may have a diapause in this stage. Occasionally, some moths will not emerge from the pupa at

Above: Mayflies are remarkable, for they molt again after they have once got their wings. From the aquatic nymph (lower) hatches out the first winged form, the subimago (top). This casts a thin skin from its whole body, including wings, and emerges as a brightly colored imago. Top right: Shed skins and emergent imagos on the window of a shop near a river.

Above: Because of its short life, this
robin moth has no need to feed and
so has no mouth parts. Its stomach is
merely filled with air.

Left: A water tiger (the larva of a diving
beetle) that has speared a three-spined
stickleback with its pincer-like mandibles.
Both larvae and adults of this species
of beetle are carnivorous and
extremely voracious.

the normal time but continue in diapause for another
whole year, or sometimes even longer. This happens
most frequently with those moths living in the far north,
where weather conditions are uncertain. Entomologists
believe such variations assure the survival of the species
in case the weather might be so bad one year as to make
breeding impossible.

The juvenile and adult stages of insects are often very
different in their habits, but this is not the case in insects
with a gradual development. Grasshoppers, bugs, and
aphids, for example, live and feed in much the same way
all through their lives.

Some of the insects that undergo complete metamorphosis also eat the same food in both larval and adult
stages. For example, quite a number of beetles lead
much the same kind of life when they are adult as they
did in the larval stage. Both the larva and adults of
ladybird beetles feed on the same kind of aphids. The
aquatic Dytiscus beetle is a carnivorous hunter in the
larval stage and remains so after its metamorphosis.
Generally speaking, however, those insects that undergo
a complete metamorphosis change their feeding habits
when they develop from larvae into adults.

Sometimes the parents are carnivorous and the larvae
vegetarian, as in one European species of beetle whose
adults feed on snails while the larvae eat beets. The
reverse may happen, as in the case of a species of water
beetle in which the adult is a peaceful plant feeder,
while its larva is a carnivorous hunter known as a water
tiger. This change in feeding habits is very marked in
the Lepidoptera, the order that includes butterflies and
moths. Adult butterflies and moths can feed only on
liquids and usually feed exclusively on nectar. Sometimes they also take sap from bruised trees, the juice of
rotting fruit, or even the liquid oozing from dead
animals.

Some species of moths and butterflies are unable to
feed as adults. Their caterpillars, however, are essentially
nothing but a digestive tract with jaws and feet. They
feed continuously on vegetable matter such as flowers,
fruits, seeds, roots, or even the wood of shrubs and
trees. Food stored in the larval tissues lasts through
metamorphosis and until the adults have emerged and
completed their breeding cycle.

Numerous gnats and mosquitoes spend their larval
lives in water feeding on minute plants and animals and
become bloodsuckers when they are adult. Many flies
with carnivorous larvae of repulsive habits become
brightly colored iridescent adults that content themselves with nectar and other sweet juices. The parasitic
insects are highly specialized in their feeding habits and
will be discussed in a later chapter.

49

How Insects Reproduce

THE different ways in which insects lay their eggs and provide for their young are so numerous that it would fill a large book to discuss them in any kind of detail. Here it is possible only to give an outline of some of the most important features of insect reproduction.

Compared to mammals and birds, insects have a very high reproductive rate. Almost all female insects are capable, when conditions are favorable, of laying a large number of eggs. The fertility of insects depends upon several factors, three of the most important being temperature, nutrition, and the presence of the juvenile hormone. (See pages 42–43).

The relationship between temperature and fertility varies among the species of insects. Each species has its own range of temperature within which it can reproduce successfully. If the temperature is too low, the eggs laid by the female will usually be infertile. If it is too high the males of certain insects, such as the fruit flies, become sterile.

Nutrition is particularly important to the female. If she does not get the right kind of food in the right quantity she will not be fertile. The food essential for fertility varies from species to species. In butterflies it is the sugar found in the nectar. In bloodsucking mosquitoes and flies it is the protein derived from a meal of blood. In the fruit flies, which feed on fermenting liquids, yeast is the necessary food.

Insects that cannot feed in the adult stage must store the essential nourishment for fertility during their larval life. If they are starved or undernourished during that stage, they will be sterile as adults. This happens quite often among silk moths reared under artificial conditions in a laboratory, where they cannot obtain all the foods that would be available to them in their natural surroundings. The resulting moths may look perfectly normal and may even mate and lay eggs in the usual way, but the eggs will be infertile.

The juvenile hormone is also a necessary factor for fertility in some insects, but not in all. Some butterflies and moths, for example, can lay fertile eggs even if the hormone is not present. But grasshoppers, flies, and some beetles and bugs can produce fully-developed, fertile eggs only if the juvenile hormone is secreted by the adult females at the time when the eggs are being formed.

Even fertile eggs will hatch successfully only if the conditions are right. The temperature must be above a certain minimum, which varies with the species, and

Above: The soldier white ant. Right: This white ant's egg-laying queen, whose body is distended by her huge ovaries. A mature queen may lay as many as 40 to 50 thousand eggs a day.

The female Kentish glory moth lays her eggs on birch twigs, so that when the young hatch they are already on their food source. Above are the feeding larvae.

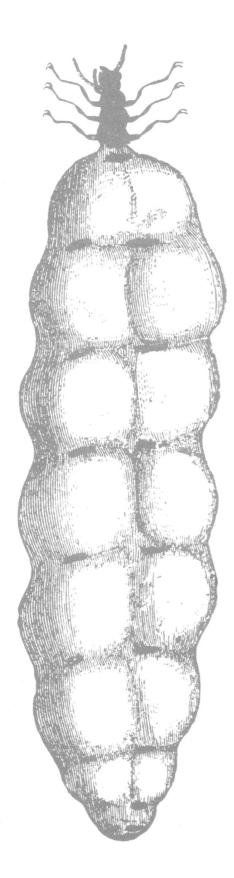

some degree of moisture is essential. Insect eggs can easily become too dry. When this happens the larva may develop fully inside the shell and then be unable to force its way out.

Most insects are comparatively short-lived in the adult stage, and the reproductive life of a female is very brief. All the eggs she will produce in her lifetime are laid in quick succession over a very short time. But in some of the social insects, such as ants, bees, and termites, the reproductive life of a female may last for several years. It has been estimated that a queen termite lays one egg every two seconds, day and night, over a period as long as ten years. Since the queen is the only breeding adult in the community, the termite population in the nest would quickly decline without her great fertility.

All the social insects lavish great care on their young. The queen bee, the queen wasp, the queen ant, and the queen termite are attended by workers who look after the eggs and feeding, clean the nest, and care for the larvae within the nest. The queen bee and the queen wasp lay an egg in each cell of the comb. Ants' and termites' eggs are laid in the queen's chamber but are immediately carried by workers to the "nurseries" where they will be looked after. The way in which the young larvae are fed and tended determines whether they will develop into workers of various kinds or into fully-sexed females. But there is still much to learn about this interesting and complicated matter.

Normally most of the eggs of social insects are raised in such a way as to produce workers, which are needed in large numbers to keep the community going. Males and females appear only at certain seasons, usually once a year. In a beehive only a few new queens, perhaps no more than two or three, are hatched in the early summer, together with a number of males, or drones. Similarly, wasps and bumblebees produce comparatively few sexually mature individuals.

Ants and termites are much more productive in this respect; during the season when they swarm, hundreds and even thousands of winged males and females can be seen pouring out of large nests.

It has been noticed again and again that all the ants of one species seem to swarm on the same day over a large area. Why this should happen and whether it is due to weather conditions or to some kind of communication among the various nests is not known. One result of this simultaneous swarming is that males and females from different nests have a good chance of meeting and mating. Thus close interbreeding is prevented.

The ants and termites shed their wings when they return to earth after this mating flight, but the female

The female earwig (above) protects and shelters her young until they are ready to fend for themselves. The nest is usually underground in a hollow. Adult earwigs frequently hide among flower petals, which also serve as their food.

bees and wasps are able to fly throughout their lives.

In the case of the solitary bees and wasps, each individual female makes provision for her own young, which will all be fully sexed individuals when they mature. A nest is built and filled with food. One egg is laid in each cell, which is then carefully sealed, and there the young insect develops in comparative safety. The solitary bees hollow out their nests in the ground or other suitable places and may line them with rose leaves, mud, chewed vegetable matter, or soft hairs gathered from the woolly leaves of certain plants. They stock each cell with a supply of pollen, moistened with honey, on which the larva will feed.

The hunting wasps, which are also solitary, build a great variety of nests, but they have a different way of providing food for the larvae. Some seal the nest when it is completed, leaving inside it caterpillars, spiders, grasshoppers, and other creatures that they have caught and paralyzed with their stings. The paralyzed creatures remain alive, although unable to move, until they are needed as food by the developing wasps. There are other species of hunting wasps that do not stock and seal the nest. Instead they remain in attendance on it, bringing flies to feed the larvae until they pupate.

Few insects take such care of their offspring as do the bees and wasps. But among the few that do are two familiar insects, the earwig and the stinkbug, whose females behave much like brooding hens — protecting and sheltering their eggs and newly hatched nymphs until they are ready to fend for themselves.

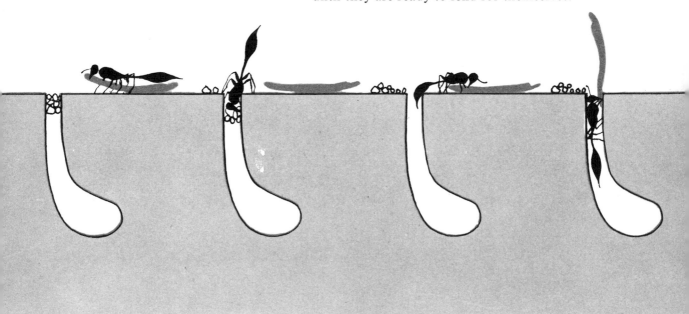

While parental care for offspring is rare in the insect world, it is also a fact that very few insects leave the fate of their eggs entirely to chance. The majority of insects lay their eggs either on or in the substance that is to serve as food for the larvae, or in a place where food can easily be found. Butterflies and moths almost always attach their eggs to the correct food plant so that the larvae can begin to feed as soon as they hatch. Occasionally a female butterfly lays her eggs on a plant poisonous to the larvae. But in these cases the poisonous plant is usually fairly closely related to the correct food plant. The larvae may even be able to feed on it for a time, although they will die before they are fully grown.

A few species of butterflies, however, do not lay directly on the food plant. One of them is an English butterfly called the silver-washed fritillary. The caterpillars of this butterfly feed on wild violets, but the egg-laying habits remained a mystery for a long time. The solution was finally found when an English naturalist discovered that late in summer the females deposit their eggs in chinks of the bark of oak trees. The larvae go into diapause immediately after hatching. In diapause they have a better chance of surviving the winter on the fairly dry tree trunks than on the ground, where they might be flooded or attacked by predators or by fungi and bacteria. When the larvae become active in the spring they come down from the trees and crawl around until they find their food plant, the wild violet.

Female sawflies actually cut slits in leaves, fruits, and buds and insert their eggs, which are then well protected

A mating pair of silver-washed fritillary butterflies (above). The female lays her eggs in chinks in the bark of an oak tree. After hatching, the larvae go into diapause until spring, then find their way to their food supply of wild violets.

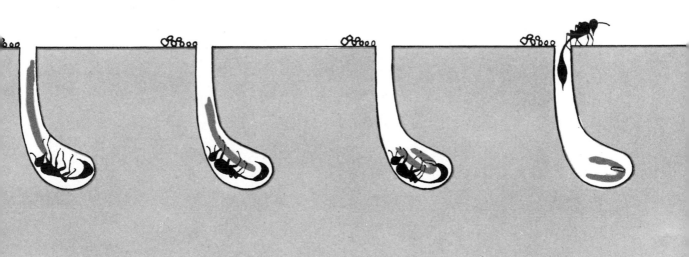

Left to right: The nesting and egg-laying behavior of the solitary wasp. The female has dug a hole and then concealed the entrance to it with large sand particles while she went to search for food. She drags back a caterpillar that she has paralyzed with her sting and places it in the nest. Then she lays an egg on the caterpillar's body and leaves the nest. When the larva hatches it will feed on the caterpillar.

Below: The scolytus beetle (enlarged; actual size shown in circle) and the tunneling pattern it has made in elm bark. The beetle bores its way through to a layer of the bark where it cuts a chamber and lays eggs in niches along it. On hatching, each larva excavates a burrow, at the end of which it forms a pupation chamber. After pupation, the new beetles tunnel their way out of the tree.

54

until they hatch. But this performance is nothing compared to that of the pigeon horntail. It can bore its ovipositor (egg-laying organ) deep into the wood of trees and place an egg far beneath the bark. These horntails very often lay their eggs in timber that has been felled and stacked ready to be shipped to sawmills. The larvae take several years to develop and the adults have been known to emerge from lumber being used for house building or carpentry.

A great many different beetles lay their eggs in the wood or bark of trees. Usually these eggs are laid fairly close to the surface, and it is not the adult beetles but the larvae that burrow into the wood and damage the timber. But in the case of the bark-borer beetles, the original tunnel is made by the adult female. She enters through a hole chewed in the bark and then works her way along the cambium layer (the pithy tissue beneath the bark). As she goes, she hollows out a corridor and lays eggs at regular intervals. As soon as the eggs hatch, the larvae begin to burrow outward from the original tunnel, but still keep within the cambium layer. The tunnel the larva makes is narrow at first. It becomes wider until, at the end, it opens out into a larger chamber where the insect pupates.

Each species of bark-borer produces a distinct and recognizable tunnel pattern. With some the main tunnel runs straight up and down the trunk, and the side tunnels radiate in all directions, making a design that looks like a centipede with very long legs. Other species make main tunnels that run horizontally across the fibers of the wood and the secondary tunnels that run up and down. The females of some species make two adjoining tunnels, branching in the shape of a Y. Sometimes several females enter through the same hole and produce a star-shaped tunnel system. If a tree trunk or branch that has been attacked by bark-borers is stripped of its bark, the marks left in the wood form a most intricate, and often attractive, pattern. But, if numerous enough, these insects can cause severe damage to growing timber and even bring about the death of trees.

The dung beetles, and their close relatives the scarab beetles, provide for their larvae as elaborately as the solitary bees and wasps. Both the adults and the larvae feed on the dung of cows, horses, or other large animals.

Above: The ovipositor of the female great woodwasp boring a hole in the bark of a tree. She lays her eggs in the safety of this hole.

The female sawfly (right) is laying her eggs under the skin of a leaf that has been perforated by a pair of sawblades at the tip of her body. When the larvae hatch they will feed on the leaf.

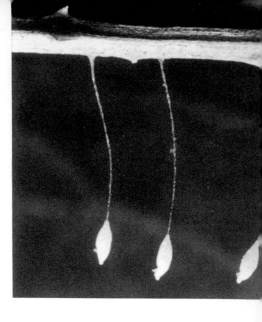

The parent beetles—male and female working together—dig deep shafts in the ground with short tunnels branching off at intervals. The short tunnels are stuffed with dung and one egg is laid in each. There the larvae develop, surrounded by enough food to last until they pupate. The adult beetles have a well-developed sense of smell and can trace a supply of dung from afar. Often innumerable beetles gather in the same place, and in a matter of hours all the dung has been buried.

The scarab beetle, which the ancient Egyptians considered to be a holy animal, makes round balls of dung. It rolls these along the ground until it finds a place where they can be buried in safety. Another related beetle found in southern Europe hollows out quite a large underground chamber, fills it with dung, and then divides the material up into seven or eight round balls, which lie in the hollow like birds' eggs in a nest. Each ball contains one egg and supplies the nourishment for the complete growth of one larva.

The shape and size of eggs are as varied as the insects that lay them. Among butterflies particularly, the eggs are often of very intricate design with numerous ridges and projections on the surface. The white admiral lays an egg that under the microscope looks surprisingly like a sea urchin.

Eggs may be laid singly or in clusters made up of anything from half a dozen to several hundred eggs. Some butterflies lay their eggs in untidy heaps, while others make neat "bracelets" of eggs around the twigs of their food plant. The cabbage white lays closely spaced batches on the undersides of leaves, with each egg attached separately to the leaf surface. There is one small butterfly that deposits six to eight eggs in a long string, with only the first one attached to a leaf and the rest attached to one another.

Ancient Egyptians mounted models of scarabs (above left) in sacred amulets. The ball of dung in which the beetle lays her eggs was thought to represent the sun god.

Below: A marble gall on an oak tree. Galls often occur when an insect lays eggs in the tissues of a growing plant. The section shows the grub in its larval chamber.

The eggs of certain lacewing flies are suspended on gossamer threads from tree twigs, safe from predators (above). The hatched larvae climb up the threads to reach their food supply.

The lackey moth (below) laying her eggs in bracelet formation around a twig; the leaves on the twig will provide food for the resulting larvae.

Many insects lay their eggs on the roots of plants or in buds and the tissues of leaves or shoots. As a result, the plant parts on which the eggs are deposited often grow in a curious distorted way and form swellings, called galls, that are quite distinct and characteristic of each species of insect. Oak leaves are a favorite host for numerous species of gall wasps. Consequently, you can find many galls of different shapes such as the oak apple, the marble gall, and the spangle gall on oak leaves. Why plants react in this way to the presence of insect eggs and what chemicals are responsible for distorted growth are problems still to be solved.

Some insects provide their own protective covering for their eggs. The praying mantis constructs an intricate cocoon, divided into as many as four hundred compartments, each containing an egg. The material used is a secretion from glands in the abdomen. This secretion flows out as a sticky fluid and then hardens to a tough, papery substance. In this protective covering, the eggs pass the winter or, in tropical countries, survive the dry season. Cockroaches lay their eggs, a few dozen at a time, enclosed in a horny capsule that splits when the eggs hatch.

Among aquatic insects there are many specialized egg-laying procedures. Certain mosquitoes and gnats lay their eggs in long strings or compact little "rafts." These float on the surface of the water until the eggs hatch. One large water beetle constructs a cocoon of silk, furnished with a curved "mast" at one end. Its eggs are laid in this air-filled container and the cocoon floats on the surface like a little boat, bobbing in the wind but never capsizing or sinking.

Some dragonflies lay their eggs in clumps or in long strings that are dropped into the water and soon become surrounded by a jellylike substance. Others insert

The above photograph shows female aphids reproducing parthenogenetically (without fertilization) and viviparously (giving birth to living young).

Top left: Blue damselflies mating. The male grips the female's head with his pincer-like terminal appendages. The female turns her abdomen forward under that of the male to receive sperm. He maintains his grip on her while she lays her eggs under water (bottom left). Then he helps her to the surface.

their eggs carefully into the stems of water plants. In at least one species of dragonfly, the adults work their way right under the water in order to do this. The male holds on to the female's neck with his claspers and helps her to surface when the egg laying is finished. Still other dragonflies lay their eggs in branches overhanging the water, from which the larvae drop when they hatch.

Unlike the higher animals, many insects can reproduce themselves without the mating of male and female. Reproduction through eggs that hatch without fertilization by the male is called *parthenogenesis*. In some species this is the normal method. The stick insect is an example. The males are extremely rare and the females begin to lay unfertilized eggs as soon as they are mature. These eggs develop and hatch normally into more females, and so one generation of females follows another without a break. This also happens occasionally, but not as a general rule, among many grasshoppers and some butterflies and moths. Queen bees and the queens of other social hymenoptera can also lay unfertilized eggs that will produce larvae. These larvae always develop into males.

A slightly different form of parthenogenesis occurs among aphids. During the summer the females give birth to living young females without mating. These first-generation females in turn produce more parthenogenetic daughters, thus building up the population very rapidly. In the autumn, however, males are hatched also as a result of parthenogenesis. Normal mating then takes place, and the females lay eggs that pass over the winter and hatch the following spring.

Except for aphids, viviparous females—that is, females that give birth to living young—are not common among insects. They are to be found among a few species of flies. In some of these flies the egg hatches just the moment before it is laid. Among others, as in the tsetse fly, the larva develops inside the mother's body and the offspring is not born until it is ready to pupate. In some of the parasitic wasps a single egg, laid in the normal way, may divide repeatedly until anything from two to 2000 offspring result. This phenomenon is known as polyembryony.

In a very few species of insects the larvae can reproduce themselves by a process known as *pedogenesis*. In this case a number of larvae develop from unfertilized eggs within the body of another older larva and behave almost like parasites. They feed on the tissues of their "mother" and finally make their way out through its skin. These offspring repeat the process, so that many larvae develop from the original one. Finally, the "daughter" larvae mature into adult insects and mate normally.

Insect Parasites

A PARASITE is a plant or an animal that attaches itself to another plant or animal, called the host. The parasite then lives a part of its life, at least, entirely upon and at the expense of its host. A parasite is an enemy of the host, and few insects are free from parasitic insect enemies, whose existence helps to preserve a balance in the insect world.

In nature insects increase so rapidly that their numbers are limited only by losses caused by adverse factors in their environment. One of these factors is parasitism. Anyone who has collected caterpillars and tried to raise them and let them develop into moths or butterflies is almost certain to have found that many of the caterpillars have merely produced flies or small wasplike creatures. This disappointing result happens because the caterpillars are infected with parasites.

The common cabbage white butterfly is a good example of an insect that seems always to be attacked by a parasite. Even when cabbage butterfly caterpillars appear in large numbers, very few reach maturity and produce another generation of butterflies. Nine out of ten have been "stung" by a species of small ichneumon wasp, which lays its eggs in the larvae. The ichneumon eggs hatch into parasitic grubs that do not kill the caterpillar while it is growing. But when the caterpillar is almost fully fed and ready to become a pupa, dozens of parasite grubs bore their way out through its skin and pupate in little yellow cocoons all around it. In the process they kill the caterpillars. This is the reason why a huge influx of cabbage white butterflies is never followed by a big second brood.

There are many thousands of species of parasitic insects, especially in the order Hymenoptera, which includes wasps, bees, and ants. Some species in the order Diptera, which includes the "true" or two-winged flies, are also parasitic. Some insects are parasites of insects; some are parasites of man and other animals.

The ichneumon wasps are thought by many to be the most important parasites of other insects. Some of them are quite large. The adults feed on nectar, but the larvae of all ichneumons are parasitic on other insects. One particularly interesting species of ichneumon wasps is parasitic on the wood-boring larvae of the great horntail. With the aid of incredibly sensitive and constantly moving antennae, a female ichneumon can locate the horntail larvae feeding in a piece of wood, even if they are an inch or more beneath the surface. Then, with her

Right: An ichneumon wasp is attracted by the scent of a wood-wasp larva inside a pine tree. She bores through the pine with her ovipositor, then lays eggs in the larva.

60

Top: Steel engraving of the larvae of
the ichneumon wasp on a caterpillar
host. The fly lays eggs in the caterpillar;
the developed larvae eat their way
out through its skin, killing it in the
process. Bottom: An engraving of a
single larva, much enlarged.

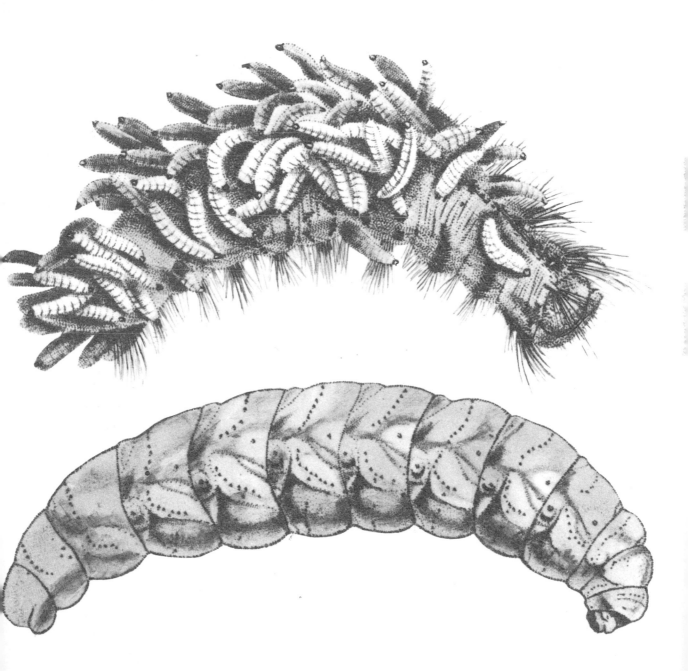

long, thin ovipositor, she bores down right through bark and wood until she reaches a horntail larva and can lay an egg in its body.

Some ichneumons attack the aquatic larvae of certain caddis flies and go diving right under the water to locate them. Observers have reported that these wasps are able to stay submerged for as long as ten minutes at a time. Before the parasitic grub finally pupates inside the empty skin of its dead host it spins a curious curled streamer that trails out into the water.

Another group of parasitic wasps is the braconids, of which some of the tropical species have ovipositors up to 4½ inches long. One braconid parasitizes adult lady-bug beetles while others attack various moths, including quite a number that are pests in stored grain. Some braconids are not internal parasites but *ectoparasites* — that is, they attach themselves to the outside of a host and live by sucking its blood.

Another group of wasps, the big family of Aphididae are very useful parasites from man's point of view, since they attack many aphids. It is quite easy to recognize a parasitized aphid. It has a peculiar swollen look; and it becomes motionless and very quickly dies. The parasite attacks its victims in a very curious way. It approaches them head on and then bends its tail under its own body and between its legs until its ovipositor is in position to bore a hole in the aphid's back. Some of these parasites even have a tonglike arrangement that grips the aphid firmly while the egg is being inserted.

The most beautiful of the parasitic wasps, shimmering in metallic colors of gold, blue, green, and purple, are members of the family Chrysididae. They are found all over the world and are parasitic mainly on other hunting wasps and solitary bees. Some of the Chrysididae prey on more than one host, and the adults vary in appearance according to the host on which they have grown. The wasp *Chrysis ignita* belongs to this family and it is much slimmer when it has emerged from the nest of a hunting wasp than when its juvenile stage was spent in the nest of a solitary bee. Since the hunting wasp stocks its nest with meat (other insects) and the solitary bee stocks its nest with pollen, this is a rather interesting illustration of the fact that a meat diet is less fattening than one consisting mainly of sugar and starch.

Some of the members of this family have wingless females. The so-called velvet ants are an example. Looking much like large ants covered with velvety fur, they hang around the nesting holes of solitary bees. There they wait for an opportunity to sneak in and lay their eggs as soon as the cells have been well stocked with food. The egg of the parasite usually hatches before that of the owner of the nest, and the parasitic larva first

Above: Cocoons of Braconid wasps beneath the bodies of their dead aphid hosts. Before pupation the wasp leaves its host, which it has sucked dry; makes a tentlike cocoon around itself as a protective shelter; sticks this to a stem or leaf by a warp of silk; and then fastens the dead host on top as a roof.

Right: A parasitic fly on a sunflower. This fly lays eggs only in places she knows to be frequented by her chosen host, usually a solitary bee. The hatched larvae bore their way into the bee.

devours the host's egg before starting on the food supplies. But sometimes the host's egg is not eaten, and the
rightful inhabitant may even reach a fair size before it
is attacked and devoured by the more aggressive parasite.

A great deal of research into the habits of some tiny
wasps known as chalcid wasps was done by an Italian
entomologist, who found more than 2000 larvae of one
small chalcid in the larva of a single moth. This does not
mean that the parasite actually laid 2000 eggs; it is an
example of polyembryony discussed in the previous
chapter. The parasite probably laid only a single egg,
but the embryo in the egg divided repeatedly until 2000
larvae resulted.

One common chalcid wasp attacks the pupae of many
butterflies immediately after their final molt, while they
are still soft and vulnerable. The pupae quickly become
discolored and then rigid. If one is broken open it will be
seen to be completely filled by a thick mass of parasitic
larvae. When these leave their host the shell is riddled
with tiny holes, like a sieve. Chalcids also attack aphids,
scale insects, bark beetles, and gall wasps, and many are
parasitic on the eggs of various insects.

Quite a number of these very small wasps parasitize
aquatic insects and swim under water with the aid of

Above: Chalcid wasps newly emerged
from a swallowtail pupa. The chalcid
probably only lays a single egg in
the pupa; this divides repeatedly,
resulting in up to 2000 larvae.

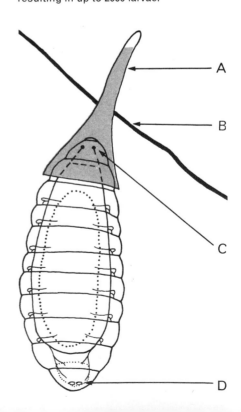

Above: A mud-dauber wasp storing her nest of mud with spiders paralyzed by her sting, before laying eggs on their bodies. When the eggs hatch several weeks later, the larvae have a ready store of meat, preserved within the mud.

Diagram of how the newly hatched larva respires while still in its host. As the larva hatches from the egg, it thrusts the pedicel of the egg (A) through the body wall of its host (B). Air passes along the pedicel, through the spiracles (C) to the body and head (D).

their fringed wings in order to find their victims. An English naturalist, Sir John Lubbock, discovered a tiny chalcid which laid its eggs in the eggs of water boatmen, dragonflies, and other water creatures.

Among the smallest of the parasitic wasps are close relatives of the chalcids, called the fairy flies, which measure only 0.5 to 0.8 millimeters in length and are visible only if they happen to settle on a light background, where they can just be seen as tiny dark dots. In spite of their incredibly small size they are highly developed insects. They have all the organs you find in larger species, except that some have no tracheal tubes and appear to use their fringed wings as breathing organs instead. It is very difficult to investigate the life history of such tiny creatures, but many of them have been found to parasitize the eggs of aquatic insects.

The praying mantis is parasitized by an unusual wasp that begins its development in a mantis egg but later transfers itself to an adult mantis as a bloodsucking ectoparasite. The mantis may be weakened but does not die. If the mantis is a female and produces a capsule of eggs, the parasite at once moves over to the capsule and there lays its own eggs.

The parasitic wasps of the group known as Dryinidae

inject a poison into their hosts at the same time that they lay their eggs. This causes a temporary paralysis and makes the work of attaching the eggs easier.

Many of the parasitic wasps attack insects that are a great nuisance to man. One beetle that is kept in check by parasites is the museum beetle. Another insect pest partially controlled by parasitic wasps is the Hessian fly, a serious pest of cereal crops, which was introduced from Europe into the United States. This pest is attacked by a small parasitic wasp named *Platygaster*. The possibility of controlling pests by encouraging their parasites was discussed by Linnaeus some two hundred years ago. At the present time the principles of biological control are receiving a great deal of attention.

The order Hymenoptera, important though it is, by no means comprises all the parasitic insects. Two-winged flies of the order Diptera often attack the larvae of other insects. The parasitic flies lay their eggs on the skin of their host. From there the larvae burrow into the body and gradually, by their feeding, kill the host larvae.

There are also a number of flies that are parasitic on warm-blooded animals. The warble fly, the sheep botfly, the deer fly, and several others live, in their early stages, in the flesh, the nasal passages, the bronchial tubes, or the intestines of living animals. Some flies, particularly wingless species, are ectoparasites on bats and birds. When large numbers are present they can even kill their hosts, particularly young birds still in the nest.

Other permanent parasites on warm-blooded animals are lice and fleas. There are very many different species, each one parasitic on certain animals and unable to live

Below: The wild rabbit that is native to Central and Southern Europe but has also been introduced into Australia and New Zealand. Top: The mosquito *Anopheles annulipes*, the chief vector of myxomatosis, a disease that infects the rabbits in Australia. The other insect is the rabbit flea that is chief vector of the disease in England.

for any length of time except on their proper hosts. Extensive studies of fleas, especially those found on rabbits and martens, have revealed that the fleas attack the adults and not the young. The rabbit flea is also, in Europe, the chief agent in the spread of myxomatosis, a fatal disease of rabbits. In Australia the same disease in spread by mosquitoes.

In the case of fleas, it is the adult insects that live as parasites, feeding on the blood of their host. The larvae develop among the debris in the nest and do not become bloodsuckers until after their metamorphosis is completed.

Few beetles are truly parasitic, although some species live as permanent guests in the nests of ants. There they are fed and tended by their hosts and often consume large quantities of the ants' eggs and larvae. These beetles are accepted and even welcomed because they secrete certain sweet and aromatic substances for which the ants develop a strong craving.

The oil beetles, on the other hand, must be classified as true parasites; there are a number of species, with a world-wide distribution. They all contain a strong acrid poison which makes them both dangerous and distasteful to most animals. This substance was formerly thought to be useful as a drug.

The big oil beetle is a dark, clumsy insect, with a huge bulging abdomen. The females lay large batches of eggs numbering several thousands in heaps on the ground. These hatch into very active, long-legged larvae which at once make their way to a plant, climb upward onto its flowers, and then sit waiting for bees to come and gather nectar or pollen. As soon as a bee lands, the larvae cling to its furry body and are carried away. Before their life history was known they had often been seen and described as bee lice. In order to continue its development each larva must attach itself to a female of one of the solitary bees and be carried to her nest. It remains attached to its host until the moment when the bee lays an egg. Then the beetle larva jumps down, lands on the egg — which is often floating on a pool of honey — and is sealed into the cell, where its future food supply is assured. Its first action now is to consume the egg. It then changes from its active state into a fat sluggish grub and continues to feed on the stores laid in by the bee until it finally pupates. It then emerges as a fully developed oil beetle the following spring. The chances that the larva of this oil beetle will find the right host are very small and so, in spite of the large number of eggs that are laid, this insect is rather scarce. Other kinds of oil beetles have a very similar life history, most of them being parasitic on solitary bees, but some related species feed in the larval stage on the eggs of grasshoppers.

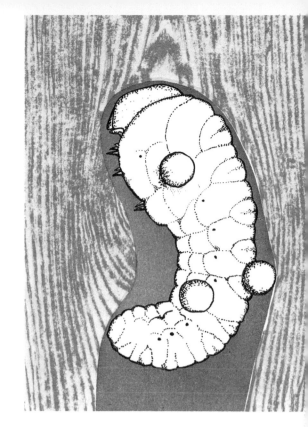

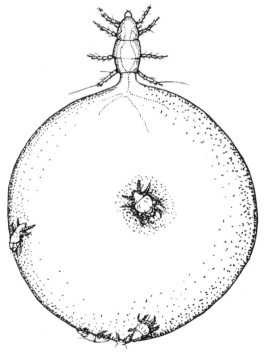

Top: Larva of the common furniture beetle being parasitized by three female Pyemotes, members of the spider class. They suck the juices of the larva's body. Below this is a gorged female Pyemote. Her male offspring, which are very small, never leave the surface of her body. They mate with their sisters which, as soon as they are fertilized, drop off their mother and seek out a host of their own.

Flight and Migration

THE earliest known fossil insects are all wingless. Most entomologists agree that flying insects did not appear until three hundred million years ago. It seems probable, however, that at an earlier period there were insects with fixed ridges on their bodies. These projections may have served as stabilizers during a fall or a jump, and possibly they also enabled the insects to be carried along by the wind. Movable wings—and with them the power of controlled flight—seem to have developed gradually from these ridges.

Only adult insects have fully developed wings; larvae and pupae all lack the means to fly. In fact, few insects do much moving about of any kind until they are fully adult. There are a few exceptions such as grasshopper larvae, some wandering caterpillars, and the larvae of a small European midge, which are sometimes seen in woodlands, crawling along in broad, densely packed processions. Generally speaking, insect larvae live in one place, surrounded by the food they require. Adult insects, on the other hand, often have to travel quite long distances—to find food, to mate, and to find suitable places in which to lay their eggs.

Some insects are so small and light that they can be carried a considerable distance by the wind, without the help of wings. Small hairy caterpillars, wingless ants, aphids, and small beetles and their larvae, have been found as high as 5000 feet, where they have been carried up by rising air currents. Even a specimen of the common flea was once caught sailing along at 200 feet above sea level. However, the majority of insects rely upon their wings to carry them from one place to another.

Insect wings come in many shapes and sizes, but all are developed on the same general plan. This consists of a thin, double-layered membrane supported by a network of ribs, or veins. The vein pattern of the wings differs from one species to another as human fingerprints differ from one individual to another. Often a slight variation in the vein pattern is the only difference between two species that otherwise look identical.

The most common wing arrangement in insects is four wings arranged in two pairs—the forewings and the hindwings. Among insects, such as bees, wasps, butterflies, and moths, each forewing is linked by tiny hooks, or barbs, to the corresponding hindwing. In flight the two pairs move in unison as one large wing. In so-called primitive insects, such as dragonflies and grasshoppers, the forewings and hindwings are not joined together, and the two pairs move independently.

At first glance the wings of these seven species of robber flies seem identical. Closer comparison of the patterns of vein formation (marked blue) reveals structural differences. Such precise observation of detail is often the only outward means of identifying an insect.

During flight the hindwings of this rhinoceros beetle provide all the propulsion. The forewings stay fixed like airplane wings, providing some lift; they fold to form a protective encasement for the gossamer hindwings when the beetle is at rest.

There is often a great difference in size and appearance between the forewings and the hindwings. In some species there is also a difference in function. In several groups of insects the hindwings do all the work of flying while the forewings serve only as protective coverings under which the hindwings are folded when not in use. All winged beetles have this kind of arrangement. Their forewings are covered with the same kind of hard layer as the rest of the body; their hindwings are thin and transparent and have hinged ribs that can be folded. Anyone who has watched a ladybird beetle settling after a flight has seen the hindwings being folded and tucked away under the wing cases, or *elytra,* which are in fact the forewings. This putting away of the wings, although quick, is not instantaneous. And, when a beetle takes off, there is a slight time lag between the lifting of the elytra and the first wing beats, while the hindwings are unfolded and stretched out.

Earwigs, too, use only their hindwings in flight. Their long, narrow wings are folded like a fan and then

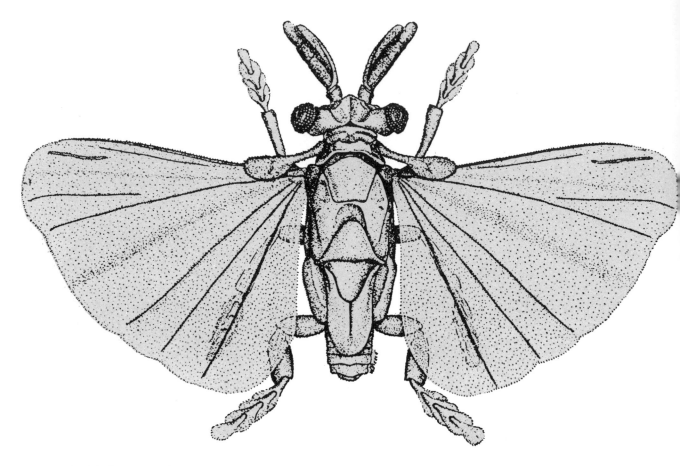

doubled over to fit under the forewings, which are no more than very short leathery flaps. Some observers claim to have seen earwigs using their tail forceps to help fold away their wings after a flight. But since earwigs seldom fly except at night, observation is difficult. Casual observers, in fact, often do not realize that earwigs have any wings.

In many species of insects the hindwings are much smaller than the forewings. In some the hind pair has disappeared entirely, leaving them with only two wings. Some species, belonging to orders that are normally winged, have lost their powers of flight and become wingless. Quite a few grasshoppers never develop wings, but their strong legs enable them to leap so well that leaping almost takes the place of flight. Many beetles cannot fly, and there are wingless forms among most other insect orders.

Often only one sex has retained its wings. In these cases, it is usually the males that fly while the females simply sit and wait for their mates. The females attract the males either by scent or, as does a female glowworm, by light signals. One exception to this practice is a small chalcid wasp, which fertilizes the fig. Its female is

Above: The male of a minute parasitic insect from North America. Its forewings have degenerated to small clublike processes; its large fanlike hindwings have no cross-veins at all. The female of the species is wingless and legless and remains larviform all her life, never leaving her host.

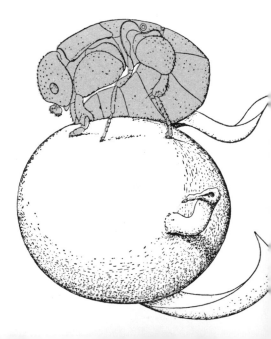

A male chalcid wasp fertilizing the female that has developed inside a gall in a fig. The male is wingless and slow-moving; the female later flies freely and pollinates figs.

winged and very mobile while the male is wingless and can only crawl about very slowly on the trees.

Entomologists have noticed that insects living near the sea, especially on small exposed islands, tend to be wingless. This adaptation may be a safety device, because in such regions flying insects are in danger of being swept out to sea on the wind and drowned. On the lonely Kerguelen Island in the Indian Ocean, none of the insects has wings. On an island off the coast of Alaska there is a crane fly that has useless, tiny wings, although elsewhere the same species is able to fly.

In flying, insects make use of two separate sets of muscles, the *indirect* and the *direct* flight muscles. It is the indirect muscles that produce the beating movements of the wings. They are attached not to the wings themselves but to the inside walls of the thorax. As they alternately raise and lower the top of the thorax, the up-and-down movement is transmitted to the hinges of the wings.

The direct flight muscles move the wings backwards and forwards or make them turn. These comparatively slight movements make it possible for the insect to steer and maneuver in the air. If the wings moved only straight up and down, flight would be feeble and uncontrolled. But because the wings can be twisted, they direct the air stream in various ways so that flight in different directions is possible. Some insects with very mobile wings, like the dragonflies, can even fly backwards. Many flies and bees can perform intricate aerobatics at high speed.

One of the earliest experiments on the movements of insects wings was done by the nineteenth-century French entomologist, E. J. Marey. Taking a common wasp, he glued tiny pieces of gold leaf to the tips of the wings. He then held the insect in such a way that, although it could not escape, it was able to move its wings quite freely. A strong beam of light was then directed onto the wasp. Reflected by the gold leaf, the beam traced an elongated figure-eight pattern in the air. Later experiments have shown that not all insects move their

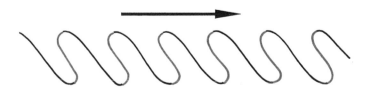

Left: High speed photographs, taken in Paris in 1907, showing the movement and direction of each wing of the small blue dragonfly during flight. Only a small portion of the whole of one cycle is shown. Above: The diagram follows the course of the wing tip of a blow fly in flight. The arrow gives direction of flight; the reddish-brown line marks the upward and backward stroke of the wing, the black line the downward and forward movement. Both up and down strokes give propulsion, although the down stroke is the more effective.

Hornet	100		
Hive-bee	250		
Large White Butterfly	12		
Housefly	190		
Humming-bird Hawk Moth	85		
Bumblebee	130		
Cockchafer	46		
Aeshna Dragonfly	38		

wings in this way. Flies, for example, trace out a pattern consisting of a series of loops.

Wing movements are difficult to study because they are so fast. But much research has been done since Marey's day, using high-speed cameras and other modern equipment. By such means it has been possible to record the speed of the wingbeats in many insects.

The honeybee moves very fast, with 250 wingbeats per second. The bumblebee registers only 130, and the cabbage white butterfly as few as 12. The rate of wingbeat, however, is not in direct proportion to the speed of flight. The hummingbird hawk moth, with only 85 beats per second, has a speed of just over 11 miles an hour. But a larger dragonfly, with only 38 beats per second, can fly at 15½ miles per hour. The housefly, whose wings beat at the rate of 190 per second, is a slower flier with a speed of only 6½ miles per hour.

Claims are sometimes made that certain insects can fly at a speed of over 100 miles per hour, but this is almost certainly much exaggerated. In general, insects cannot fly as fast as birds.

Because of their small size and weight, insects soon reach a speed at which air resistance becomes too great

Above: Diagram illustrating the number of wingbeats and the relative distance traveled per second, of eight species of insects. Neither the rate of wingbeat nor the size of insects is in direct proportion to distance covered.

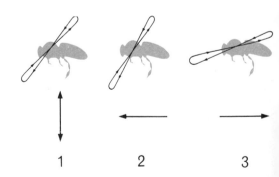

Above: The plane of the wingbeat regulates direction of flight. In (1) the near horizontal plane of the honeybee's wings results in slow or hovering flight. In forward flight the wings are more vertical (2). The plane of (3) produces backward flight.

Above: A suction trap, which is hoisted up by balloon and used to obtain specimens and determine insect density at high altitudes. Below: A fairy fly is so small that it has little wing control and is blown around by the wind.

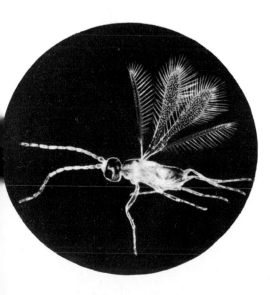

for their muscular power to overcome. Indeed, calculations based on wing area, body weight, and so on, have shown that it is theoretically impossible for certain insects, such as some beetles and bumblebees, to fly at all. Nevertheless they do fly. This goes to prove that the power of flight is not just a matter of the right size of wing combined with a certain weight and volume of body, but that the way in which the wing moves is at least equally important.

Many of the small winged insects are so light that they can make controlled flights only when the air is quite still. Normally they travel only short distances and seem to float in the air rather than fly. But aphids and many of the tiny parasitic flies are sometimes swept up on rising air currents and carried by the wind for hundreds of miles. Descending currents finally bring them down to earth again. When kites equipped with insect traps are sent up to collect samples at 1000 feet or more, a great many aphids are often caught, together with small flies and tiny chalcid wasps. Larger and stronger insects, which can to some extent resist being carried by the winds, are seldom found more than about 200 feet up.

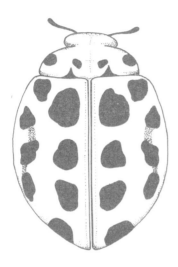

Widespread infestations of aphids often begin in the spring, when the winged female forms emerge from the eggs. Soon after the First World War, when very little was known about the migration of insects, a party of naturalists was amazed to find large numbers of spruce aphids on the snow-covered mountains of Spitsbergen. With them was a kind of fly that in the larval stage preys on aphids. There are no spruce trees in the Norwegian islands of Spitsbergen, and the nearest spruce forest the insects could have come from is 800 miles away on the Kola Peninsula in Russia. These spruce aphids were probably swept helplessly along by the winds. Their long journey was almost certainly an involuntary migration. It is possible, however, that the migration was to some degree controlled, for sometimes aphids and tiny parasitic flies seem deliberately to launch themselves into the air when the wind is strong, as though to take advantage of it.

Whether this particular migration was voluntary or not, it is certain that many insects do deliberately set out on journeys or migrations. Such insects may cover only quite short distances. But sometimes the insects are on the wing for weeks at a time and cover distances of hundreds or even thousands of miles. Among the short-distance migrations are those of certain beetles, which move from the open fields where they breed to woodlands a few miles away where they feed on the leaves of the trees. Many mosquitoes, too, alternate between their feeding and breeding grounds, which may be several miles apart. In some regions, especially in North America, ladybird beetles migrate in order to find suitable quarters in the mountains for hibernating. There are also several records of certain flies migrating, although few details are as yet known.

Prominent among insects that make longer and more spectacular migrations are locusts and butterflies. Since

Many species of ladybirds migrate from their summer feeding and breeding grounds to hibernate, usually in cool places at a high altitude; they may travel several hundred miles.
The 16-spot ladybird (above) is one such migrant. The swarm below stayed inert, immune to cold, all winter.

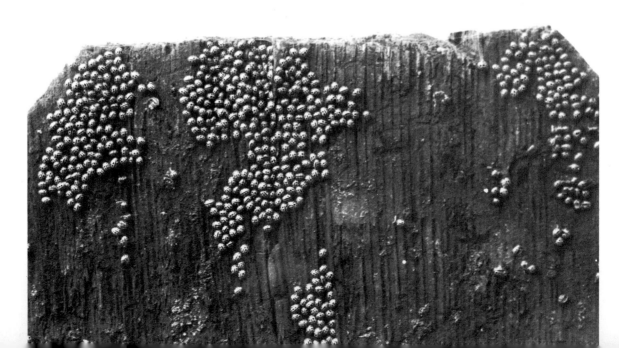

Left: A locust swarm in Africa. A single swarm of desert locusts may consist of a thousand million insects, covering eight square miles and consuming 3,000 tons of food per day. Above: The burrowing wasp is not a true migrant but will fly with a swarm of locusts. It paralyzes a locust with its sting and buries it as food for its young when they hatch.

Right: A female large cabbage white
butterfly. Below right: Excerpt
from Turpyn's Chronicles of Calais,
describing a vast swarm of white
butterflies "thicke as flakes of snowe"
seen in Calais, France, heading
from northeast to southwest in July
1508. The exact routes of migratory
butterflies have now been plotted.
The accuracy of Turpyn's record is
borne out by the above map of the
observed migration of cabbage whites.
This movement through central Europe
towards the south occurs at the end of
July and the beginning of August.

another chapter is devoted to locusts, we shall deal here only with butterfly migrations. This subject has been studied in great detail.

Most species of migrating butterflies seem to set out on their travels toward distant breeding grounds in spring. This movement comes very soon after they have emerged from their chrysalises. Invariably they fly in one direction only—usually northward in the Northern Hemisphere. Far fewer observations have been made of their movements in autumn, but the evidence suggests that they then make the return journey southward.

Butterfly migrations are often observed near coastlines, where the insects may actually be seen coming in from the sea. On the south and east coasts of England observers have frequently watched great swarms of cabbage whites and clouded yellows landing exhausted to feed on the first available flowers. This can be a spectacular sight: the landing of a swarm of cabbage whites has been likened to a sudden snowstorm of fluttering white butterflies. Red admirals migrate in somewhat less dense swarms, but these butterflies often land in very large numbers and very quickly spread out over the countryside. Bath whites are very rare migrants to England, but now and then large numbers arrive, as they did in 1945, when they were seen all along the south coast.

Other migrant butterflies, like the Queen of Spain fritillary and the long-tailed and short-tailed blues, occasionally travel from Europe and Africa to England, but never in large numbers. Very often several different species of butterflies, and moths as well, migrate at the same time. Probably this is because weather conditions happen to be exactly right for a long flight.

Many butterfly migrations start from the Mediterranean area—from North Africa, southern Spain, Italy, or the French Riviera—where butterflies often continue breeding throughout the year. The painted lady is one of the most noted travelers among butterflies. Its migratory flights have been traced from Algeria or Egypt right across Europe to England and even to Scandinavia. The actual start of a big migration of butterflies is seldom observed by people who can understand and record what is happening. But in the case of the painted lady there are several interesting records of this kind.

The first observation was made in March, 1879—the year of one big migration—by an Englishman named Skertchly. While traveling in the Sudan in Africa, he came upon an area of rough grass where he saw thousands of painted ladies emerging from chrysalises suspended on the grass stems. As soon as their wings were dry, the butterflies rose into the air all at one time and

Above: Map of the British Isles showing observations, recorded in 1945, of the usually rare immigrant, the bath white butterfly.

Most Camberwell beauty butterflies are late summer immigrants from Scandinavia. The map below shows where they have been recorded since the first two were caught at Camberwell in 1748. They have never been known to breed in Britain.

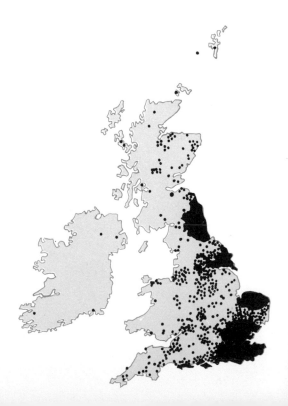

A convolvulus hawk moth, and a record from an entomologist's diary of its abundance in Germany in 1719. It is a migrant in Europe, Africa, Asia, and Australia. A strong flier, one was caught in 1880 on a ship 350 miles northwest of the Azores.

set off toward the east, the most direct route to the sea. There they probably turned north to fly over Israel and Jordan to Asia Minor and then over the Caucasus into southern Russia and eastern Europe.

A similar experience was recorded toward the end of the Second World War. A young soldier standing on a beach in Algeria saw swarms of painted ladies emerging in the scrubby vegetation close to the shore. As soon as their wings were dry, these also took to the air and flew off northward across the Mediterranean. The painted lady occurs in many parts of the world, and wherever it is found spectacular migrations have been recorded — in North America, Australia, New Zealand and the Pacific Islands, India and Ceylon, southern and central Africa, all parts of Europe, and the Middle East.

Most butterfly migrants travel only in one direction in spring. Since they often breed on the way, it may take more than one generation to complete the journey. When a return flight in the opposite direction takes place, it is usually made by the descendants of the original migrants.

The only species in which the same individual makes the two-way journey is the famous monarch butterfly so common in the United States. These big, strong butterflies summer as far north as Canada. In the autumn they regularly fly to southern California and Florida. There large numbers gather in certain favorite localities in order to spend the winter in semi-hibernation.

These autumn flights begin in Canada and in northern parts of the United States during August. Later the swarms grow larger and larger as monarchs from more southerly areas join the flight. In March, when their food plant, the milkweed, begins to grow, the northward return journey starts again. The monarchs then move off singly, the females laying eggs as they go. Some fly only a comparatively short distance, while others continue right into Canada. Some have even been known to reach Hudson Bay. In the southern regions several generations of monarchs are bred during the summer, but farther north the number is smaller. Observers agree that in Virginia there may be as many as four generations; in New York State three; in Iowa two; and in Ontario only one.

Quite a few moths also migrate, and the most regular traveler is the silver Y moth. This is a medium-sized moth whose caterpillars feed on a great variety of low-growing plants. These moths fly by day as well as by night, and often appear in huge swarms. Some of the larger hawk moths, such as the famous death's–head, also migrate; so do the Convolvulus moth, the striped hawk, and several others. Only one moth, the bogong

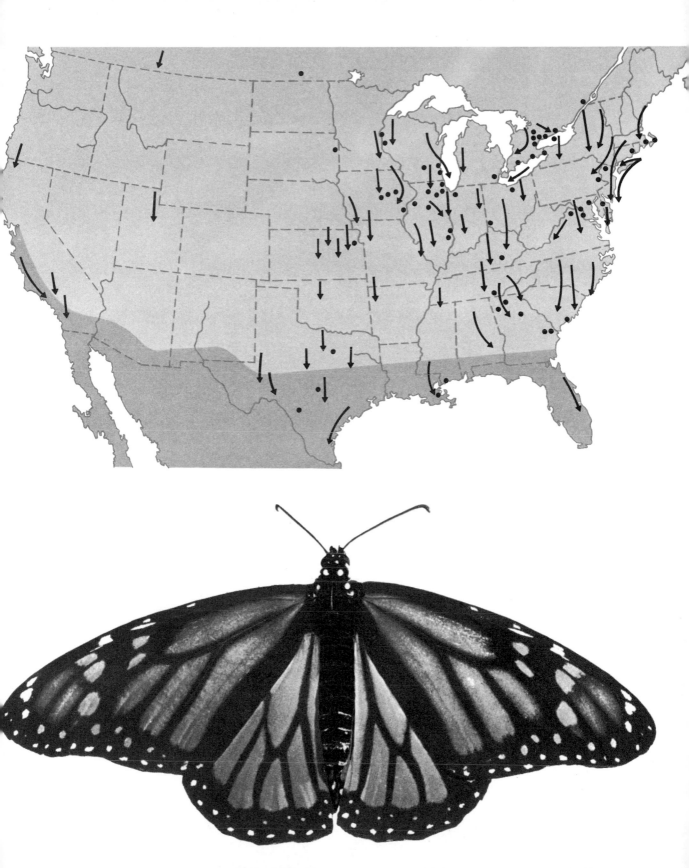

Above: The monarch, or milkweed, butterfly. Their main migrations occur in North America. Arrows in the map of the United States and southern Canada show the direction of their migration. They move at first in groups of two's and three's, but later join up in swarms.

Their massing points are marked by spots on the map. Migration begins in August; they go south to warm areas (shown dark). Few flights occur in the Rocky Mountains region.

moth of Australia, behaves like the monarch butterfly. The bogong also migrates in order to hibernate and returns in the spring to repopulate its old living area.

Although a great deal of study and research has been devoted to the subject of migration, the reasons why insects migrate are not yet fully understood. In some cases the urge to migrate is obviously triggered off by overcrowding or an extreme food shortage. But this is not always the case. Changes in temperature and in the length of night and day may also have an influence. Some entomologists have suggested that electric storms and changes in atmospheric pressure can bring about a migratory flight. It is certainly true that large migrations frequently take place just before a storm, when the wind has not yet sprung up to blow the insects along.

In the case of insects that migrate regularly every year, it seems obvious that migration is somehow linked to the rhythm of the seasons. In many tropical countries migrations seem to be linked with severe drought. However, in those insects that migrate only occasionally, it is extremely difficult to discover what causes the migrations.

Much research remains to be done on the question,

Some migratory insects keep to their determined course in a very definite way. Right: Migrating butterflies hit a bungalow obstructing their path. After beating against the wall they retreat and rise rather than turn aside.

A migrating dragonfly is the vector of a parasite harmful to fowl. Below are the hosts in the parasite's life cycle. First the eggs of the parasite are eaten by a water snail. They develop, are excreted by the snail, and are then drawn into the nymph of the dragonfly by breathing movements. If the chicken eats nymph or adult dragonfly containing parasites, it becomes infected. The parasite causes inflammation of the oviduct and egg-laying is disturbed or halted; peritonitis can develop. Thus this migrating dragonfly can cause food shortage.

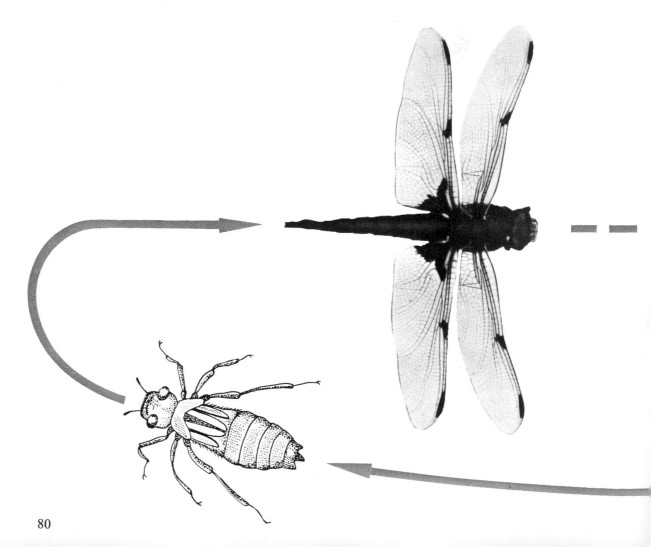

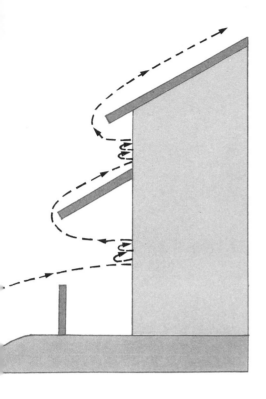

but one thing is quite clear. That is, once migration has started, the urge to go on traveling is very strong. Until this urge is exhausted, the insects will continue on their way undeterred by natural obstacles, even if the majority of them perish in the process. Migrating insects almost always move steadily onward, seemingly confident of their direction, pausing only briefly to rest and feed. Quite often insects that normally fly only in daylight will, when migrating, continue through the night. (Migrating butterflies such as red admirals have been seen at lighthouses and have been caught in moth traps at night.) They often travel fast and will work their way in the desired direction even against the wind. They cross wide stretches of water and fly over high mountain passes. If obstructed by tall buildings or hills, they will ascend and fly over them rather than be turned aside from their course. The whole behavior of migrating insects suggests that they are in the grip of a powerful instinct, which has been compared to mass hysteria. What finally halts the migration nobody knows. Assuming that some hormone triggers off the move, it can only be said that migration probably comes to an end when this chemical is no longer produced in the insects' bodies.

Cycles of Insects

THE number of insects that may be seen in any one place varies from season to season, from day to day, and even from hour to hour. These changes in number — or even complete disappearances and reappearances — of insects follow regular patterns or cycles.

The daily cycles are the easiest to observe. When conditions are normal, certain insects appear at certain times of day. Their movements depend on the intensity of the light, the temperature, and the humidity that suits them best. Until the sun is shining warmly, butterflies will not fly. Beetles and flies will not become active until the morning is well advanced. Bees will not leave their hives until the sun has reached a certain height.

At midday, when the light is most intense and the temperature at its highest, some insects will disappear to rest in the shade until the cool of late afternoon. Others prefer this warmest part of the day. Ants, for example, become very active, many flies are present, and grasshoppers begin to "sing." Then, as dusk falls, midges and mosquitoes begin to bite. After sunset the night-flying insects such as moths, June bugs, and water boatmen take to the wing. Even indoors, as the daylight fades, silverfish, cockroaches, and beetles not normally seen during the day emerge from their hiding places to search for food.

The daily cycle may be upset by unseasonable weather. Extremes of heat or cold, strong winds, or heavy rain may temporarily cancel out the factors that normally influence the cycle. The seasonal cycles tend to be more constant because they depend mainly upon the temperature. But there are many other factors to take into consideration, for the seasonal cycles of the various insects are based on their life cycles.

The majority of insects go through one complete life cycle in a year. Some produce several generations in that time and are seen in two or three separate cycles of abundance during the year.

This sand fly (above) is active at dusk and again at dawn. The female is blood-sucking and can be the vector of a number of parasitic diseases.

Top right: A carpenter bee on a thistle. This bee thrives in warmth and sunlight. It is called "carpenter" because it will bore a foot deep into wood to lay its eggs.

The cockroach (right) shuns light. By day it hides in cracks and crevices, but at night it emerges in unclean living quarters. These insects first lived in the tropics, but have now spread to all temperate zones.

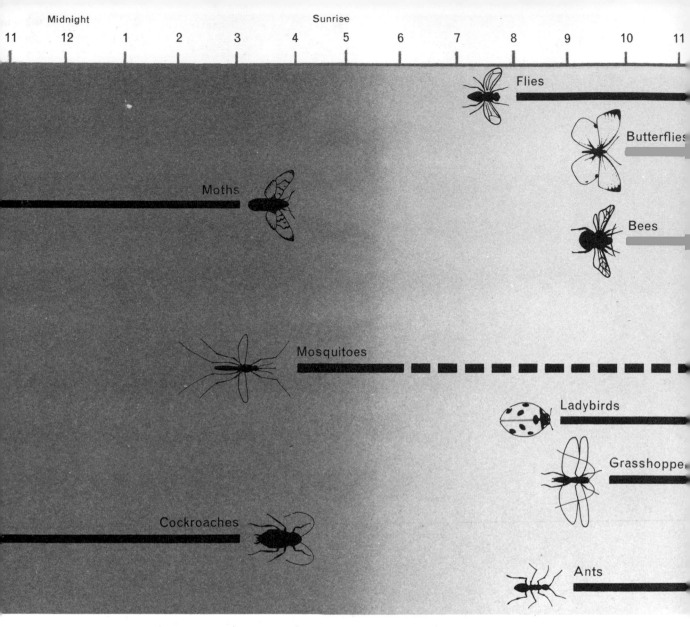

The chart shows the periods of activity during 24 hours of certain common insects. June 21st in southern England was the date and situation chosen, but a similar chart could be

The small tortoise-shell butterfly of Europe is an example. The adults hibernate throughout the winter and do not appear in any numbers until the spring, when they come out to feed and lay their eggs. They can be seen for some weeks, until they die from old age. In July there is another cycle when the second-generation butterflies are on the wing. These too lay their eggs and die. Then there is another gap until the autumn, when the third generation is feeding on the autumn flowers. This third generation goes into hibernation and will start the cycle again in the following year.

Butterflies that produce only one generation each year appear for two weeks or a little longer at their correct season. After that the adults are not seen again until about the same time the following year. The

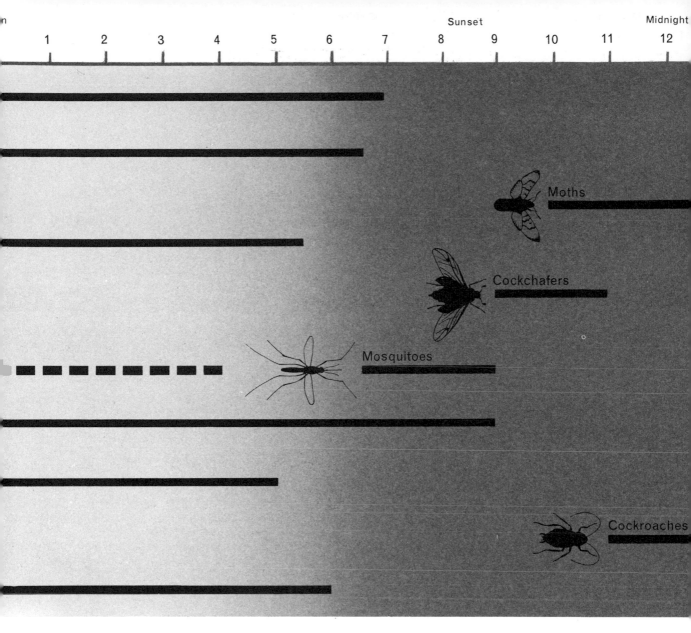

made for any other time and place. The entire 24 hours is occupied by a continuous relay of insects. As might be expected, the daylight hours are favored by most of the species.

orange-tip, for example, flies only during May and the white admiral is normally seen only in July.

Insects that go on breeding right through the summer appear at first in quite small numbers. Gradually they grow more and more abundant before they disappear. This is very noticeable with the social wasps. In the spring only an occasional queen wasp can be seen. As the summer goes on, worker wasps become more common. In August, when the nests have reached their maximum size, workers are abundant. Then they die off in September, and only the queens are left.

Some species of insects that breed and increase very quickly have a brief period of great abundance followed by an equally quick decline. This scarcity usually is caused by predators and parasites that have killed great

Aphids increase very rapidly in early summer. The above two photographs of an infested broad bean plant were taken within a few days of each other at the beginning of June.

numbers. Aphids are a good example. In early summer, plants may be covered with certain species, but by late summer it is often difficult to find a single survivor of those species. Other periods of abundance of particular insects are due to the vast numbers that emerge from the pupal stage at the same time. The "rise" of the May fly has been mentioned and often craneflies appear in great numbers in late summer or early autumn.

A few insects, because they have a life cycle that spans several years, can be seen only at long intervals. The seventeen-year cicada appears in large numbers only three or four times during a normal human life. Many of the larger beetles are seen in any number only once in every three or four years. And enormous swarms of grasshoppers and locusts build up only from time to time, without any special seasonal rhythm.

Some insects take different forms or live on different foods according to the seasonal cycle in which they appear. In many butterflies that produce two generations in a year, those flying about in summer look very different from those of the parent generation that flew in the spring. Certain aphids feed in one generation on the roots of plants and in the next on the leaves or shoots, or even on an entirely different plant. Many of the gall wasps have alternating generations of winged and wingless individuals.

The great majority of insects are most active when warm and humid weather coincides with a season of the year when food is available both for the adults and for the larvae. In temperate climates, this means the summer; in the tropics, the rainy season.

A few insects prefer cooler conditions, and the adults' flying season occurs in the autumn and winter. One example of this is the small, fragile-looking winter moth. The adult males of this species fly at night, often in cold and foggy weather when the temperature is only a few degrees above freezing. The females, which are wingless, lay their eggs at a time when most other insects are hibernating. But even the winter moth cannot stand freezing weather, and so its flying season is earlier in the colder countries of Europe than in the more temperate ones. In northern Russia and Scandinavia this season is as early as September. In central Russia it occurs toward the end of October and in France and Germany during November. Winter moths breed in England during December and in Sicily during January and February.

Wherever there is a distinct contrast in climate between winter and summer, or dry season and wet season, the great majority of insects go through a dormant stage during the season when conditions are least favorable. Even if they are not completely dormant, their body

The colors of the map butterfly show
seasonal variations. Top is the spring
variety; the lower, which resembles
a white admiral butterfly, is the
summer variety.

processes are much slower than normal. They usually retire into sheltered places where they are protected against extremes of heat or cold. Buildings, caves, hollow tree trunks, underground cavities, heaps of leaves, rock fissures, and spaces under bark, roots, moss, and stones are all favorite hiding places.

Many insects pass the winter or other unfavorable conditions in the egg stage. In mild, moist climates the eggs can often survive quite unprotected. But in conditions of extreme heat or drought the chances of hatching are much diminished unless the eggs are laid under bark, in the ground, or in vegetable debris that will protect them from drying out too much.

Another large group of insects pass the winter as pupae. They remain in diapause until, with the coming of the warmer weather, they emerge as adults. The pupae are protected in various ways from extremes of both heat or cold and from drying out. Some are enclosed in a very tough cocoon, spun from many layers of silk glued together and interwoven with leaves. Others pupate underground in a hollow chamber whose walls have been "cemented" and made moisture-resistant with secretions from the mouth of the larva.

Insects that spend the winter as larvae also have ways of insulating themselves from the weather. Those that live in the soil tend to move much deeper when the weather turns too cold, and wood-boring larvae move deeper into the wood. Many larvae, both solitary ones and those that live in groups, make themselves a *hibernaculum*—a Latin word meaning a winter residence. This is a protective casing made by binding together parts of the food plant with a silken web. It protects the larvae from many predators as well as from the weather and gives them a good chance of surviving.

Social insects, such as ants and bees, spend the winter deep inside their nests or hives. There, clustered together for warmth, they eat their stored food and keep up just enough movement to assure that the temperature in the nest remains above danger level. Aquatic insects pass the difficult season in one of their underwater stages and so lessen the risk of being frozen or dried out. In extreme weather, if ponds freeze solid or dry out completely, many may perish.

It may seem surprising that so many insects are provided with means of protecting themselves from cold. It is widely believed that insects are capable of withstanding extreme cold without ill effects. It is certainly true that some insects can survive very low temperatures, at least for a short time. As long ago as 1736, Réaumur conducted experiments showing that certain caterpillars could be frozen until they were stiff and hard and then be thawed out again unharmed. In 1835, Sir John Ross,

Monarch butterflies hibernating on a tree in California. The monarch has a regular seasonal migration and subsequent return flight. Certain trees are settled on each winter.

leader of an arctic expedition in search of the North-west Passage, found that larvae of one species of arctic moth could be chilled to minus 47°C. without dying. The larva of the goat moth can be chilled, while it is hibernating, to minus 20°C. and still survive. But it is impossible to generalize from these examples, for insects vary a great deal in their ability to resist cold.

Some species, especially those that normally live in subarctic regions, are highly resistant. Others die if the temperature falls by only a few degrees below the normal. Those insects that normally live under conditions where they never experience freezing temperatures—such as the weevils that feed on stored grain—are easily killed by cold. So are tropical insects.

For a large number of insects the critical temperature seems to be about minus 10°C. They can survive this temperature, particularly if they are cooled down gradually. (A sudden drop in temperature is much more dangerous because the body cells of the insect have no time to adapt themselves to the change.) Below this temperature the body fluids begin to freeze. When this happens the insects die.

The degree of cold that an insect can withstand varies also with the condition of the insect. When it is in an active state, feeding and flying or running about, its body contains a good deal of water; then it is quickly killed by cold. When it is in diapause—whether as egg, larva, pupa, or adult—it is much more resistant to cold. Caterpillars, for example, can withstand temperatures several degrees below freezing when hibernating. Once they have begun to feed again, a late spring frost will kill most of them. Moreover, all insects seem to be more resistant to cold during winter, when temperatures in their natural habitat are normally low. In summer they are much less resistant to unseasonable cold spells.

Above: The hibernaculum ("winter home") of the white admiral caterpillar. It forms this by drawing the edges of a leaf of its food plant into a tube with silk threads that it spins and attaches to the leaf edges. All winter it stays inside, protected from weather and predators. Below: Trees covered in webs spun by feeding caterpillars.

Tropical nights are cold; when the sun rises, locusts seek its warmth. The ground (top), where the photographer's shadow rested for five minutes when the temperature was 18.5° C., is almost bare of locusts. But in the heat of the day, 32° C., they quickly sought his shadow (bottom).

An insect that has been starved has a better chance of surviving a cold spell than one that has been well fed, particularly one fed on moist food. This is because the well-fed insect's body has a higher ratio of water to fat and is therefore more likely to freeze solid. The higher the percentage of fat, and the lower the water content in the body's cells, the better the insect is able to resist cold. For this reason, eggs and pupae generally come through cold winters better than caterpillars and adults.

A prolonged period of cold, even if temperatures do not drop below freezing point, can prove fatal to many insects. Fruit flies, for example, will die after seven weeks in cold storage at a temperature between 4°C. and 7°C. Some other insects are not killed by prolonged exposure to cold but may either slow down in their development or develop abnormally. Much research still remains to be done on this subject. But it seems likely that if the body's cell processes slow down too much, as they will during a cold spell at the wrong season, chemical processes in the body go wrong. These cannot be corrected later when the temperature rises, and so the insect is permanently damaged.

Equally dangerous is extreme heat, even for a very short period. Few insects can stand a temperature of more than 50°C. without serious damage or death within a few minutes. In countries where the temperature rises steeply at midday, most insects seek shelter. They may hide under foliage or under stones, burrow down into the ground, or retire to shady moist places. Insects that live in sandy deserts often have unusually long legs that enable them to keep their bodies from contact with the burning sand.

In very hot weather insects tend to be much more short-lived than when the weather is cool. Everything is speeded up. Eggs hatch more quickly, larvae feed up and pupate in a shorter time than normal. When there is no diapause the period in the pupa is shortened also.

Insects raised at high temperatures often tend to be smaller than normal. So-called temperature varieties of butterflies, usually with a much darker coloring than normal, can be produced if the pupae are subjected to abnormally warm conditions at a particular stage. In nature insects are rarely exposed to long periods of extreme heat, because the temperature falls at night. Variations of this kind seldom occur naturally.

There has been an interesting discovery about the responses of insects to alternate heat and cold. That is the way in which their development can be speeded up, not so much by heat alone, but by chilling followed by unusual warmth. If grasshopper eggs are kept at freezing point for 30 days they will then hatch in 25 days if placed in a temperature of 27°C. If the eggs are chilled

Above: Delousing soldiers' clothing in mobile steam sterilizers during World War I. Lice cannot tolerate high temperatures; this treatment kills them.

This bee circulates air in the hive by standing at the entrance and vibrating its wings. Bees die if it gets too hot, but are inactive outside until the morning sun gives some warmth.

to freezing for 120 days they will hatch after 20 days. If chilled for 500 days they will hatch in only 15 days.

Cold, in fact, can often act as a stimulant. That is probably why, in northern countries, the development of insects is so rapid once the winter is over and warm spring weather begins. (Much the same thing also occurs in certain plants, which can be forced into bloom much more quickly if they have previously been kept in cold storage.) However, this is not a general rule that applies to all insects, and especially not to those that would normally be easily damaged by cold.

Many laboratory experiments have been made on the effect of both constant and variable temperatures on insects. It has been found that variable temperatures, such as occur under natural conditions, are generally better. Under variable temperature conditions insects live longer and lay more eggs. The larvae also develop better, and greater numbers reach the adult stage.

Most insects are stimulated by warmth. If the temperature is very low they are more or less inactive. As it rises they become more active: they eat more, move about more quickly, and mate more successfully. But warmth is beneficial to them only within certain limits. After a certain point, which varies in different insects, it can cause a heat stupor and death. That insects cannot stand constant heat is obvious to any keen observer: in the heat of the day comparatively few insects are on the move. All beekeepers know that in hot weather honeybees expend a lot of energy on ventilating their hives by fanning cooler air into the warm interior.

Insect Populations

This beetle from the Canadian Rockies is adapted to develop at 0° C., although when inert it can withstand lower temperatures. It is colorless, wingless, and about an inch long.

THE insect population of the world is astronomical in number. With the exception of the permanently frozen polar wastes and the completely arid deserts, almost every square yard of the earth's land surface supports a teeming insect population. And the insects' world is not only at ground level, but extends into the air as high as the treetops and down into the ground for several feet.

It is only in the twentieth century that entomologists have really begun to deal with the problems of the distribution and balance of insect populations and the way in which they are affected by climate and other factors. Even now field studies are not very far advanced, although a great deal of work has been done in the laboratory.

The general distribution of different types of insects throughout the world depends to a great extent on geological factors. Next in importance to these is the effect of climate. Climatic conditions not only govern the distribution of insects but also control the size of insect populations in different areas. In a natural community of insects a state of balance is usually preserved. Thus, although numbers may vary they normally neither rise to a tremendous height nor fall so low that survival becomes impossible.

As the preceding chapter showed, severe drought and extremes of heat or cold can all be fatal to insects at some stage of their development. The largest numbers of insects are found, therefore, in countries where the climate is warm and rather humid. But it is seldom that conditions, even in warm climates, are ideal for any length of time. If this were so, insects would multiply so rapidly that they would become seriously overcrowded in a short time. Instead, most insects in the world have to fight for survival, with the result that a state of balance is more or less maintained over the years. Predators and parasites play their part in keeping down insect populations, but climate is the most important factor.

In countries where cold winters are common the native insects are adapted to withstand cold. Even so a great many die of cold each year, especially if the winter is unusually severe or the protective snow covering is not sufficiently thick. A sudden, unusually early onset of cold weather, or very heavy autumn rains followed by sudden cold, can cause a high percentage of deaths.

So, too, can an unsettled winter of alternate mild and cold spells that interfere with hibernation.

In most of the temperate regions of the world weather varies from year to year and all sorts of adverse conditions at different times contribute to insect deaths. Even during the summer, when the weather tends to favor the increase of insects, a spell of bad weather during a critical period can have a very noticeable effect. Some insects have only a short time as adults. If very bad weather, with heavy rain and strong winds, makes it difficult or impossible for them to find their mates and lay their eggs, then their numbers will be wiped out altogether.

Excessive heat and drought can be almost as harmful. This is very evident during abnormally hot, dry summers. In such periods many desirable species of insects such as butterflies may almost vanish from their usual areas because the vegetation dries up and the caterpillars can find no food. Insects that are normally natives of temperate climates may often be killed by the direct heat of the sun. Sudden heat waves, when the temperature soars high above the normal even for a comparatively short time, can prove fatal. The cotton boll weevil and the vine moth, certain aphids, and scale insects have all been found to decrease dramatically in numbers after a heat wave. Heat can also prevent certain insects from spreading to new territories, because it cuts down on their fertility. The cabbage white butterfly disperses as a migrant over large areas, but the heat prevents it from colonizing the countries south of the Mediterranean. Even in Israel it can breed only in the winter. In summer the temperature is too high and the eggs and young larvae are killed by the heat.

Wherever a dry season alternates with a rainy season, the rate of insect deaths is higher during the dry season, even in a normal year. But if the dry season is abnormally prolonged, the death rate soars and whole insect populations may be almost wiped out. A good example of an insect that is kept down by a climate of this kind is the Australian swift. This insect of high fertility has increased in numbers because the development of sheep and cattle herding has made available to it larger areas of the grassland in which it lays its eggs. But so many of the eggs are killed by the long summer droughts that the population reaches great numbers only on the rare occasions when two wet seasons follow each other. This happens only once in about 75 years.

Prolonged drought can also be harmful to insects in more indirect ways. It may prevent the growth of their food plants. Drought may also make the surface of the soil so hard that insects cannot emerge from their underground hiding places to feed or mate. Too much rain

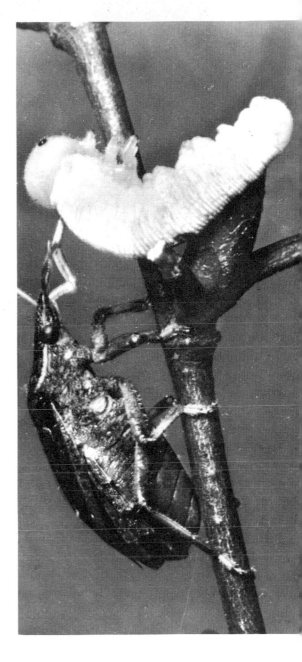

Parasites and predators as well as adverse weather conditions keep insect numbers in check. Here a sawfly larva is being attacked and killed by a carnivorous shield bug.

Above: An adult flesh fly feeding on the juice of a blackberry. Both fly and larva also feed on dead and decaying animals. Life cycle from egg to adult is about five days, so if the food source is abundant the number of flies devouring it increases quickly.

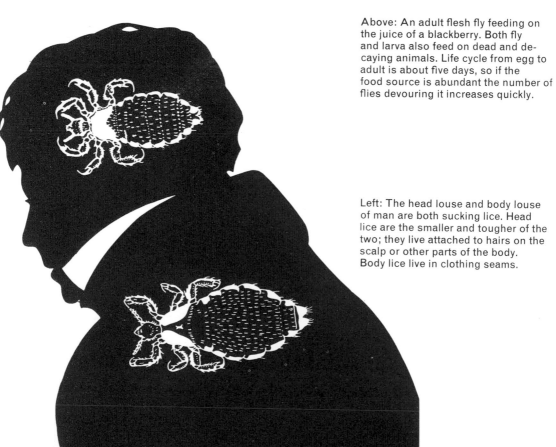

Left: The head louse and body louse of man are both sucking lice. Head lice are the smaller and tougher of the two; they live attached to hairs on the scalp or other parts of the body. Body lice live in clothing seams.

can be equally harmful. It may cause waterlogging and death by drowning, or it may cause an increase of the fungus diseases that often infect insects in diapause.

Some insect species are so widespread that their members are found in widely differing climates. Usually, however, each local race of the species has its own distinctive habits, and each has become adapted to life in its own locality. During the years of their gradual spread, these insects adapt to different conditions, and even their breeding habits may change. They may, for example, produce only one generation a year instead of two, or two instead of one.

In a natural insect population, the numbers may also be controlled by a shortage of food in general or by competition for food between different species of insects. Sometimes the food may be present, but not in the right condition for the needs of the insects. It may be growing in the shade while the insects live in sunlight, or in a dry place while the insects need moist air. Many insects are not very mobile in the larval stage. If their food runs out the larvae cannot wander around and find more, even if it is fairly near. Occasionally cannibalism breaks out. Adults may eat their own eggs, as the Colorado beetle is apt to do in cool weather. Caterpillars, when they are overcrowded on a food plant, may eat one another soon after they hatch.

Sometimes, if there is a general scarcity of food, there are only a few places available for the females to lay their eggs. When this happens so many eggs are laid in the same place that few of the resulting larvae get enough food to complete their development. Among the flies that lay their eggs on the carcasses of dead animals, this is a common occurrence. When the flies discover a carcass it is soon smothered in eggs—all laid within a short time. Great numbers of larvae hatch out at the same time and quickly devour the carcass. But almost all the larvae perish, either from overheating in the general scramble or from starvation when the food supply gives out.

A lack of suitable breeding places can greatly restrict insect populations, for many insects demand rather special conditions. Water, soft soil in which to hollow out nests, hollow stems for cell-building—the absence of any of these can reduce the numbers of insects. Some insects are adaptable and can survive in a wide range of differing conditions. Others thrive only under very special conditions. The tsetse fly in Africa is an example of an insect that is very sensitive to its surroundings. The scrub vegetation in which it lives has to be of just the right density or the fly cannot survive. Once this was discovered, it became possible to wipe out the fly over

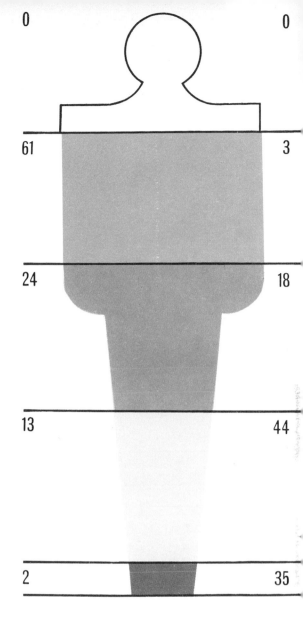

0		0
61		3
24		18
13		44
2		35

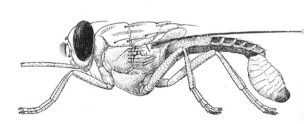

Above: A tsetse fly giving birth to a fully grown larva. The adult lives for about three months and will produce 8–10 larvae. The diagram shows the height at which the tsetse flies Glossina palpalis (left) and G. tachinoides (right) hunt. A man stood in a stream bed in Nigeria in the dry season, counting the flies that settled on him at different levels. 79% of G. tachinoides attacked below the knee (the level at which their food source is found), compared with 15% of G. palpalis.

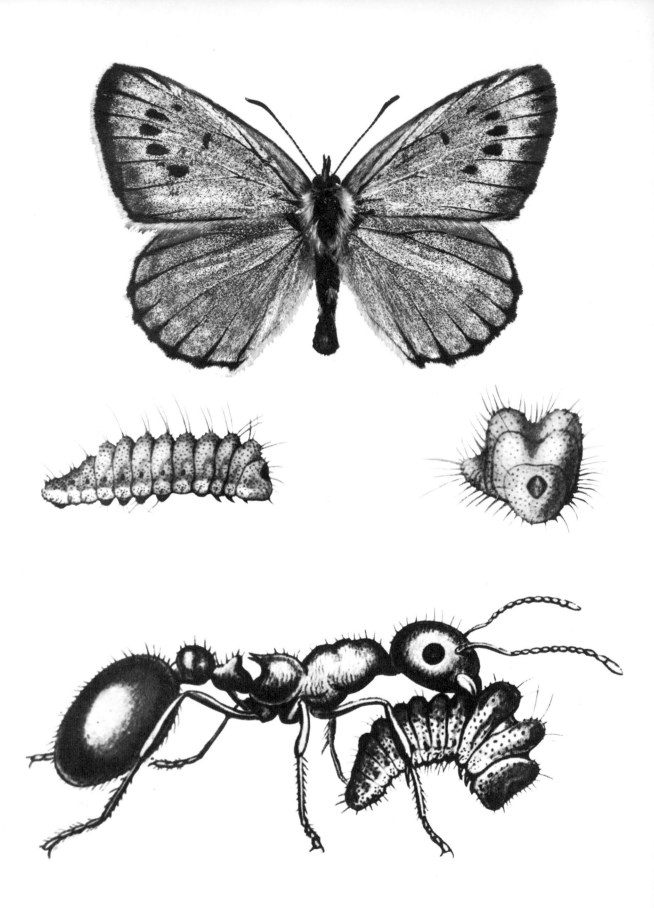

wide areas either by simply cutting and thinning the scrub or planting it too thickly for the fly to live in.

Microclimate is a recently coined word that refers to the weather conditions—temperature, humidity, air pressure, and air currents—that exist within a small area. Microclimate may refer to the nesting hole of a bee, the space beneath the bark of a tree where beetle grubs are feeding, a spot under a canopy of green leaves in a hollow. Or perhaps it refers to a slightly larger place such as a small woods or a meadow. The microclimate of places a few hundred yards, or even a few feet, apart may well be very different. As a result the insect populations will be very different, too.

Although the study of microclimates is relatively new, entomologists already know enough to realize how important a microclimate's influence is on local populations. A knowledge of microclimates may also be of practical use in the control of insect pests. For example, it may be found that a certain pest can be controlled by spacing the plants that it attacks farther apart. Or the plants may be arranged along the line of the prevailing

Right: Experiment measuring the relative density of Drosophila flies in a Brazilian forest. Baited traps were set at 10-meter intervals along the two intersecting lines, each 200 meters long. The height of the black columns is proportional to the percentage of flies collected at that point. The number of flies caught was counted at regular intervals. The experiment was repeated on different dates. Top: December 1948; center: February 1949; bottom: June 1949. Seasonal variations, abundance of food plants, and microclimate are the main causes of changes in numbers.

Microclimate is only one of the factors that restricts an insect to a specific locality. The large blue butterfly has a strange life history (left), which was only solved in 1924 by the entomologist F. W. Frohawk. The young caterpillars feed initially on wild thyme. But after their second molt, they wait to be collected by a red ant. In return for a honey secretion, the ant carries the caterpillar to its nest and allows it to feed on ant grubs. It stays in the nest from August to June, hibernating in winter and pupating in May, when the adult emerges. So the large blue butterfly is restricted to those areas where wild thyme and red ants are found together.

wind instead of across it. In both cases, the microclimate is altered.

Microclimate explains what observant naturalists
have often noticed and that is how some insects are
found year after year only in tiny areas. These insects
never spread into the surrounding countryside although
there seems little to differentiate it from the spot they
have chosen. The reason is that the needs of these insects
are highly specialized. The rare large blue butterfly in
England is an example; it is found only in a few spots in

Feeding on the body of this dead
bat are some insects related to the
earwig. They have developed in dark
caves in Sarawak, on Borneo,
and show various adaptations to this
environment, such as lack of coloring,
vestigial eyes, and no wings.

Light and dark forms of the peppered moth. In northern England 150 years ago the dark variety was rare; its color made it conspicuous to predators. Now the dark strain tones in with smoky northern cities, so by natural selection it outnumbers the lighter variety.

southwestern England. Similarly, the British swallowtail is restricted to certain parts of eastern England. Some aquatic insects can live only in water of a certain chemical composition. There are species of beetles that can exist only in caves where the air is always perfectly still.

Many human activities have a very widespread effect on insect populations. Among the most important in this respect is the draining of land, because this lowers the humidity of an area and changes the local vege-

Above: A dead housefly on a window-pane surrounded by spores of the fungus that has killed it. During damp winters pupae are especially vulnerable to attack by such fungi.

Man is perhaps the greatest enemy of insects, for he is constantly developing new techniques of exterminating them. Below: An aircraft spraying crops with insecticide.

tation. Cutting down forests, plowing up grasslands, building dams, polluting air and water with fumes and waste materials—all such activities tend to do away with many insects. Harvesting crops while insect larvae are still feeding on the leaves can often wipe out a local population completely. So can building or plowing in a place where a small local colony of insects is breeding. This has been happening more and more frequently in recent years, due to the rapid growth of towns and villages and the tendency toward a more intensive agriculture. The effects are most noticeable among butterflies, which are becoming increasingly scarce in densely populated industrial countries.

Changes of the kind mentioned above never wipe out all insect life. Often the more sensitive species disappear, while the more adaptable survive. The survivors may even increase rapidly, because there is less competition for food and living space. Then, too, many of their predators and parasites may also have disappeared. Ants can easily adapt themselves to city conditions; in fact, they are a serious nuisance in many large towns.

When huge acreages of a certain crop are planted in one district, those insects whose food plant it is may increase in numbers until they become a pest. Drastic measures may have to be taken to reduce their numbers.

In the chapter on parasitism many examples were given of insects that control the increase of others. The control effect works both ways: the parasite depends on

the host, and if the parasite reduces the numbers of the host to a very low level, its own numbers will go down rapidly soon afterwards. This gives the host a chance to recover and increase, until once again the parasite becomes active. Thus there is a continuous cycle of alternating large and small populations of two different species.

In nature it is rare for one species of insect to exterminate another. But it does happen occasionally, particularly among ants, which are unusually aggressive creatures. When introduced into new localities, the Argentine ant and the fire ant both exterminate local ants. This has happened in Alabama and Madeira and in parts of Australia. On the other hand, some ants encourage the increase of certain other insects—particularly aphids. The ants protect the aphids from enemies and give them shelter for the sake of the honeydew they produce.

Diseases caused by viruses or bacteria sometimes sweep through local insect populations and reduce their numbers drastically. But the effects are not usually long-lasting. Control measures initiated by man, such as heavy spraying with insecticides, may also cause sudden changes in the insect population. However, insects can recover their ground fairly quickly and may even become more numerous than before. The reasons for this will be discussed in a later chapter.

Above: Six varieties of the chalk-hill blue, the butterfly that so suddenly disappeared from Royston in England. Below: An aerial view of the town. The white line shows the extent of expansion from a small village at the time of the butterfly's disappearance. Such urban expansion can so alter a butterfly's delicately balanced habitat that it is no longer able to breed.

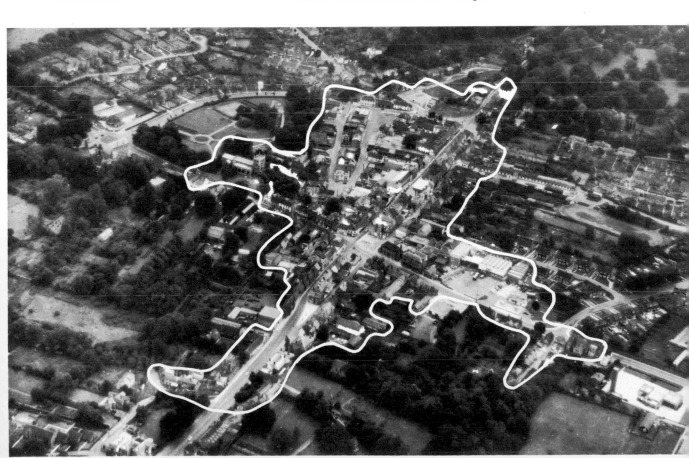

How Insects Spread

THE general distribution of insects over the world depends mainly on the climate and on their own adaptability. Those that require special conditions and can feed on only a certain kind of plant are very local. More adaptable species and those whose food plant is widely cultivated may be found in many different countries. Cockroaches—which will eat practically anything, including shoe polish—follow man wherever he goes and are found almost everywhere in the world. Many flies, ants, and mosquitoes are distributed over huge areas. Certain butterflies, like the painted lady, are found the world over. And innumerable insect pests of agricultural crops are spread over two or more continents with greatly differing climates.

Insects disperse, or spread, in many ways. Most winged insects have an inbred tendency to fly some distance away from the place where they are hatched. For some species these individual flights are the only means of dispersal. Such species spread only very gradually and are soon halted by unsuitable climate, absence of food, or physical barriers such as high mountain ranges. Species that migrate spread more rapidly; they may suddenly appear in places far distant from the countries where they have been breeding. Aphids frequently colonize new areas in this way. But the record is probably held by the monarch butterfly, a very powerful flier with a strong migratory instinct. The monarch has spread from North America across the Pacific to the East Indies, Australia, and New Zealand; it has also gone across the Atlantic to the Azores and the Canary Islands. It has established itself wherever its food plant, the milkweed, grows.

But the most effective agent in assisting the spread of insects is man himself. Few insect species have managed long-range colonization from one continent to another without human help, often unwittingly given. Before men began to travel extensively throughout the world each continent had its own distinct insect population.

It is only since the comparatively recent development of easy, rapid human transportation that insects have managed to spread on an intercontinental scale. Many of them are so tiny (and their eggs even tinier) that they may easily be carried unnoticed in ships or airplanes, on travelers' clothing or among cargoes—especially when plants are carried from one country to another. A single fertile female mosquito emerging from the hold of a ship in a foreign harbor can start a plague of mos-

The warble fly (right) is a parasite of cattle. It lays eggs between June and August on the hairs of a beast's leg (A). Some eggs hatch, first instar larvae (B) penetrate the skin and from November on migrate to the fat surrounding the vertebral column (C). In the following January to March the larvae move to the skin of the back. Here they form cysts and develop into second, then third, instar larvae. These bore through the skin (D), fall to the ground, and pupate (E). From June to August adult flies emerge from the pupae to start a fresh cycle.

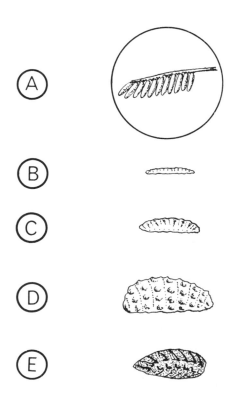

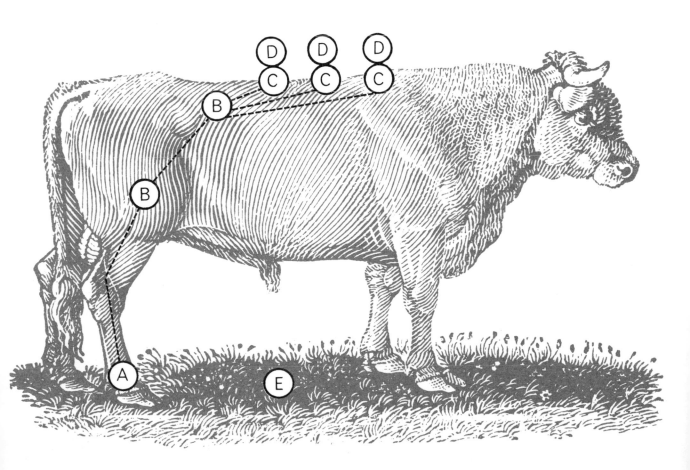

January | February | Mar

quitoes in a country where they did not exist before. A few scale insects clinging to the bark of an imported fruit tree can start a great pest problem. Insects introduced into a new country often increase so quickly that the process is rightly termed a "population explosion." Often the intruders' natural enemies are absent from the new area. Thus, if the climate is favorable and suitable food is available, they are able to spread over a wide area in a surprisingly short time.

Many bark beetles and wood-boring insects are spread by the export of timber from one country to another. As a preventive measure, timber is now usually stripped of its bark before it is shipped abroad, but this cannot always stop the spread. Insects that feed on stored grain, on dried peas and beans, on dried fruit, or on unprocessed crops have spread tremendously. So, too, have clothes moths, carpet beetles, museum beetles, and furniture beetles. Many of them are now so widely distributed and so long established that it is no longer possible to tell where they originated. Others, like the gallerid moth that feeds on stored nuts and dried fruits,

Above left: A United States Department of Agriculture bulletin on ways of controlling the Japanese beetle—a pest of crops and fruit trees. Its life history is pictured above. From November to April the grub hibernates in a cell buried in the earth. Then it tunnels toward the surface to feed. It forms a new cell, pupates, and then the adult beetle bores its way out of the ground in June and feeds on foliage and fruit until September. It lays its eggs in grass in July; these hatch in August into grubs, which feed on the roots of the plants until winter sets in again.

Right: The adult webbing clothes moth and its larvae. The eggs of this moth have spread to all countries in clothes and wool. The larvae cause the damage.

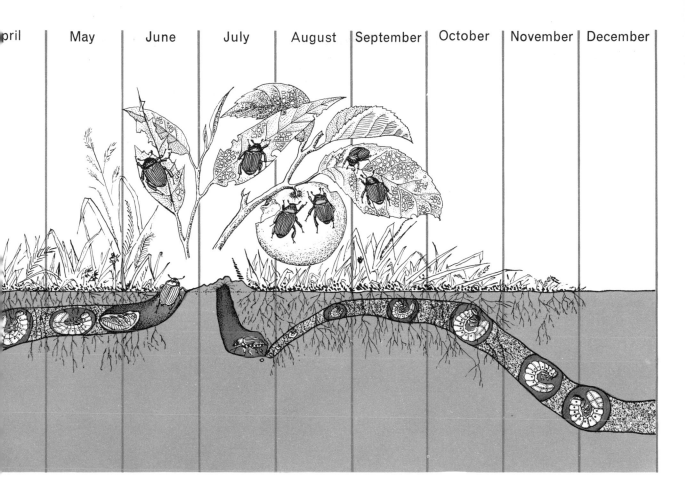

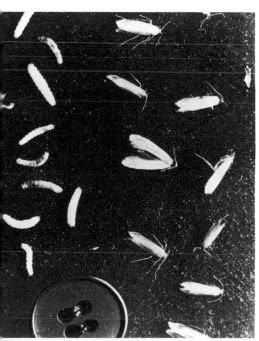

have only fairly recently begun to spread from China and Japan to the coastal areas of Europe and the United States. The moth is obviously being imported in food.

The United States offers many examples of invasions by foreign insects. It is estimated that more than half of our major agricultural pests are not native insects but introductions from other countries.

In 1916 a few small insects previously unknown in the United States were found among plants in a nursery garden at New Jersey. Because they were identified as beetles whose homeland was Japan, they soon became popularly known as Japanese beetles. Within a year they had spread over three square miles of land; by 1923 they had colonized 2442 square miles; and by 1941, twenty-five years after their arrival, they covered 20,000 square miles. During the first few years the beetles bred so fast that workers were gathering and destroying them in thousands. In one small orchard 208 gallons of beetles were collected in a couple of hours. Yet the numbers that swarmed over the orchard did not seem to lessen. Japanese beetles caused tremendous damage

Top: A 19th-century slide lecture explaining the drastic measures being attempted in France to stamp out the vine aphis, which threatened to ruin all their grape vines. The solution was to graft resistant American root stock on to French vines. The monument (below) symbolizes the French vine being aided by the young, healthy American vine.

A GUSTAVE FOËX

to crops, although in Japan they had never been a serious pest. They were able to spread over a large area because of their ability to feed on almost any kind of tree or shrub.

A very similar story is that of the camphor scale insect. Like the Japanese beetle, it came to the United States from Japan and could feed on a wide variety of plants. It found no difficulty in establishing itself and is now widespread in the southern States. It is especially troublesome where citrus fruits are grown.

In 1869, a few eggs of the European gypsy moth were imported into the United States and raised for study. Although carefully kept, some of the moths escaped in the Boston area and found the climate and vegetation to their liking. Soon they became a serious pest, stripping the leaves off trees in an ever-widening area. They continued to spread right up to the 1930s, when they reached the limits of the area within which the climate was suitable for them. Today, although gypsy moths have ceased to gain ground, they still remain a serious pest. In spite of vigorous measures taken against the moths, major outbreaks occur from time to time.

Another pest, the small cabbage white butterfly, came from Europe in the middle of the nineteenth century and is now found throughout the United States and many parts of Canada and Mexico. It has also appeared in Bermuda, Hawaii, Australia, and New Zealand. Almost certainly this butterfly has been imported with agricultural produce, for it is a feeble flier and could not migrate over such great distances.

Insect movements across the Atlantic have not all been westward. Two very serious pests, the vine aphid and the Colorado beetle, traveled in the opposite direction—from the United States to Europe. The vine aphid, which at one time threatened the entire wine production of France, first arrived on some imported wild vines at Bordeaux, the French port. Its original habitat was in the United States, east of the Rocky Mountains, where it was never a troublesome insect. In France, however, it quickly spread, destroying European vines in three million acres of vineyards.

The vine aphid has two different stages: one feeds on the leaves and the other causes galls on the roots of the vines. It was found that the second stage killed the European vines by completely destroying their roots. Then a Frenchman suggested grafting the French vines on to American root stocks that were resistant to the aphids' attacks. The vineyards were replanted with grafted vines and the vine aphid is not an economic danger.

The Colorado beetle also is a native of the Rocky Mountains. It originally fed on a wild relative of the potato plant and remained fairly localized. But when the cultivated potato was introduced into the area in the middle of the nineteenth century, the beetle quickly transferred to the new food plant. It began to spread toward the Atlantic, reaching the coast in 1874. From there small numbers of beetles several times crossed to Europe; some were found in Germany as early as 1876. But European potato growers were alert to the danger and the pest was stamped out quickly before it could gain a hold.

In the end, however, the beetle achieved a bridgehead in Europe at Bordeaux, France. By 1935 it was well established in France and from there it spread over most of central and southern Europe. So far it has been kept out of Scandinavia and England by strict controls. It has appeared in those countries on several occasions, but it has always been exterminated. It is also possible that the climate, both in England and in Scandinavia, is not really suitable. Although the beetle seems to be very adaptable, its original home was in a fairly dry climate. There may be limits to the amount of humidity it can stand in cooler regions.

The absence of natural enemies, especially insect predators and parasites, is one of the chief reasons why introduced insects spread with explosive rapidity.

The spruce sawfly is a native of Europe. It was first

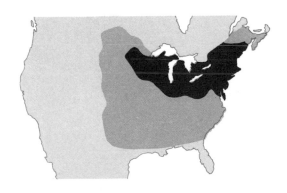

Maps showing distribution of Colorado beetle; densely infested areas are marked black, milder areas, gray. Top: Extent of the infested area in Europe in 1958. Middle: The beetles' place of origin, where it fed on wild potatoes. Bottom: Its spread to eastern America; this dates from 1859, when potatoes were first grown in this area as a food crop.

The ladybird is a fierce enemy of all aphids; here it is seen devouring one. An Australian species has been introduced in America in the fight against scale insects.

Left: A spruce forest in Canada. Huge rafts of logs are being floated downstream to the pulp mills. Spruce sawflies (insert) are a menace to this industry. To kill them, forests were sprayed by plane with insecticides. Now parasites have also been imported and released in infested areas.

discovered in Canada in the 1820s and very soon it had become so numerous that thousands of valuable timber trees were being killed annually. By 1937 it was the most abundant of all spruce-eating insects in northeastern forest regions of the United States and Canada. In Europe it never did much harm and was certainly not of economic importance, because it was kept in check by a number of parasites. These parasites have since been introduced into the United States and Canada in an attempt to control the spruce sawfly there.

The cottony-cushion scale insect originally came from Australia. Now it is found in New Zealand, Japan, China, India, South Africa, Madagascar, all around the Mediterranean, over most of South America, in the southern United States, and in the West Indies. It attacks orange and other citrus trees, but it has now been brought under control by the introduction of one of its predators, an Australian ladybird. The predator keeps the scale insect population at a level where it does not do any serious economic damage.

When insects that are themselves predators are introduced into a new country they can have a very serious influence on the native insects. Ants in particular

—being highly organized, aggressive, and voracious—can quickly wipe out native insects, including other species of ants. This has been recorded within fairly recent times in the Hawaiian Islands. There the introduced leaf-cutting ant almost completely exterminated the native ant population up to 2000 feet above sea level. The leaf-cutting ant also invaded Madeira and the Canary Islands. But here it was followed fairly soon by an even fiercer creature, the Argentine ant, which wiped out the leaf-cutting ant.

In its homeland the Argentine ant is not a serious pest, but when it came to the United States at the end of the nineteenth century, it soon became one. It probably came in coffee imported from Brazil. In any case, the ant spread across the southern states. It took up its quarters in houses, gardens, and orchards, raided pantries and food supplies, and destroyed many native insects, including other species of ants. At the same time it allowed such pests as aphids and scale insects to thrive. The same sort of thing happened in South Africa and Australia, where the Argentine ant was introduced just before the outbreak of the Second World War. Vigorous extermination campaigns have been conducted against this ant. When it has been eradicated by poison

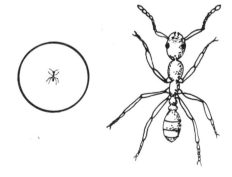

The Pharaoh's ant, above (actual size in circle), is a difficult pest to eradicate. Top: Spraying the insulation jackets of a hospital heating system with an insecticide. Such pipes form an ideal highway for the spread of these tiny, persistent ants.

Different crops are susceptible to attack by different insects. In the 1850's John Curtis produced the first report on this aspect of entomology for England's newly formed Royal Agricultural Society. Top right: His drawings of the moths and flies that attack carrot and parsnip crops, and their natural parasites. Bottom right: Moths and caterpillars that live on turnip and mangel-wurzel roots.

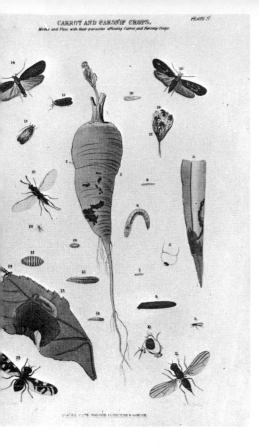

sprays, the native ants soon return and re-establish themselves in their old territories.

One of the smallest of all the ants is the barely two-millimeter-long Pharaoh's ant. It is thought to have originated in Egypt, but in the last 150 years it has spread all over the world. Originally this ant was adapted to a warm climate. But because of its habit of nesting in buildings, it has been able to survive even in places as cold as Tobolsk in Siberia. Today there is scarcely a city in the world where this tiny ant cannot be found. It is almost impossible to wipe out because it hides in the walls and foundations of any warm building. From this secure base it makes forays for food and spreads to other buildings, often along underground pipelines.

Farmers today cultivate the land more intensively than in the past. More and more are also practicing monoculture—the cultivation of a single crop over a large area. Such modern agricultural methods increase the danger of insect explosions. Introduced insects—unless they are of a species that will eat practically anything—spread far more slowly in an area where the vegetation is mixed.

It is well known, for example, that you find fewer timber pests in a mixed forest than in a forest consisting entirely of one kind of tree, like a spruce plantation. Deciduous trees break up the denser masses of evergreens and create conditions of light and humidity that are less favorable to pests. Such conditions are often more favorable to their predators and parasites.

When an insect is introduced into a new environment, whether by accident or design, the result cannot really be predicted. The newcomer may not be able to gain a foothold at all, or it may spread with frightening speed.

Since so many accidental introductions have caused serious trouble, authorities all over the world now take strict measures to prevent the introduction of foreign insects of any kind, not only those that are known to be pests or disease-carriers. Plants have to undergo very careful inspections and insecticidal treatments before being allowed to enter a country. Certain plants may be prohibited altogether and so may packing materials such as straw, hay, or dried leaves. Cargoes of all kinds are inspected before they may be unloaded at the docks, and every precaution is taken to see that stowaway insects do not land. But in spite of these controls, the dispersal of insects continues.

The insect populations of the world are becoming more and more mixed and sudden explosions of insect populations will almost certainly continue to occur. Whether or not a state of balance will finally be reached nobody can tell. The world has become one vast melting pot and the real mixing has only just begun.

Insects and Man

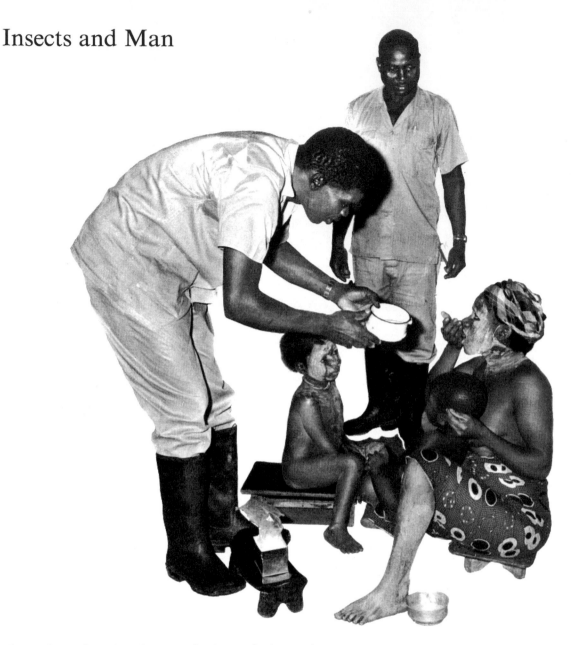

ONE of the favorite themes of science fiction writers is the near-destruction of human civilization by hordes of insects that have developed into giants as the result of some genetic accident. The sober truth is that insects have been enough trouble to humanity at their present size. Since the beginning of recorded history insects have caused the death by disease of more people than all the wars, earthquakes, hurricanes, floods, droughts, and fires combined. To this immense toll of human life can be added the incalculable economic losses caused by insects attacking food and textile crops, forests, buildings, furniture, and much else.

Superstition is a barrier to the scientific control of disease. Above: An African woman and her child suffering from malaria. On the advice of a witch doctor they have painted their faces to chase away evil spirits. Two officials from an anti-malaria campaign distribute efficient drugs. Top right: Two mosquitoes (Aedes aegypti), the vector for yellow fever, feed on human blood. Below right: A malaria control party in Africa spray a swamp with oil. The mosquito larvae cannot get access to air and so die.

The Bible describes several plagues in Egypt that led to the exodus of the Israelites. These plagues were caused by sudden invasions or "explosions" of insects, and the Bible gives a vivid account of the locusts, flies, and lice (the last were probably some kind of midges). We know now that it was swarms of such bloodsuckers that helped to spread fatal disease among the cattle and illness among the people in the Nile Valley. Throughout history many a military campaign has failed because the armies were stricken by disease spread by insects. Whole civilizations have declined because the vigor of their peoples was undermined by malaria and other illnesses. Vast regions of the world have long remained undeveloped and almost uninhabited because insects made it impossible for men to settle in them.

With the exception of locusts—which are about two inches long when adult—most of the really dangerous insects are small. The flea and the louse, the mosquito and the fly are potentially the most deadly of all insects. This is because they are so numerous and because they act as carriers of serious, and often deadly, diseases that would otherwise not be infectious.

Malaria, yellow fever, plague, and typhus germs are not usually spread through the air. Malaria and yellow fever are never passed by direct physical contact between people. They are spread only when certain species of mosquitoes pass the disease-causing organisms by first sucking the blood of a person sick with one of these diseases, and then biting other people.

It took mankind a long time to realize that many of its worst diseases are spread by insects. It took even longer to develop the right methods to combat them. Until quite recent times cleanliness was never an outstanding human trait. Unsanitary dwellings, dirty clothes, and a lack of soap and water have been the cause of untold suffering.

Many people around the world still live in primitive conditions in overcrowded and dirty dwellings where fleas, lice, and flies establish themselves and multiply rapidly. There the trouble begins.

In the case of malaria, yellow fever, and sleeping sickness the situation is somewhat different. Their carriers, or *vectors,* depend less on the domestic conditions of the people they attack than on the type of country they inhabit. Mosquitoes, for instance, must have water in which to breed, although they like to rest inside houses during the day. This knowledge has led to the means of destroying them. In the same way, patient research into the habits of the tsetse fly has enabled men to control the spread of sleeping sickness and its associated diseases.

Warm-blooded animals, both domestic and wild, are just as apt to get insect-borne diseases as are humans.

Most of the serious diseases of cattle, sheep, and horses are spread by insects or are the direct result of insect attack. For thousands of years, people all over the world have depended for a large part of their food supply on various domestic animals that are almost defenseless against their insect enemies. In addition to protecting themselves, therefore, men have had to develop means of protecting their animals.

Today veterinary entomology—the study of the relationships between animal diseases and insects—is an important subject. Before insecticides were developed, very little could be done to control bloodsucking flies and other insects that are pests of animals. But during the present century great advances have been made and many different kinds of insect-killing sprays and dusts are now in general use. These have done away with much suffering among animals and have helped to improve their health. Even the reindeer herds in Lapland and arctic Russia are now sprayed with insecticides to prevent them from being attacked by botflies. At the present time veterinary entomologists are trying to develop substances that cattle could eat without harm but that would be fatal to their insect pests.

The dangerous insects include more than the carriers of human and animal diseases or the well-known food-destroyers such as locusts. Ever since he began to grow crops, man has also been troubled by thousands of insects that compete with him for food. Beetles, caterpillars, plant lice, leaf miners, corn borers, and many others are always present, ready to damage or destroy vital crops needed for food and clothing. By devoting large areas to the cultivation of single crops, man has unintentionally aided pests. In developing a world-wide network of transportation, he has helped pests migrate from one continent to another. When a comparatively small human population within a limited area can grow more food than it needs, a certain amount of wastage by insect damage is not important. But with the world population increasing at its present rate and needing more living space as well as more food, it becomes essential to get the best possible return from the agricultural land available. Loss and damage through insects is no longer a minor matter, and pest control is a vital necessity.

Food crops of every kind, timber, houses, stored products—all are attacked to some extent by insects. To wipe out these pests completely is almost impossible. Most of them can be controlled. But constant and costly research is needed if we are to learn about the life cycles and behavior of pests and to develop practical methods of fighting them. It is this work of applied science that is the field of the economic entomologist.

Above: Photograph of squalid living conditions in 1950 in Bombay, India. When people have to live in insanitary dwellings and close to livestock, then flies, lice, and other disease-carrying insects thrive. Now most buffaloes in Bombay are housed in modern stables on a nearby cooperative dairy farm. Below: Spraying sheep with insecticide on a Canadian ranch. Ticks spread a large number of virus and bacterial diseases among domestic animals.

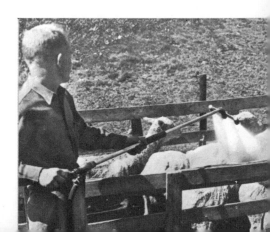

Above: A female desert locust. These locusts form vast swarms that travel over wide areas, devastating natural and cultivated vegetation wherever they feed. Below: A crop damaged by the European corn borer. This insect bores into the stalks of the corn, then feeds on the kernels. In 1949 it caused American farmers more than 353 million dollars worth of damage. With the help of insecticides, by 1952 damage was reduced to 85 million dollars.

Until the late nineteenth century, few people considered that pest control could become the subject of a vitally important scientific discipline. The earliest researchers in this field were treated with considerable scorn by traditional, academic entomologists. They regarded those interested in control as farmers dabbling with a subject beyond their understanding and were often unwilling to help them in any way. Gradually, however, the skeptics were forced to abandon this attitude. The change came when government agencies responsible for agriculture in several countries realized the need for organized, scientifically based action against

crop pests. The need was first acted upon in the United States as early as 1845, when Dr. Asa Fitch was appointed state entomologist of New York. Similar appointments began to be made in other countries in the decades that followed. By the early 1900's, economic entomology had become scientifically respectable.

Today the wheel has turned full circle. Those men whose entomological work has led to important practical results in insect control are often given greater general respect than the pure scientists. When the first International Entomological Congress was held at Brussels in 1910, few of the delegates were interested in the economic applications of their science. Today the majority of the papers read at such gatherings deal with some aspect or other of pest control. The scientific community now realizes that all the different branches of entomology support and complement each other.

It is not difficult to prepare a poison that will kill insects. But entomologists have discovered that poisonous liquids or dusts spread over an infested area may have unexpected widespread and undesirable effects. The insecticides may destroy useful insects such as bees, ladybirds, and parasitic wasps as well as pests. Insecticides may also be harmful to the crops or leave a residue that is also poisonous to humans and other animals. Sometimes insects develop resistance to certain poisons and new strains of the species appear that are not harmed by the sprays and dusts. This happened fairly quickly after DDT first came into general use against flies and mosquitoes in the 1940s. Sometimes the insecticide is too difficult to manufacture, or too expensive, or effective only under certain climatic conditions.

Very often the details of a pest's life history are difficult to discover. For instance, it may be a small creature, easily overlooked; or it may spend part of its life hidden inside the tissues of plants where it cannot be seen. The insect may migrate from place to place or from plant to plant, or appear in much different forms at different seasons. Then it may take years before people realize that various creatures are, in fact, separate phases in the life of one species. Some insects are very resistant to poisons. Other, less adaptable species are so well protected by their habitat or by some aspect of their behavior that they are difficult to attack effectively. For instance, some insects are active only in the middle of the night, while others nest and feed underground.

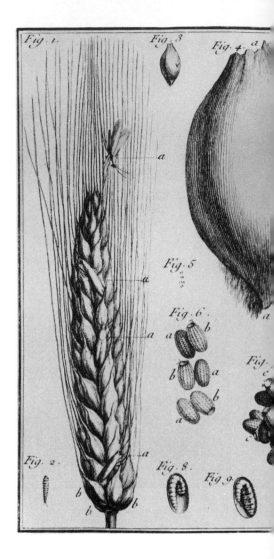

Right: The first International Entomological Congress, held in Brussels in 1910. In these early years, aspects of pure entomology were discussed. Now such meetings deal mainly with problems of pest control.

118

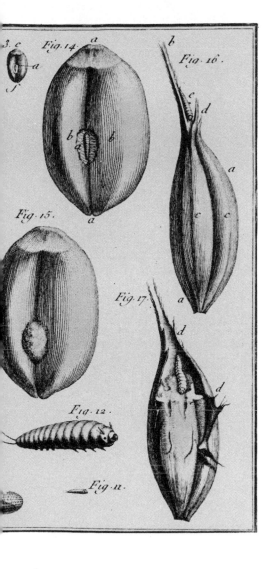

The seemingly limitless variety in the forms and behavior of insect pests poses major and often exasperating problems for economic entomologists. Moreover, they are constantly being called away from their laboratories to take immediate and urgent action out in the field. If crops are threatened by a sudden invasion of hordes of insects there is no time to study the problem at leisure. Drastic measures are required at once. Too often, such emergencies leave entomologists no alternative but to spray the affected area with powerful insecticides — and to risk the secondary effects described above.

As the science of pest control develops, researchers are becoming increasingly aware of the importance of studying insect ecology. Ecology is the study of the complex system of relationships that exist between all animals and their environment. It is a very wide field of study. For even one species of an insect pest, ecology includes the climate and geography of the pest's habitat; the plants (wild as well as cultivated) on which the pest feeds and breeds; the predators, parasites, and diseases that attack the pest at different stages in its life cycle. One of the most important discoveries of this kind of study is that many pests can be controlled, or even wiped out, by means other than the indiscriminate and often ineffective use of dangerous insecticides.

The accumulation of knowledge about insects demands lengthy, painstaking research. Sometimes, it seems that entomologists are doing research on problems that have little relation to the practical control of pests. The fact is, however, that every scrap of information about a pest may make a small but important contribution to the conquest of a disease, the safeguarding of crops, or the preservation of forests, textiles, foods, and other materials that are attacked by insects.

The importance of economic entomology today is shown by the vast and constantly increasing sums of money that governments are spending on pest control. Many spectacular victories have already been gained over man's insect enemies, but the war never ends and flare-ups continue to occur all over the world. Often the work of controlling pests in underdeveloped regions is hampered by poor road, rail, and other transportation or by lack of finance. But thanks to the world-wide community of economic entomologists, man now has the means to defend himself against most of the destructive or disease-carrying insects.

Top: Drawings from 18th-century report by Duhamel du Menceau of the moth attacking wheat in France. This early work of economic entomology was scientific at a time when belief in "spontaneous generation" was widespread.

Insects as Disease-Carriers

A HUNDRED years ago no entomologist had yet suggested that any link existed between insects and disease. Today we know that as many as two hundred diseases of men and animals are spread by insects, and more are still being discovered. The most important disease carried by insects is malaria, which in the past caused more deaths than any other disease. Proof that mosquitoes spread malaria was not established until the late nineteenth century. Before that time scientists found it hard to believe that an insect could be the *vector*, or carrier of a disease. Indeed, ordinary observation and intelligent guesswork were well in advance of scientific findings. Some ancient Indian physicians apparently suspected the connection between mosquitoes and malaria as early as the sixth century B.C. The Babylonians depicted their god of pestilence as an insect, and certain African tribes long ago attributed malaria to insects.

The connection between low-lying marshy land and malaria had been noticed in ancient Greece and Rome. The Greek physician Hippocrates, for instance, was aware of the link. But he was misled, as were nearly all medical men during the next two thousand years. He believed that it was the foul air, or *miasma*, rising from the marshes at night that caused the alternating bouts of fever and chills characteristic of malaria. We may laugh now at the idea that night air was dangerous and should be kept out of the house at all costs. But the idea was sensible, for by staying indoors and closing their windows to shut out the "dangerous" air, people unknowingly protected themselves against night-flying mosquitoes that carried the disease.

The theory that malaria was caused by some kind of invisible tiny animal or germ was first proposed in 1848. From that time on scientists began to search for the specific cause of malaria. Finally, in 1878 the parasite was found in the blood of malaria patients by Alphonse Laveran, a French army surgeon working in North Africa. Although Laveran's findings were soon confirmed by others, many medical scientists refused to believe them. By 1890, however, Laveran's ideas were generally accepted, and he later received a Nobel Prize for his discovery.

The way in which the disease was spread, however, still remained a mystery. In 1882 A. F. A. King read a report before the Philosophical Society in Washington, D.C., in which he suggested that malaria was carried from person to person by mosquitoes. His listeners took little notice and decided he was eccentric.

The coin above (fifth century B.C.) was struck in honor of Empedocles, who checked an outbreak of malaria in Sicily by draining a swamp. He believed malaria to be caused by vapors rising from stagnant water and did not realize the role played by insects.

Below: The life cycle of the malaria parasite within red blood corpuscles, drawn by Laveran in his original communication to the Société Medicale des Hôpitaux, 1880. It was Laveran who first discovered the parasite in the blood of a malaria patient.

Fig. 1. Globule rouge du sang. — Fig. 2. Leucocyte granuleux. (Ces éléments sont destinés à servir de point de comparaison pour apprécier les dimensions des autres éléments dessinés au même grossissement de 1000 diametres environ.) — Fig. 3 et 4. Corps n° 1. — Fig. 5. Corps ovalaire intermediaire aux corps n° 1 et n° 2. — Fig. 6. Corps n° 2 immobile. — Fig. 7. Corps n° 2 avec ses filaments periphériques mobiles, renflés a leur extremité libre. — Fig. 8. Corps n° 2 avec appendices mobiles groupés lateralement. — Fig. 9. Filament mobile devenu libre. — Fig. 10. Corps spherique rempli de granulations pigmentaires mobiles. — Fig. 11. Corps n° 3. — Fig. 12 et 13. Corps n° 3 deformés. — Fig. 14. Élément pigmentés provenant du sang d'un homme mort de fièvre pernicieuse: a, a' éléments analogues aux corps n° 1; b, b', b" elements analogues aux corps n° 3. — Fig. 15. Éléments dissociés de la rate d'un homme mort de fièvre pernicieuse ; éléments analogues aux corps n° 3.

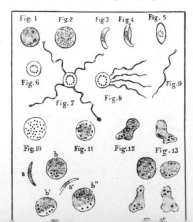

Two years later, a new discovery made it less easy to brush aside King's suggestion. Patrick Manson, a Scottish doctor who had been working in China, published a report about a parasitic disease, known as *filiariasis*, that he had found to be transmitted by mosquitoes. If mosquitoes could transmit one disease, it was at least possible that they could transmit another.

In 1894 Ronald Ross, a surgeon in the Indian Medical Service, visited Manson in London and was shown malaria parasites under a powerful microscope. Manson suggested that malaria, like filiariasis, might be carried from one person to another by mosquitoes. When Ross returned to India he systematically examined and dissected many different species of mosquitoes to discover whether any of them contained malaria parasites. Eventually he experimented with the "dapple-winged" mosquito, *Anopheles stephensi*. He allowed it to feed on a malaria patient and later found the characteristic malaria parasites in the mosquito's stomach. The age-old mystery was solved at last. In recognition of his pioneer work Ross also received a Nobel Prize.

Later, many other species of malaria-carrying mosquitoes were discovered. All of them belong to the anopheles group. Further experiments showed that man and the anopheles mosquitoes are two alternating hosts

Above: "Ague and Fever," an 18th-century artist's representation of demons as the cause of malaria. Below: Sir Ronald Ross in his laboratory. In 1897 Ross discovered malaria parasites in the anopheles mosquito's stomach. Thus the vector of the disease was determined.

Man and Mosquito

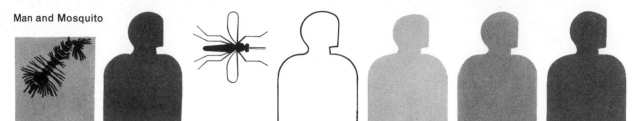

After mosquito larvae grow in water (1), adult female mosquito flies off and bites man sick with malaria (2). Blood-carrying parasites go into mosquito's stomach where they multiply (3). When healthy man is bitten (4), parasites enter his blood and disease develops (5–7) in from six days to six weeks.

Parasites

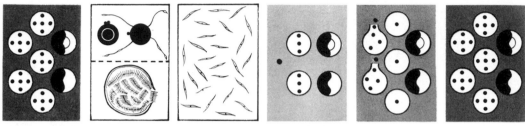

Life cycle of malaria organism is traced starting within red blood cells of infected man (8) where two forms of parasite exist: asexual schizonts (dotted circles) and male and female gametocytes (halved circles). When blood of sick man enters mosquito, male form puts forth flagella (9 top) that break off and fertilize female; fertilized form penetrates stomach wall and grows within cysts (9 bottom). Cysts burst and free masses of threadlike sporozoites (10) that move to mosquito's salivary gland, from where they enter another man's red blood cells and develop into schizonts and gametocytes (11). Asexual schizonts begin to multiply by segmentation (12), destroying cell; this bursts, releasing parasites into other cells (13). Continual bursting and releasing of parasites from cells causes recurrent bouts of fever in patient. Sexual gametocytes, meanwhile, will not pair and multiply until taken into mosquito's stomach.

Defense

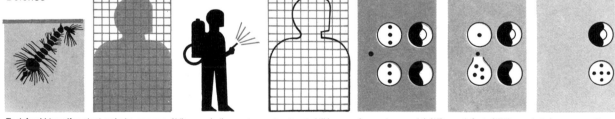

To defend himself against malaria, man can: (14) spread oil over stagnant waters to kill larvae; place nets over sick (15) or uninfected (17) people to keep mosquitoes away; (16) spray adult mosquitoes with insecticides; (18–20) take drugs that kill parasites in blood and cut down their multiplication.

for different stages in the development of the parasites that cause malaria. The parasites can complete their life cycle only by passing from one host to the other. Many other scientists then took up the work. Soon every stage in the transmission and development of malaria was known in detail.

About the year 1600, Juan Lopez, a Jesuit missionary working in Peru, was cured of malaria by an Indian chief who gave him a medicine prepared from the bark of a tree. This was the "fever tree," or *cinchona,* the bark of which contains quinine. From that time on, cinchona —and later quinine itself—was used more and more as a remedy for malaria, and large quantities were exported from South America. In 1854 the Dutch started plantations of cinchona trees in Java. A few years later more plantations were established near Madras, in India. Quinine is still used in the treatment of malaria, although

Understanding the cause and course of malaria is essential for scientific control of the disease. The above diagram illustrates the life cycle of the malaria parasite, one of several species of small protozoa of the genus Plasmodium. Section One shows how mosquitoes go on transmitting the infecting parasite from sick to healthy men. Section Two traces the series of changes undergone by the parasites in man and mosquito. Section Three shows some of the ways of controlling mosquitoes' breeding places and of protecting and curing people.

it has largely been replaced by newer synthetic drugs that were developed during the Second World War to protect troops fighting in the tropics.

The treatment of malaria patients is the concern of physicians, but prevention of the disease is very much the concern of entomologists. (This applies also to yellow fever, an even more deadly disease, which is also spread by mosquitoes.) An important feature of every large-scale anti-malaria campaign is the simple — but often very expensive — procedure of draining swamps and marshes. The efficient drainage of the Pontine marshes southeast of Rome is one example of this.

The Pontine marshes were a hotbed of malaria infection even before the great Roman civilization arose. Several Roman emperors and, later, several popes initiated vast schemes to drain the marshes, but none had more than a temporary success. It was not until Benito Mussolini launched a great drainage plan in 1930 that the marshlands began to be safe for human settlement.

Today, with the aid of insecticides, house screens, and anti-malaria drugs, the area has been turned from a wasteland into a thriving agricultural community. Much of the area is now rich agricultural land that will eventually repay in crops the enormous cost of the drainage project.

One of the most famous of all anti-mosquito campaigns was carried out between 1904 and 1913 in the Panama Canal Zone by William Crawford Gorgas, an American army doctor.

Before taking charge of disease-control in the newly established Canal Zone, Gorgas had carried out a successful campaign against yellow fever in Havana, Cuba. He began work in Havana in March 1901 by systematically removing all the breeding places for mosquitoes and confining all yellow fever victims in screened rooms. Within five months, he managed practically to wipe out the disease, which had been widespread in the city since 1761.

Attempts to build the canal had been started in the 1880s by the French. But even the most skilled engineers of the time, with plenty of labor at their disposal, failed to make progress because of the terribly unhealthy conditions in the region. The whole area was described as "one sweltering miasma of death and disease." In eight years 50,000 laborers died of malaria, yellow fever, and plague. In May 1904 the United States Government took over the canal project from the French.

The American Medical Association suggested to the Panama Canal Commission that Gorgas be appointed to tackle the problem of disease in the Canal Zone. The suggestion was rejected at first, but the surgeon general of the United States put Gorgas in charge of

QUININE THE REMEDY FOR MALARIA

The above poster, distributed in India in 1927 by Public Health Authorities, shows the way in which malaria brought poverty and death if the sufferer failed to take quinine. Below: A modern method of sterilizing female mosquito larvae by irradiating them with cobalt-60. The adult mosquitoes are released in natural surroundings, where they mate but do not produce live offspring.

William Crawford Gorgas (1854–1920) pioneered malaria control by draining swamps, cutting brush and grass, oiling ponds, and advocating the use of larvicides and quinine.

Work in progress on the Panama Canal in 1909. Early attempts to cut the canal were thwarted by continual outbreaks of malaria and yellow fever. Gorgas succeeded in controlling these diseases, and the canal was completed in 1914.

the disease-control work in the Canal Zone in 1904. The members of the commission were furious. They ridiculed Gorgas' work and tried in every way to hinder him. President Theodore Roosevelt, however, believed in Gorgas and his method.

The first two years of American effort were devoted to controlling the diseases that had defeated the French efforts to build the canal.

Gorgas attacked mosquitoes in every possible way. He drained or filled in stagnant pools, sprayed the larger areas of water with oil to kill the larvae, cleared the undergrowth where the mosquitoes hid, screened the sleeping quarters of the men, killed adult mosquitoes wherever they were found in buildings, and dosed everybody with quinine.

His work showed immediate results. By the end of 1906 he had wiped out yellow fever and eliminated the rats that carried bubonic plague in the Canal Zone. Malaria was more difficult to control because the anopheles mosquitoes proved harder to eradicate. Not until 1913 could it be said that the Canal Zone was relatively free of malaria. It was the greatest victory man had yet gained over an insect enemy.

A more recent successful campaign against a specific malaria-transmitting mosquito was conducted in Brazil. In March 1930 an entomologist on the staff of the Rockefeller Foundation found a new malaria-carrying mosquito in Natal, Brazil. This was an African mosquito that had not previously been reported in Brazil. How it had arrived there nobody knew, but it is likely that the mosquitoes that started the colonization of Brazil had traveled from Dakar in a French ship.

By 1931 these African newcomers had spread 115 miles along the coast. By 1938 they had multiplied to such an extent that a tremendous malaria epidemic began to rage. In the first six months of the epidemic, 14,000 Brazilians died. It was clear that the mosquitoes were spreading fast both along the coast and inland.

The Brazilian government decided that the routine anti-malaria measures were not enough, and started an all-out campaign to exterminate this particular species completely. By presidential decree, two million dollars were provided to establish a special malaria service staffed by some 4000 scientists and technicians.

The affected region was divided into squares of workable size. Each square was assigned to a separate team who went over it, almost yard by yard. They applied poison to all possible breeding sites and thoroughly sprayed houses and other resting places for mosquitoes. To the great surprise even of many experts, the campaign was completely successful. The last live mosquito of this particular species in Brazil was re-

ported on November 14, 1940. Since then, not a single live adult or larva has been found, apart from three mosquitoes that were found in 1943 in a hut near a transatlantic airport and were at once killed. And so it was proved that an all-out effort like this can achieve remarkable results in a very short time.

The fight against malaria goes on continually in many parts of the world. Any relaxation of vigilance is dangerous, for a single person suffering from malaria can be a source of infection and start an epidemic.

Wars and troop movements have always tended to increase the occurrence of malaria, partly because anti-mosquito measures are often disrupted and partly because infected people move from place to place. For example, Finland had virtually stamped out malaria at the beginning of the twentieth century but Russian soldiers reintroduced it in 1945. More recently in the United States a malaria-infected Marine, returning from the

Malaria parasites are spread when an infected female anopheles mosquito bites a human host. Above: An Anopheles gambia mosquito. It is found in tropical Africa and the Upper Nile basin. It breeds in sunlight in small pools of stagnant water. It is active from midnight to dawn, and its favorite host is man.

war in Korea, slept outdoors for several nights without any protection against mosquitoes. The result was a local outbreak of the disease.

The first national project to wipe out malaria was begun in Venezuela in 1945. Since then many countries have followed suit, while in 1955 the World Health Organization began an intensive international campaign. Today, malaria is in decline all over the world. It no longer occurs in Scandinavia, Britain, Germany, Cyprus, Italy, or the United States. Vigorous efforts are being made to stamp it out in India, Burma, Egypt, France, Greece, the Middle East, the U.S.S.R., and South Africa. Still malaria remains a threat in many parts of Africa, Malaysia, Pakistan, and Saudi Arabia. While there is still a tremendous amount of work to be done, there is little doubt that the time will come when a malaria epidemic will be a thing of the past.

Another deadly disease that has almost been overcome is bubonic plague. It gets its name from swellings, or *buboes,* which appear in the lymph nodes under the arms or in the groin. The plague has been known since 430 B.C. and has repeatedly wiped out large sections of the populations of Europe and the Far East. Yet it was not until the beginning of the twentieth century that scientists discovered that it was spread by a flea, *Xenopsylla cheopis,* that lives on rats and other rodents. When it feeds on rats—which catch the disease easily and which live among men—this flea is dangerous.

The germ that causes plague was discovered by two independent research workers almost at the same time in 1894. These two men were a Japanese scientist,

In 1955 a world-wide campaign was launched by WHO to eradicate malaria. The map shows the progress of the campaign by April 1963. Pale brown areas: total eradication. Dark brown areas: eradication nearly completed. Gray areas: still malarial.

Below: Constructing a drainage ditch in Venezuela in 1954. A division of malariology, dedicated to the control and eradication of malaria, was instituted there as early as 1937.

126

S. Kitazato, and a Danish scientist, A. Yersen, who was working in Indochina. They both identified the cause of plague as a bacterium (plural: bacteria), which was named *Pasteurella pestis*. Kitazato generously credited Yersen with its discovery, since Yersen had described it more accurately, although not the first to see it.

In 1907 the Second Indian Plague Commission was set up. After many experiments with rats they found that the bacteria were transmitted from one rat to another, or from rats to humans, or from one infected human to another, through the bites of the rat fleas. It was shown that the fleas became partially choked with the bacteria after sucking blood from an infected host. Then when biting another host, they spit back some of the blood, now infected with germs, into the wound. Once the links between the plague, fleas, and rats had been exposed, the disease became easier to deal with, since the control of rats was clearly the first objective.

Even before Yersen and Kitazato's discovery, bubonic plague had ceased to be a terrible threat in Europe. Few Europeans were still living, as their ancestors had lived, in overcrowded, unsanitary, rat-infested dwellings. But in India and the Far East bubonic plague still exists. There are a few cases each year, although its occurrence is rarer than ever before. In 1957, for instance, only 514 deaths were reported (although this figure does not include outbreaks in Iron Curtain countries, for which statistics are not available).

Another form of plague, called sylvatic plague, is carried by fleas infesting wild woodland animals such as marmots and ground squirrels. It still occurs in many parts of the world, including the United States.

In 1910–11 and again in 1920–21 violent epidemics broke out in Manchuria and killed a total of about 70,000 people. This type of plague may cause pneumonia. Once an epidemic of pneumonic plague begins the disease can be passed from one person to another as the germs are spread by coughing. It is therefore likely to spread more quickly than the bubonic form.

A fourth disease that has had a tremendous influence on the history of mankind, particularly in Africa, is sleeping sickness. Sleeping sickness, which is transmitted by the tsetse fly, affects humans. But a similar disease — also carried by tsetse flies — affects cattle and other hoofed animals. It has been known in Africa since the fourteenth century. Early European slave traders were well aware of its existence. They were always careful to examine the slaves they were offered to see if they had swollen neck glands, one of the early signs of the disease.

Until the late nineteenth century sleeping sickness occurred only in a small region of West Africa. But by then European colonists put an end to much of the

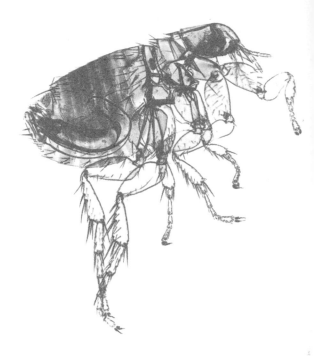

The rat flea (above) is the main vector of bubonic plague. Plague is transmitted to man by the bite of a flea that has been infected by bacteria in the blood of a rat. The house, or black, rat and the sewer, or brown, rat are the two rodents most often associated with human plague. It is a disease of communities living in poor hygienic conditions and southern India is one of the areas hardest hit. Below: A WHO worker and Indian villagers bait traps to catch rats.

tribal warfare that had kept the different African peoples confined to their own territories. Tribes began to move about more freely and sleeping sickness quickly spread. It is now known in the Congo region, in Zambia, Rhodesia, Mozambique, Tanzania, Uganda, and Kenya. The related disease of live stock, *nagana,* has made it almost impossible to raise domestic animals over an area of more than two million square miles. This, in turn, means that many of the people of this region are undernourished for lack of protein food. Other cattle-raising people have crowded into certain more healthy areas until pastures have become so overgrazed that widespread soil erosion has occurred. There is little doubt that sleeping sickness and nagana, together with malaria, are to blame for much of the poverty and economic underdevelopment of many African societies.

The control of sleeping sickness and nagana is a far more difficult task for the entomologist than the control of plague or malaria. There are twenty-two different species of tsetse flies, inhabiting every kind of terrain from rain forest to scrub and savanna. Unlike mosquitoes, the tsetse flies do not have any special breeding places because the female flies produce full-grown larvae that pupate immediately. The flies fall into three distinct groups: two of the groups transmit nagana and one spreads sleeping sickness. Among the last group, two species of tsetse flies are the chief culprits. These flies collect near water. During the dry season the concentration of flies becomes very heavy around the few remaining streams and water holes. When villagers come to collect water they are very likely to be bitten. If the disease is active in the area it soon spreads. It has long been known that those tribes that have their own covered wells in the villages are much healthier than those that rely on nearby streams or animal water holes.

At present it is not known for certain whether sleeping sickness is confined to humans or whether there is an animal "reservoir" of the disease. Some entomologists suspect that pigs may be carriers, and one form of the disease may be carried by two species of antelope.

Animals infected with nagana die very quickly, even though they look healthy right up until the time they die. Effective drugs are now available for human use and much research goes on to discover drugs that will prevent or cure the disease in cattle and horses.

The fight against the tsetse flies themselves is far from easy because of their varied habits, but much useful work has already been done and new methods are constantly being tested. According to their habits the flies can be divided into three categories: riverine flies that congregate near water, savanna flies that inhabit open country, and forest flies that live in the rain forests.

Above: The tsetse fly Glossina palpalis, a vector of sleeping sickness in western Africa. These flies give no warning buzz. Insecticides can be used to kill off the adults, but their pupae lie buried deep in damp, shady ground. Below: Map showing distribution of tsetse flies in Africa. Parts marked light red show the vast distribution of 20 species. The area in dark red marks the distribution of outbreaks of sleeping sickness recorded since 1920. Red dots show isolated cases of the disease.

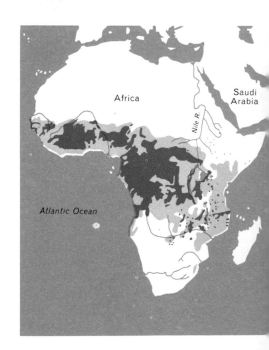

The riverine flies are the easiest to deal with. If the river banks are cleared of bushes the flies can find no moist, shady resting places and will quickly disperse. Since the areas involved are of manageable size, the bush-clearing work has been neither very difficult nor very costly. The savanna flies present a similar but much larger problem. They too like to roost in brush of a certain type. Clearing the brush over vast areas of savanna is very effective but also very costly. Now this method has been successfully replaced by insecticide spraying. The dense, tall rain forest, however, has so far defied any method of controlling the tsetse.

There is another method of controlling tsetse flies, especially those that spread nagana. This method has been to eliminate the wild game on which they feed and so kill them by starvation. This has undoubtedly helped, especially in Uganda. But it has never been a popular method because it involved slaughtering thousands of wild animals that are both beautiful and—to some at least—exciting to hunt. So this method is now seldom used and entomologists and veterinarians engaged in tsetse fly research are now concentrating on developing sprays and drugs that will kill the flies and make their animal hosts resistant to nagana.

The three groups of insects—mosquitoes, fleas, and tsetse flies—that we have considered in this chapter are by no means the only disease-carrying insects. The tiny sandflies, for instance, are responsible for the spread of several diseases. Sandflies are difficult to control because they conceal their eggs in the soil, in decaying vegetation, in water, and in wet sand. They also act as carriers of diseases between humans and dogs.

Some tsetse flies attack both man and domestic animals. In areas such as the Sudan where water is scarce (above) people and animals are forced to take water from rivers around which these flies are likely to congregate.

Below: Cattle in Africa being captured and prepared for inoculation against nagana—the form of sleeping sickness that affects animals.

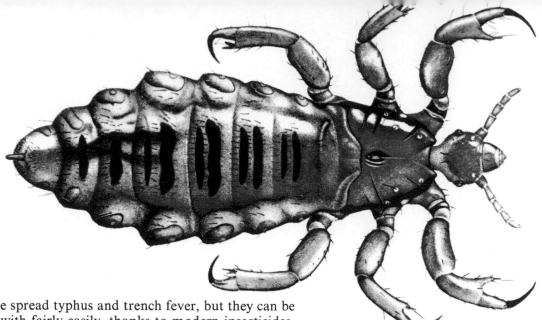

Lice spread typhus and trench fever, but they can be dealt with fairly easily, thanks to modern insecticides. Lice seldom cause trouble nowadays except when people are temporarily herded together under very unhygienic conditions during wars or after some natural disaster. The housefly, although it does not suck blood, is a noted disease carrier because it feeds and lays eggs on both food and feces of animals and humans. Thus, houseflies are responsible mainly for spreading dysentery and other stomach disorders. Great efforts have been made to control the housefly, particularly in the United States. The health authorities in many countries have succeeded in making most people aware of how dangerous this insect can be. Horse and cow manure are the most favorable breeding materials for houseflies,

Above: The body louse, vector of the organisms that cause typhus. These organisms are sucked up from infected human blood by the louse; they multiply in its gut and pass from its excrement into the blood stream of the next human bitten.

Below: Workers at the Aswan Dam camp in Egypt being sprayed with DDT in a talcum powder base to kill lice.

The housefly is a formidable disease carrier because it feeds and lays eggs on both food and excrement. Above: Spraying a foodshop with an anti-fly preparation. Below: A team of public health officials in England inspect meat for traces of contamination. Every day they visit markets, warehouses, retail shops, and slaughterhouses.

and when the automobile replaced the horse in Europe and America, the housefly population fell dramatically.

But in many countries sanitation remains primitive, and cattle, donkeys, and camels are still common in the towns. Flies continue to swarm and carry severe intestinal diseases that cause many deaths, especially among babies and young children. Unfortunately the housefly has proved very difficult to wipe out because it rapidly becomes immune to almost every type of insecticide. So the most effective answer to its menace—although inevitably a slow one—is to improve standards of sanitation and hygiene throughout the world.

Not many years ago biting and stinging insects and houseflies were dismissed as merely annoyances. We know now that all insects of this kind are potentially dangerous, both to ourselves and to our domestic animals. We know, too, that protection against them is vitally important. Tremendous advances have been made in the fight against insects that help to spread germs. But we still have a long way to go and it seems unlikely that these insects will ever be completely wiped out. However, if entomologists can at least manage to keep the insects under control, while doctors suppress the diseases with drugs, there is a remote possibility that the actual disease organisms may in time disappear. If this happened the insects that now carry these organisms would no longer be dangerous. Meanwhile many hundreds of scientists are working on these problems and are constantly finding new ways to handle them. Year by year the world becomes a healthier place, and fewer people die from insect-borne diseases.

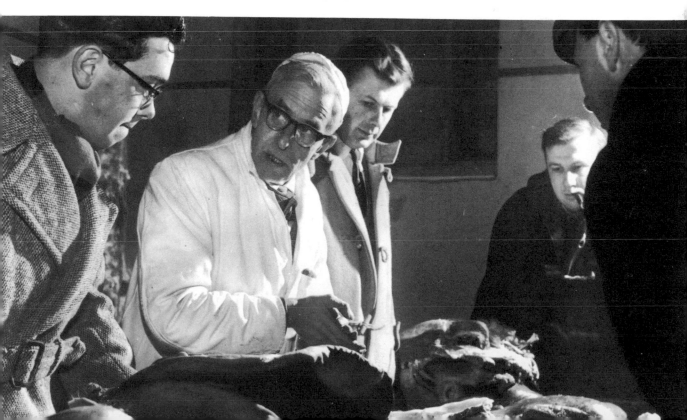

The Fight Against Locusts

NOBODY knows when locust swarms first began to range across vast areas of the world destroying all green vegetation in their path. Locusts were undoubtedly known and feared by the ancient civilizations of the Nile, Tigris, Euphrates, and Indus river valleys five thousand years ago. Probably they threatened the livelihood of many food-gathering peoples even before this period.

Today, various species of swarming locusts are found in North and South America, Africa, the Middle East, southern U.S.S.R., India, Pakistan, China, and Australia. Except for southern Spain and Portugal, Europe is now free of these pests, but it was not always so. Until a little more than two hundred years ago locusts occasionally penetrated into western Europe. Apparently they came from areas around the Caspian Sea and migrated westward through Rumania, Hungary, Poland, and Germany.

A German chronicle of the year 1569 describes an invasion of locusts devouring the crops. During 1693 and 1694 enormous swarms made their way through Hungary, Austria, Germany, and eastern France, and the same thing happened again in 1730. In more recent times, however, locusts have been confined mainly to countries south and east of the Mediterranean, where they are still a very serious pest.

There are several distinct species of migratory grasshoppers, commonly known as locusts. The most important are the red locust, the brown locust, the African migratory locust, and the desert locust. The first three are confined to Africa, while the fourth and most destructive ranges over Africa and the Middle East as far as India and East Pakistan. The North American locust has not been a serious pest since 1876, when a large outbreak occurred, but the South American form is still troublesome. All these grasshoppers have the common trait of grouping together in large numbers under certain conditions and then setting out on long migrations.

The story of the fight against locusts is an excellent example of how vital it is to know everything possible about an insect if it is to be successfully controlled. It was not until the present century that locust behavior began to be understood. Until then, the sudden appearance of locust swarms had remained a complete mystery and nobody knew what happened to the insects between periods of swarming. Then in 1921 the Russian-born Boris Uvarov published his discovery that locusts lead

The drawing above, from a bas-relief of about 700 B.C., shows the servants of King Sennacherib of Assyria bringing locusts impaled on sticks to be eaten at a feast. The relief, right, comes from an Egyptian tomb. Dated about 2300 B.C., it shows two locusts eating leaves.

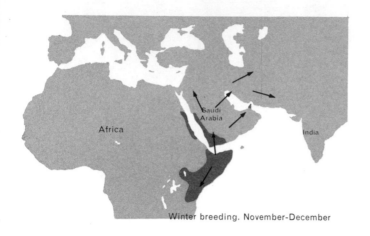

Winter breeding. November-December

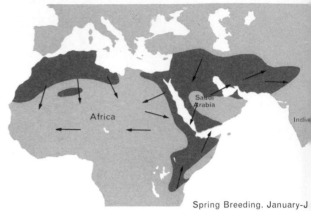

Spring Breeding. January-J

a double life. That is, sometimes they are solitary animals; but at other times they are gregarious, or group-seeking. He also noted that their physical appearance alters as they change from one phase to the other.

In the solitary phase locusts behave and look like any other harmless grasshopper. They live in one place and feed moderately on the local vegetation, mainly grasses. Their color blends with the surroundings, for they are mostly green or brown, speckled and marked in various ways. This solitary phase may continue for many generations.

The gregarious phase, which may occur suddenly, is triggered off when many solitary locusts are crowded together. This may happen when more eggs than usual are laid because of especially favorable conditions during the breeding season. Or it may happen because the suitable breeding area shrinks so that the females are forced to lay their eggs close together. Thus, when the young locusts—known as hoppers—hatch out they find themselves surrounded and jostled by their fellows. This closeness to other hoppers causes a remarkable change both in their appearance and their behavior. Instead of developing their normal protective coloring they now become much brighter. They take on a coloration of red and yellow, set off with black. Changes occur in the structure of their legs; they become much more lively and excitable; they eat more. They also show a strong gregarious instinct, forming first into small groups and then into larger and larger bands that soon begin to move out from their hatching grounds. This movement of the hoppers is called a *trek*.

If any of these swarming locusts become separated from the swarm, they will go back to a solitary existence and gradually lose their bright colors in favor of dull greens and browns. On the other hand, a hopper that has settled down to a solitary life can take up a gregarious existence if it is introduced into a swarm. After

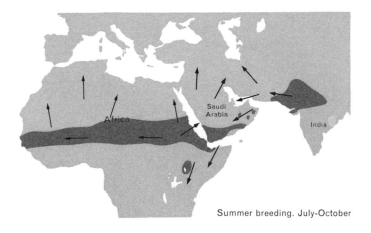

Desert locusts breed somewhere within the infestation zone during every month of the year. These maps mark the seasonal breeding areas; the arrows show how the flow of migration continually replenishes each area with new generations of locusts. Far left: Winter area, November-December; the rains of Somaliland and the coastal areas of the southern Red Sea favor breeding at this time. Middle: Spring area, January–June. This is the main breeding time; where winter breeding took place, a second generation may now appear. Right: Summer area, July–October. Here the summer monsoon is favorable to breeding.

Summer breeding. July-October

Below: A band of desert locusts on the march in Africa. If living space becomes crowded, or climatic conditions unsuitable, the locusts march to new ground in thousands or millions, feeding continually en route. This exodus stops about 30 days after hatching. During this time they pass through five instars, or stages of growth, before becoming winged adults.

some time it will take on the swarming colors. Because it is gradual, this color-changing process makes identification very difficult. In addition to the typical solitary and gregarious colorations, there will be a certain number of both swarming and non-swarming locusts in a transitional stage of coloration.

Locusts, in their different phases, have been compared to soldiers and civilians. The peaceful civilians live quiet lives in their own little villages. When war fever sets in, they join a huge army, dress in distinctive, bright uniforms, become excited and restless, and set off to conquer the world. But if they are discharged for some reason, they once more adopt civilian clothing and their old habits of quiet civilian life.

Although the migratory locusts begin their trek soon after hatching, they do not usually get very far while they are still in the immature hopper stage. They start moving in the morning, as soon as the sun has warmed the ground, and hop along, feeding as they go. When it becomes hot at midday they stop for a rest and climb onto plants and grasses to get away from the hot ground. Later they set off again and continue until sunset, when they rest for the night, usually on bushes and plants well above the ground. Different species of hoppers show a certain variation in trekking behavior. Some move in very close formation, while others spread out on a broad front. Desert locusts, for instance, tend to keep close together in the early stages of their trek. As the hoppers molt and approach maturity—at about five weeks of age—they space themselves farther apart.

When locusts are full-grown and have developed wings, they immediately take to the air. For the first day or two they take only short, practice flights in various directions. Then the real migration begins.

Migrating locusts usually fly downwind at a speed of about ten miles an hour in swarms so dense that they may cast dark shadows on the ground. The number of

locusts in a swarm varies, but a medium-sized swarm may contain more than a trillion—a million million insects. Much larger swarms than this have been reported. Swarming locusts have huge appetites and each insect will eat its own weight in food every day. To put it another way, an average swarm consumes daily something like 3000 tons of vegetation. When a swarm lands to feed in a field or in an orchard, nothing is left after a few hours except the thickest stalks and the bare branches of the trees. When the locusts have finished feeding they fly off on their journey, which may continue for as much as 3000 miles.

The adult locust has a normal life span of about six months. In that period the female will lay an average of 300 eggs in three or four separate batches. Under especially favorable conditions she may lay twice or three times this number. The eggs are enclosed in a pod-shaped capsule that she buries in the ground. There they remain until they hatch (usually after ten to twenty days) and the young hoppers wriggle to the surface. The eggs will not hatch unless they are laid in damp ground or are moistened by rain after laying. Thus the breeding season generally falls in the monsoon, or rainy, period of the specific region. At this time, too, natural vegetation is at its most abundant, and the newly hatched hoppers have a good supply of food. By the time the dry weather returns the locusts will have reached maturity and can migrate to other regions where food is more abundant.

When locusts are swarming their strongest instinct is to keep together. Thus, at breeding times, the females will all lay their eggs close to one another. The crowding together of the newly hatched hoppers then induces the

Swarming desert locusts cause vast destruction of plants and crops. The dense swarm (above), clouding from view an orange grove in the Souss Valley of Morocco, is stripping it of leaves. A single swarm may number 1000 million; it may range over an area of 3000 square miles, leaving devastation in its trail.

Below: The orange tree has been stripped of all its leaves by a marauding swarm of locusts. A single swarm can eat up to 20,000 tons of green food in one day.

gregarious phase in the new generation. Thus, once a serious outbreak of swarming has started it may go on for many years. The swarms will move backward and forward over a vast area. Careful observations of the red locust and the African migratory locust have shown that the initial outbreaks of these species always start from certain well-defined and fairly small areas, where a nucleus of the locusts live permanently in the solitary phase and from which they may spread over thousands of square miles.

The outbreak areas of the red locust are in Tanganyika, and during the serious plague period that lasted from the 1920s to 1944 the locusts spread southward to South Africa and westward into the Congo basin and the Atlantic coast of Africa. The migratory locust begins its migrations from the Niger River flood plains near Timbuktu in the Mali Republic, in northwest Africa. Between 1928 and 1942 it invaded almost the whole of Africa south of the Sahara Desert. Eventually the plagues died out. That there have been no further outbreaks of these two locusts is due mainly to two organizations, the International Red Locust Control Service and the Migratory Locust Organization which keep a constant watch on the outbreak areas and attack hopper bands as soon as they are reported.

The brown locust (large swarms of which appeared in South Africa during the autumn of 1963) and, more especially, the desert locust, are now the principal troublemakers. Up to now no special outbreak areas have been discovered for the desert locust. It seems to be able to breed almost anywhere in all the sixty countries in which it is found. This area covers Africa (although swarms are not found south of Nigeria and Tanzania), Saudi Arabia, Jordan, Syria, Iraq, eastern Turkey, Iran, Afghanistan, West Pakistan, and a large part of India stretching as far as East Pakistan. In all of these countries food is a serious problem. No crops can be spared for locusts. So this pest presents a constant and very serious economic problem, causing tremendous monetary loss and a great deal of fear and suffering.

Systematic locust research began in England in 1920 when a small staff of English entomologists set about collecting locust data from all over the world. In 1929, after locust outbreaks had occurred in Africa, a small grant of money was made from government funds to carry on this work for a year and to distribute information about locusts wherever it was needed. The efforts of the English scientists were so successful and aroused such interest that in 1931 the first International Locust Conference was organized in Rome. There it was decided that a permanent research center should be set up in London. Today it is called the Anti-Locust

Research Centre. Here intensive locust research goes on all the time, helped by information that comes in from all the regions where locusts are a pest. The Centre also organizes anti-locust campaigns in all the territories where outbreaks occur.

Many different aspects of the locust problem are studied at the Centre. The various species are bred in large numbers, and their anatomy, physiology, life histories, and behavior are investigated. Locusts are raised under different conditions of temperature, humidity, and light intensity to find out exactly how they react to changes in their environment. They are fed on different foods, their transitions from the solitary to the gregarious stage are studied, and their methods of flight are investigated in a wind tunnel.

By collecting and analyzing reports from the locust areas the staff at the Centre can keep up to date with the distribution and movements of the insects. Such reports, the first of which date from the early 1930s, have made it possible to forecast fairly accurately the direction in which swarms will move at certain seasons. Warnings can then be sent out to threatened areas to prepare them to deal with the insects when they arrive. The study of seasonal temperature, rainfall, and prevailing winds in commonly affected areas helps to increase the accuracy of these forecasts. It has also revealed differences in behavior between different species of locusts. Testing insecticides and developing the best methods of applying them are other important activities of the Centre.

Ever since governments first made efforts to wipe out locusts, it has been obvious that individual countries, acting independently of one another, could never hope to succeed. Locusts, after all, do not stop their migrations when they reach a national frontier, but spread quickly from one country to another. To be effective, anti-locust campaigns must be carried out on an international scale. This is especially true as far as the desert locust is concerned.

At one time, in African countries, responsibility for exterminating red and migratory locusts rested with individuals on whose land they were first found. The result was that farmers often hesitated to report outbreaks because this meant that they had to try to exterminate the insects at their own expense. Obviously the only way to tackle the problem was for every threatened country to have special anti-locust organizations staffed by entomologists to plan the campaigns and trained personnel always ready to go into action.

Although the need for such organizations was apparent, it was difficult to persuade all the affected countries to establish them. Locust control is expensive and many governments did not want to finance a permanent

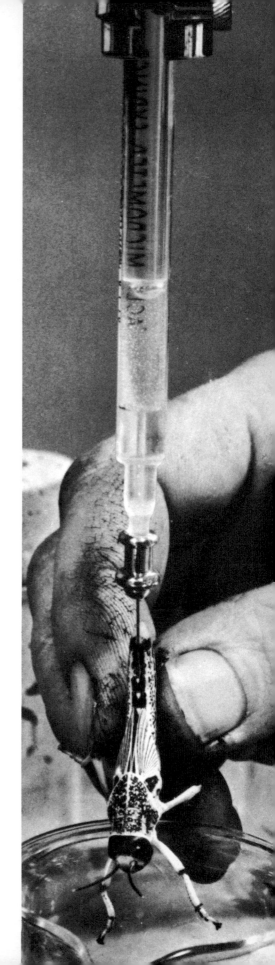

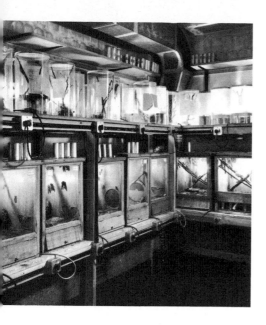

Above: Observation cages used for breeding locusts at the Anti-Locust Research Centre in London. Left: An experiment to test the reaction of an insecticidal liquid on a desert locust. Below: Fieldwork in progress in the Souss Valley, Morocco. Here the action of insecticides on locusts is tested in their natural surroundings; at the same time the effect of insecticides on crop growth is studied.

organization to deal with outbreaks that might occur only at irregular intervals. Moreover co-operation was difficult to obtain between countries that were politically at odds with each other. Even now full co-operation has not been achieved. But great advances have been made, and most countries that lie in the locust belt have agreed to support an international control system.

A very widespread migration of desert locusts began late in 1951, when swarms were reported in the Somali peninsula in east Africa. Early in 1952 these same locusts began to move northward into Ethiopia. From Ethiopia the swarms moved westward into the Sudan, and eastward across the Red Sea into the Arabian peninsula.

By the beginning of February they had reached Iraq, and from there they spread westward into Jordan, and had started eastward toward Iran, Pakistan, and India. Although the swarms stopped frequently to feed and to lay their eggs, it took them only three months to travel 3000 miles. The young hoppers began to hatch in March and strenuous efforts were needed to control them. The British Desert Locust Control, the Egyptian Anti-Locust Mission, and motorized army units of the Arab Legion, as well as soldiers from Saudi Arabia, worked ceaselessly and managed to prevent new swarms from forming. In Iraq, with the help of American airplanes, it was possible to stop the spread of the pests. In Jordan the campaign was carried on with help from Turkey, Syria, Lebanon, and the United Nations Food and Agriculture Organization, which by this time was playing a vital part in anti-locust work. In Iran the government arranged for the army to help, and vehicles and personnel were also sent from India, Pakistan, the Soviet Union, and the United States.

U.S.S.R.

Black Sea

Caspian Sea

Turkey

Syria

Iraq

Jordan

Iran

Afganistan

Egypt

Saudi Arabia

Pakistan

Red Sea

Oman

Africa

Nile R.

Yemen

Hadhramaut

Sudan

Ethiopia

Somaliland

Uganda

Kenya

Indian Ocean

Map showing dramatic spread of locusts in 1952. Dark red marks the area infested in December 1951. In five months swarms traveled 3000 miles, repeatedly stopping to lay eggs. Over five million dollars was spent on control efforts.

Thanks to international co-operation the campaign proved successful over most of this area. However, some swarms managed to escape from Iran and invaded India and Pakistan. There they bred on a large scale during the monsoon season. In spite of ceaseless efforts, which did succeed in preventing any very serious damage, new swarms built up and started to fly westward after the monsoon had passed. By October they had reached Arabia, and by the end of the year they were back again in Ethiopia and Somalia.

Although the intensive campaign of 1952 was only partially successful, it did protect most of the standing crops from attack. Above all, it demonstrated the value of international co-operation. The campaign cost over five million dollars. This seems like a great deal of money, but it is small compared with the cost of the damage these insects can do if they are not controlled. In the winter of 1954–55, for instance, Morocco was invaded from the south by desert locusts. In six weeks they had ruined crops valued at nearly $12 million. Two years later there were further serious attacks in northwest Africa and in Arabia, Iraq, and Iran. All these locusts stemmed from the original Somalian outbreak of 1951.

Until the present century there were no really effective weapons against locusts. Beating and trampling the creatures, digging trenches in which to burn or bury them, frightening them with gunfire—all these methods were common. They were never very effective and, in the light of present-day knowledge, seem pathetically inadequate. We know now that the locusts lost through such methods could easily be replaced through breeding. The only way in which the menace can be controlled is by exterminating the swarms before they begin to fly. If this cannot be done, then the locusts must be killed before they have had a chance to breed.

To do this, anti-locust units constantly patrol vast areas of the desert searching for bands of young hoppers that are just beginning to move. The earlier they are discovered, the easier they are to deal with. The commonest method is to put down a line of poisoned bait in their path. This consists of grain mixed with about 4 per cent of an insecticide that acts as a stomach poison. When the hoppers reach the grain they stop to eat it and soon die. The amount of poison required is very small: 4 pounds of poison mixed with 96 pounds of grain is enough to deal with a band of hoppers covering as much as four acres of land.

Between March and June 1952 about 10,000 hopper bands were destroyed in this way in an area of Saudi Arabia covering about 10,000 square miles. The following October, in Somalia, 12,000 hopper bands were

Aircraft fitted with mechanisms for
spraying insecticides make widespread
locust control possible. The above
photograph shows preparations for
reloading two helicopters with insecticide
in Morocco in 1960.

killed using only 350 tons of poison bait. The operational area covered 24,000 square miles, and about 500 people were employed under the guidance of 13 trained entomologists. The cost of the poison bait is not at all high. But the enormous area that has to be covered, and the need for many motor vehicles capable of operating in almost trackless country, makes such a campaign very expensive.

In an effort to cut the cost, experiments have been made in spraying threatened vegetation with poison dissolved in water. Either aircraft or ground vehicles have been used. The method is sound enough but it has been difficult to prepare an insecticide that would remain potent for a number of days without harming the plants or leaving an unpleasant or poisonous residue on food crops. It is also possible to spray flying locust swarms from an aircraft, especially when they are in dense formations. One aircraft killed 400 tons of locusts in 14 minutes while spraying a swarm in Somalia. Another method that has been used successfully is to spray the vegetation on and around locust-egg beds before the eggs are due to hatch. When the baby hoppers emerge they begin to feed and are poisoned, before they have had time to begin their trek. Baiting the path of advancing hoppers is still perhaps the most useful and universal method. But, like spraying the egg beds, its success depends on an efficient information service. It is essential that the hopper bands be spotted as soon as possible after hatching. Their size, their stage of development, and the direction in which they are moving must then be reported at once to the local anti-locust headquarters.

As we have already noted, the study of weather conditions — especially rainfall — in the locust areas can be of great importance. Such knowledge helps in forecasting the most likely districts where breeding will take place at a certain time. It has long been known that flying swarms often stop to lay their eggs at the beginning of a rainy period. Reports of breeding locusts are constantly pouring in by telegraph to the Anti-Locust Research Centre from almost every country within the desert locust zone. Locust warnings are then sent out from the Centre to the regions concerned, just as a weather bureau sends out storm warnings to shipping.

The desert locust has not yet been beaten, but great advances have been made. Today it is not so much a question of developing methods to deal with the locusts. The problem is to build up the anti-locust organization to a high pitch of efficiency. In time, full international co-operation must, and will, be achieved. When that time comes, the days of serious devastation by locusts will be numbered.

Above left: Trench burial of locusts in Argentina. Millions of the insects have been channeled into this pit by canvas screens. Overhanging zinc plates defeat escape attempts. The captured locusts will then be burned. Below left: The Anti-Locust Service combating an invasion in Morocco in 1954. Sprays of liquid insecticide are applied by an airplane.

Above: Poison-baiting a band of desert locusts in Somaliland. When the band (brown) reaches the line of bait, it eats it, then dies. Below: Insecticide sprayer being used in the campaign to control locusts in Central America. A laboratory was set up in Nicaragua in 1960 to study locust biology and to organize anti-locust control departments in five other countries.

Protecting the World's Crops

PESTS have probably been attacking crops since man first began to cultivate crops. But it is only during the last one hundred years or so that crop pests have become a critical world-wide problem. Before then most agricultural regions of the world were divided into relatively small units in which a variety of crops were raised. Thus, because a particular pest usually attacks only one particular crop, insect damage tended to be confined to local outbreaks.

But since the mid-nineteenth century, the situation has altered a great deal as the result of changes in farming methods. Not only has the crop yield, and therefore the value, of each acre increased greatly. More important, huge tracts of country have become devoted almost exclusively to the raising of a single crop. Obvious examples of such specialization in the United States are the vast corn belt of the Middle West and, until recently, the cotton belt of the South. Once a pest establishes itself in a mainly one-crop area of this kind, it multiplies and spreads rapidly and may threaten a nation's entire output of a particular crop.

No fewer than 5000 different species of insects are known to be important pests of crops. Almost every crop grown anywhere in the world is attacked by at least one, and often quite a number, of insect pests. The problem of food crops is especially serious. For the majority of the human population the world is a hungry place. In many regions the destruction of food by crop pests can lead to malnutrition, or even starvation, for thousands of people. Economically, too, the price can be crippling. In the United States, for instance, the cost of insect damage to all crops is estimated to be $4 billion a year.

Few subjects are more controversial at the present time than that of pest control. Most experts agree that control is necessary, but there is deep disagreement about the methods that should be used. Some powerful insecticides are not selective in their action. That is, they will kill all insects—useful as well as harmful—that come in contact with them. Many of them will also kill birds and animals, and even humans may be harmed by poisonous residues left on food plants.

Among the most dangerous insecticides are the chlorinated hydrocarbon compounds, such as DDT, which have been used all over the world by professional entomologists as well as by farmers and gardeners. Many of these powerful insecticides are very effective when correctly applied as sprays or dusts. They have been invaluable in big campaigns, such as the fight against

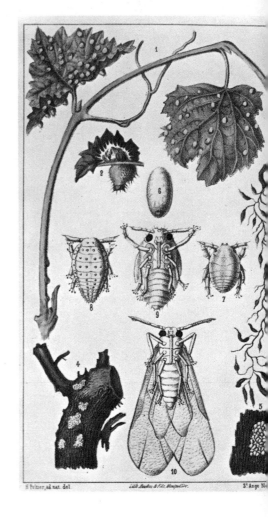

Above: Drawings of the eggs, galls, and adult of the aphid Phylloxera, and a root and leaves of a vine blighted by this insect. Above right: 19th-century French government officials inspect blighted vines. From 1865–1875 over half the vines of France were destroyed by Phylloxera, causing the country more economic harm than the Franco-Prussian War. Right: The soil of an infected vineyard being treated with carbon bisulphide. This treatment was only temporarily effective; the final solution was to graft susceptible French vines onto resistant root stock from America.

malaria mosquitoes. But their drawbacks are now becoming apparent, and entomologists and chemists are trying to find new insecticides that will be equally good but more selective.

The ideal insecticide has yet to be found. There are certain preparations derived from plants, such as derris root and pyrethrum powder. These are deadly to many insects on contact, although harmless to birds, mammals, and man. Unfortunately, these products remain poisonous for such a short time that frequent spraying or dusting is necessary to keep crops free from pests.

The new *systemic* insecticides hold much promise, but they are still in the experimental stage and have yet to be tested on a large scale. Systemic insecticides act on

quite a different principle from sprays or dusts of the old type. When applied to the plants, either by watering or spraying, they penetrate right into the plant tissues. The only insects poisoned are those that actually feed on the plants by sucking the sap or eating the leaves. Harmless insects, which may settle on but do not eat any part of the plant, are not affected. Insecticides of this type should be particularly useful against aphids, leaf hoppers, and such pests as leaf miners, which feed inside the plants. Up to now systemic poisons are recommended only for ornamental plants. Although these poisonous chemicals seem to break down into harmless compounds after a few weeks, we need to know much more about their effects before they can be considered safe for use on food crops.

One of the weaknesses of many modern insecticides is that insects of different kinds can develop a resistance against them in a remarkably few generations. Another drawback is that most effective sprays kill not only the insect pests but also most of their predators and parasites. Thus, if some insect pests in a given area remain alive after a spraying attack, they will breed again more quickly than before because most of their natural enemies in the immediate neighborhood have been destroyed. Frequent, heavy spraying to offset this danger is costly and in some cases may be difficult to carry out.

These and other drawbacks have stimulated much research into the possibilities of more "natural" methods of control. At present, biological control is receiving a great deal of attention. This method introduces natural predators into a particular area to kill the pests. The aim of this method is not to exterminate the pests completely but to keep their number at a level sufficiently low to make sure that the damage they do is of very little economic importance.

However, biological control is not without its dangers. It is fairly simple to upset the local balance of an insect population. To restore the balance can be ex-

Above: A chicken house in London being sprayed with a pyrethrum insecticide, which is toxic to a wide range of insect species but does not affect birds and other animals. It stays toxic for only a short time so frequent spraying is necessary. Below: Testing a chemical compound at an American research laboratory to see if it has "systemic" action on plant leaves. Insects are placed on the leaves. If the chemical is drawn up from the roots and kills insects that eat the leaves, it will be tested further. Systemic poisons have not yet been proved safe for use on food crops.

tremely difficult, especially if imported insects are involved. It has been done, however, and very successfully too, especially in the United States, where biological control methods have received much support from leading entomologists.

One of the most famous cases of successful biological control was the victory over the cottony-cushion scale. This little insect was accidentally introduced into California from Australia in about 1868. It has a waxy covering that makes it very resistant to spraying. The scale spread alarmingly and within a few years had done tremendous damage to the California citrus orchards. Yet in its native country it was not a serious pest. Clearly, in Australia some natural enemy was keeping the scale under control. So the head of the entomological services of the United States Department of Agriculture sent an assistant to Australia to identify the scale's predator and to bring some specimens back.

The American scientist discovered that the principal enemy of the scale insect was a small ladybird. He sent a container with 139 of these beetles back to California, where preparations had already been made to receive them. An orange tree heavily infested with scale insects had been covered with a gauze tent. There the beetles were released, together with some parasitic flies that also attack the scale. The flies did not prove to be of much use, but the ladybirds settled down at once and soon ate all the scale insects on the tree. Later, the beetles were let out of the tent, and they spread rapidly throughout the citrus-growing areas of California. Within two years the Australian ladybird, as it came to be called, had managed to control the scale insect. By 1890 the scale was no longer an economic problem. Since then the ladybird beetle has been introduced successfully into many other countries where the scale insect has appeared. It is, in fact, the classic example of biological control.

The successful campaign with the Australian ladybird encouraged entomologists to try similar methods

Biological control is an inexpensive way of killing specific insect pests. The photograph (above) shows Australian lady beetles feeding on cottony cushion scale insects that have infested a citrus tree. Right: Lady beetles feeding on another kind of scale insects on an orange. Two adult beetles and four of its larvae can be seen; at the lower right is an empty pupal case. Both stages of the beetle feed on the scale insects.

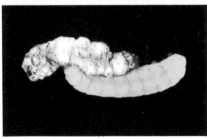

Top: An oriental fruit moth on a peach leaf. It lays its eggs on the undersurface of the leaves of peach, pear, apple or quince trees. The larvae hatch and attack the twigs and fruits. The second photograph shows its larva being parasitized by the larva of an ichneumon wasp. The adult of this parasite is seen below. This parasite is now mass cultivated, and then released in infested orchards.

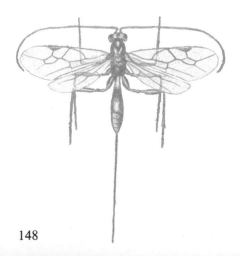

against other pests. One such pest was the gypsy moth, which was brought into the United States from Europe in 1869. Within twenty-five years it had spread all over New England and was causing serious damage to orchards and woodlands. Parasites and predators of the moth were imported from Europe and Japan and helped to keep it in check. But the manageable present-day population of this pest could not have been achieved only by biological control. Insecticide sprays had to be used also.

In Hawaii the sugar-cane leaf hopper and a species of cane borer, which caused severe losses to the sugar-cane industry, have been successfully controlled by imported parasites.

The American blight, or woolly aphid, became a serious nuisance in many parts of Europe at the beginning of the present century. It is now kept under control by a tiny parasitic wasp, less than one millimeter long, that was introduced from America. A very injurious scale insect, also of American origin, began to infest white mulberry trees in Italy. But it was soon controlled by another imported American parasite, which gained the upper hand with the help of other predators and parasites from South Africa and Japan. In the United States alone, 485 parasitic species have been imported specifically for biological control; of these, 95 have become established.

Many such schemes have failed or have been only partially successful. But biological control continues to be used all over the world, especially when pests are difficult to deal with in other ways. The fruit fly, the olive fly, the corn borer, and the alfalfa weevil are among the serious pests that are being attacked by biological warfare at the present time.

An interesting variation of biological control was suggested by the discovery that insects, like humans, are naturally susceptible to certain diseases. Might not pests be controlled by deliberately-created epidemics? The idea holds great promise, especially if diseases can be found that affect only the species that we need to exterminate.

Many larvae of butterflies and moths easily catch a disease caused by bacteria called *Bacillus thuringiensis*. The larvae of the cabbage white butterfly, for example, often catch this disease in nature, as it is very contagious. Research workers found they could put a few caterpillars that had died from the disease in a bucket of water and churn them around. The diseased caterpillars made the liquid highly infectious. The liquid could then be greatly diluted and used as a highly poisonous spray against other caterpillars. Sprays containing the bacteria that cause this disease are now

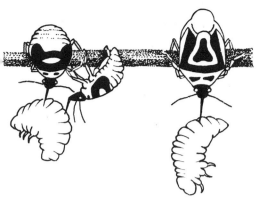

Insects such as Perillus bioculatus have been brought from North America to France because both nymphs (above left) and adults (above right) eat Colorado beetle larvae. They impale them with their beaks then suck their body fluids.

Below: A small black wasp parasitizing a larva of the alfalfa weevil. This species of wasp was brought from Italy to the United States in 1911. Now hope for economically controlling the weevil rests with it.

manufactured commercially and sold in a highly concentrated form. One of these commercial concentrates contains about 60 million bacteria spores per gram. The sprays are widely used and have been welcomed because they are not at all dangerous to other animals. They also act very quickly even though the caterpillars do not die for several days; but the caterpillars stop feeding almost immediately after they are wetted by the spray. Other bacteria sprays are also being developed. Even the once notorious Japanese beetle can now be controlled by the milky-disease bacteria, *Bacillus popilliae*.

Virus diseases can also be used for insect control. Viruses are submicroscopic agents that infect living cells and cause disease. The viruses do not take effect quite so quickly as, for instance, *Bacillus thuringiensis*. But the viruses are more persistent, and once an area has been thoroughly sprayed the virus diseases can continue to be a source of infection for many years. It has been found that insects not actually killed by a virus disease can pass it on to their offspring, which will then be killed. Sprays carrying viruses have been used with great success against the alfalfa caterpillars in the United States. Unfortunately, these are the larvae of a beautiful butterfly, the clouded yellow. But since they do tremendous damage to alfalfa, an important forage crop, they must be killed. It has so far proved more

difficult to make use of fungus diseases of insects because their effectiveness depends on relatively high humidity. But some have been successfully used, often in connection with ordinary insecticides. Research on them continues.

Entomologists have also experimented with insect attractants and repellents. Under certain conditions, and in limited areas, lights can be used to lure moths, mosquitoes, crane flies, certain beetles, and even hornets into prepared traps. The use of baits in insect research has shown that many substances rich in protein are very attractive to flies. The Mediterranean fruit fly has been successfully controlled in many places by using traps. The traps are baited with rolls of cotton that has been dipped in a solution of the attractant substance. The solution also contains a deadly poison. Sometimes the mixture of attractant and poison is simply sprayed on the fruit trees. It is not necessary to treat more than one row of trees in every three or four because the

Above: A medfly trap, taken apart to show the cotton wick, impregnated with an attractant but poisonous chemical, and a number of medflies killed by it. Lure-baited traps like this are used to locate infested areas. Below: A gypsy moth about to enter a trap baited with a sex attractant.

Left: San Jose scale insects feeding on a peach twig. Because of its hard waxy outer cover, destruction of this scale by spraying with insecticide has been unsuccessful. No effective method of controlling it has yet been evolved.

insects quickly find the bait. By this method fruit flies have, in some areas, been wiped out within months.

The possibility of using the scent of female moths to trap males has also been investigated. The idea is perfectly sound in principle, but at present it is not practical for commercial use. An enormous number of females are needed to produce even a small amount of scent. In experiments with gypsy moths, for instance, it was found that only 20 milligrams of the attractant substance could be extracted from 500,000 females. However, the attractant, known as *gypsyl*, can now be made by a chemical process.

The question has recently been considered of whether supersonic noise—or "silent sound," as it is often called—can have any practical use either as a repellent or as an insecticide. Experiments have shown that mechanical reproduction of the supersonic squeaks of bats repels certain species of moths. Other experiments seem to indicate that insects can be very much disturbed, and even killed, by certain sound waves. Very little is really known about this method. So far it has been used only in laboratory experiments, mainly because it requires very expensive apparatus.

Chemical repellents have been used mainly as a protection against mosquitoes, midges, and biting flies. It has proved very difficult, however, to find a substance that will remain effective for more than a few hours. Moreover, unless such repellents are universally employed over a wide area, the pests may sometimes be able to move to neighboring fields that are not protected. Generally speaking, destroying the pests is probably more desirable than driving them away.

During the 1880s American fruitgrowers began to be troubled by an insect called the San Jose scale. A native of China, the insect spread slowly at first. With the increase in the numbers of fruit trees, the insect multiplied rapidly until it had become a pest in almost every state of the union. Many people involved with fruitgrowing in Europe became worried that the scale would be introduced there by accident. In 1898 the Emperor of Germany issued a decree prohibiting the importation of fruit and living plants from the United States. The fight against this pest aroused a great deal of public interest, and it was the main cause of the enactment of many international quarantine laws. (No really effective method to control the San Jose scale was found, inci-

dentally. Various sprays were developed, however, and it became routine to spray while the trees are dormant over the winter.)

Quarantine laws have been invaluable in reducing the danger of pests and plant diseases spreading from one country, or continent, to another. These laws are especially strict in the United States, where they apply even to interstate movements. No plant material of any kind is allowed into the United States without authorization. If a person is given a bunch of roses when flying from England, for example, to New York, the flowers will be confiscated and burnt by the customs authorities on arrival. In 1956 nearly a quarter of a million separate items of plant material were intercepted before they entered the United States. Within them were found innumerable injurious insects, including fruit flies, bollworms, and stem borers—all highly dangerous economic pests. In Europe, too, similar rules apply. Particularly strict regulations are in force regarding potatoes due to the danger of introducing the Colorado beetle.

As we have seen, entomologists have developed (and are continuing to develop) a great variety of pest-control techniques. Many of these methods have been "tailor-made" to combat specific pests. But there have been a

In the early years of the United States Plant Quarantine Act, inspection was handled by a few officials under difficult conditions. Above left: An inspector examining imported orchids for possible insect pests in 1917. Now inspections are quick and scientific. Above: Officials look for insects among fruit taken from airline passengers' baggage.

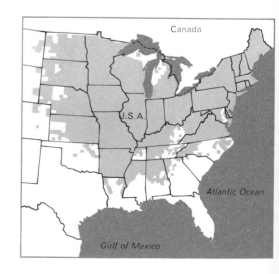

Below: An adult corn borer moth beside a stem of corn that has been cut open to show the larvae feeding inside. The corn borer has damaged North American corn crops for more than 40 years and is still a serious pest in many states. Below left: Map showing the area in the United States known to be infested by corn borers in 1961.

number of occasions when a pest has shown resistance to all known methods of control. In such cases, all the entomologist can do is to use every weapon at his disposal in the hope of at least limiting the spread of the insect.

A good example of this kind of combined operation is the campaign against the corn borer moth. This is a pest that American entomologists have been fighting with only partial success for more than forty years. In 1928, when corn borer damage became really serious, the United States Congress voted a fund of $10 million for a special campaign. The moth continued to flourish and in 1949 the pest did more damage than ever before. Although it has not been quite so destructive since then, it remains a serious economic pest. Two factors contribute to its persistence. First, it produces as many as three generations in a year; second, it feeds on various weeds and on crops other than corn, so that it cannot be controlled by protecting the corn alone. Altogether twenty-four different species of parasites have been imported in an effort to control it by biological means. Of these, only six have become established in different areas. Many kinds of sprays and dusts have been tried. Both bacterial and fungus infections have been deliberately spread among the insects with a fair amount

153

of success. Light traps have been used to capture as many adult moths as possible.

One of the latest ideas has been to release numbers of captured male moths that have been sterilized by exposure to radiation. It is hoped by this method to reduce the number of fertile eggs laid by the females. Plant breeders have also joined the fight and have developed varieties of corn that are resistant to attack. The campaign against the corn borer shows the best approach when no one method is capable of destroying a specific pest. Intelligent co-operation among entomologists, plant breeders, and government agencies can often reduce a pest's destructive activities.

There are some pests, however, that have successfully resisted every attack of entomological science. One of these is the cotton-boll weevil. This is still another pest that first appeared in North America toward the end of the last century. Few boll weevils had been reported before 1880, when large numbers were found doing considerable damage in a cotton plantation in Mexico. From there the insect gradually spread northward. By 1901 cotton growers in the southern United States had become seriously alarmed and a special investigation was started. Very few good insecticides were available at the time. Besides, spraying and dusting methods were almost useless because the weevil larvae lived and fed inside the cotton bolls. Entomologists made a number of suggestions. In particular they said that the cotton crops should be harvested earlier than usual and that all traces of old cotton should be cleared from the fields in the autumn. Few of the very conservative cotton farmers followed this advice, however, and the annual toll of ruined crops continued to increase.

At this time the economy of many southern states was founded almost entirely on this one crop. When cotton failed, the consequences were very serious. Once prosperous cotton growers lost all their money, thousands of laborers fled to the North, and many local banks failed. Nothing, apparently, could halt the advance of the boll weevil, a name that was soon adopted as a term of abuse.

No really effective answer to the weevil was found. It was gradually beaten not by science but by economic pressures. The cotton growers were faced with the choice of raising other crops or going bankrupt. Within a few years the whole economic system of the South had changed. Although cotton continued to be grown, the acreage devoted to it was much smaller than before. More important, cotton fields were separated from each

One way of suppressing harmful insects is to sterilize them by radiation. The photograph (right) shows a canister, containing thousands of the pupae of tropical fruitflies, being fitted to the arm of a hoist. This will be put in a lead cask containing radioactive cobalt-60. Adult flies emerging from the irradiated pupae will be sterile.

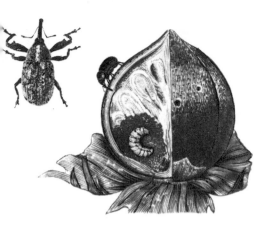

Above: Drawing of the adult boll weevil beside a cotton boll, sectioned to show the weevil's larva in its cell. Below: Map of the southern United States showing the area infested by the Mexican boll weevil in the early 20th century.

Canada

U.S.A.

Gulf of Mexico

Damage done by the boll weevil indirectly helped the economics of the Southern states, by compelling the growing of alternative crops. In recognition of this, a monument (left) to the boll weevil was erected in Enterprise, Alabama.

other by fruit orchards, fields, and gardens where many other plants were grown. As a result, the weevil could more easily be kept under control.

New methods of managing the cotton farms were adopted, strict measures of hygiene were enforced, and only the very best cotton lands were used. In the end the boll weevil tragedy turned out to be a blessing in disguise. With agriculture established on a much broader base than before, the economy of the South could not so easily be threatened if one particular crop failed. Indeed, in the town of Enterprise, Alabama, the citizens put up a statue bearing the following inscription: "In profound appreciation of the boll weevil and what it has done as the herald of prosperity."

You will have noticed that most of the examples of pest control in this chapter are taken from the United States. This is no accident, since many of the most serious problems of crop pests have been solved by American entomologists. Until the late nineteenth century, Europe was ahead of America in basic entomological research. Since then the United States has consistently led the world in applied entomology — in organizing large-scale anti-pest campaigns, in developing insecticides and other methods of controlling pests, and in training scientists and technicians in this work. Today there are probably more teachers and research workers in entomology in the United States than in all the other countries of the world combined.

The importance of pest control has been accepted by most national governments. This is underlined by the annual growth of public investment in entomological research since the beginning of this century. As might be expected, the most striking example comes from the United States. For the year 1900 the Federal Bureau of Entomology had a budget of $30,700. In 1910 the figure was almost $530,000, and by 1930 it had risen to nearly $2,500,000. The estimated 1965 appropriation for the Plant Disease and Pest Control section of the United States Agricultural Research Service is well over $26,000,000. In addition, of course, many chemical and pharmaceutical firms are investing huge sums in pesticide research and development.

Obviously, pest-control problems differ among countries according to their geography and climate. But very often the results of entomological research on one problem have value and uses in others. Today, economic entomologists are beginning to be aware of themselves as members of a world-wide association. Man's final conquest of crop pests depends on such co-operation.

Guarding Stored Food

THE entomology of stored products has always been somewhat neglected in spite of the fact that insect damage to grain and other stored foods has been a serious economic problem for centuries. In the old days of sailing, for instance, seamen on long voyages often had to face meal worms in the flour, beetles in the hard ship's biscuits, and grubs in the bacon. Many food products, especially cereals, peas, and beans, as well as all kinds of natural textiles, have always been attacked by insects while in storage. Even today heavy losses are quite common although more attention is now being given to methods of preventing damage by insects.

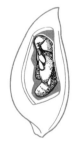

Above left: Work in progress on the building of granaries in Togo, Africa; they are built of mud, then covered with rushes. Below left: A modern American granary. Above: The three stages in the life of the granary weevil in wheat. Left: The full-grown larva. Middle: The pupa. Right: The adult, which has cut an exit hole in the kernel. The adult is never more than eight millimeters long. Top: Untreated wheat after 16 months of storage in a heavily infested storehouse; beetles are seen inside the grains of wheat.

Most of the insects that attack stored foods are beetles. The greatest amount of damage occurs in underdeveloped tropical countries, partly because the climate favors the insects and partly because storage facilities are often primitive. Damage to products still growing in the field is serious enough although it is sometimes made good. If part of the crop is destroyed, the yield from the remainder may be increased because the plants have more room to develop. By contrast, damage to stored products cannot be undone. Few reliable figures on stored-crop damage are available. But the United Nations Food and Agricultural Organization has estimated that 5 per cent of the world's food cereals and oil seeds are destroyed by insects each year after they have been harvested. Losses in some parts of the world are very much higher than in others. In Latin America, for instance, conditions are especially bad. A United Nations survey made in 1949 showed that losses of corn were 50 per cent in Honduras and 30 per cent in Nicaragua. Even in Costa Rica, where the government had made considerable efforts to prevent damage, losses were still as high as 45 per cent. Damage of this kind is not limited to homegrown goods. In Ecuador about $6 million worth of flour imported from the United States and Canada was spoiled during 1947 and 1948. In India, a million tons of stored grain are lost annually. In Nigeria, bean weevils have often eaten half the stored crop before the next harvest is due.

Pest damage can be severe even in countries where storage facilities are comparatively good and the climate is temperate. In Alabama, for instance, a loss of a quarter of the year's stored-corn crop is not uncommon. In Germany it was estimated that the granary weevil consumed 2½ per cent—about 225,000 tons—of the 1949 harvest of grain. In a world where millions of people are suffering from hunger, losses like this cannot be allowed to continue. Strenuous efforts are now being made to stop the damage.

Some of the stored-food pests are gathered in with the crop. In the case of peas and beans, for instance, the pest larvae inside the plant pods may have done a great deal of damage even before the crops are harvested. Others pests do not attack until the harvest has been put into storage. Then, with almost unlimited food and living undisturbed for many months, they breed at a terrific rate. They not only eat but also contaminate the stored food to such an extent that most of it may be unusable when the storehouse is opened.

Along with the granary weevil, one of the most important grain pests is the rice weevil, which also feeds on corn. Both these insects eat grains in their larval stage, when each larva consumes only a single grain.

157

They also eat as adults, when they move about and feed on a number of grains. They breed very quickly and can produce several generations in a year. Their tremendous rate of increase was clearly shown by an experiment in Kenya. Some bags of disinfected corn were put into an infected storehouse. After four months the bags contained about 32,000 adult rice weevils to every 220 pounds of corn. Infested grain becomes entirely unfit for use because, even if some of it is undamaged, it is contaminated by insect remains. Thus, when the grain is milled, it produces discolored and very poor flour that tastes unpleasant and may even cause sickness.

The coffee weevil attacks not only coffee beans but also cocoa, cotton seed, nuts, and dried fruits. The brass beetle — which takes its name from its coat of yellow hair — is an international pest of stored products. It will eat almost anything — grains, leather, wool, cigars, dried fruit, medicinal herbs, and even the silvering on the backs of mirrors. These beetles sometimes appear in enormous numbers when they have found suitable breeding places. Many small moths are also food pests. Among them are members of the *Galleria* and *Ephestia* groups, which infest warehouses all over the world and whose larvae feed on grain and dried fruit.

Many methods are used to combat insects of this kind. The simplest, and perhaps least appreciated, are common-sense matters of hygiene and the sensible design of storage places. It is essential to clean every nook and cranny of a storehouse, preferably with powerful vacuum cleaners. All useless remains of the previous crop must be burnt before a new shipment is brought in. Today, sacks are thoroughly sterilized and insecticidal smokes or sprays are used in empty storehouses, ships' holds, and freight cars. Such methods prevent pests in old stored goods from contaminating the new.

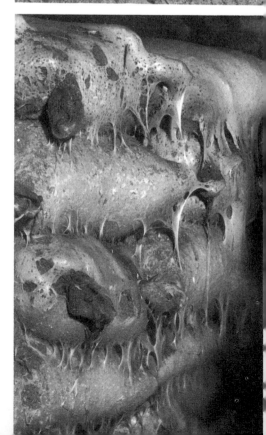

Many designers of granaries, silos, and warehouses now consult entomologists in order to avoid the type of construction that provides hiding places for insects. Designs for storehouses that can be completely sealed against insects are now being tested. If successful they should be especially valuable for crops, such as famine reserves, that are stored for longer than usual. It has been found that in a sealed — that is, airtight — storehouse, the chemical processes of the living grain decrease the oxygen and increase the carbon dioxide content. As a result any insects already in the grain are killed. If others can be prevented from entering, the grain will remain unharmed and in good condition for a long time.

The problem of effectively sealing products from pest attack also concerns foodstuffs, such as cereals and

Above: Section through a cob of corn showing the destruction done by larvae of the pink cornworm moth. They eat their way from one kernel to another, often leaving the cob bare. Below the cob is the adult moth, which has a wingspan of less than half an inch.

Left: Three photographs showing stages in the attacking of a sack of stored oil-seed by larvae of the warehouse moth. Top: Early infestation by the larvae. Center: They have begun to spin webs from sack to sack. Bottom: Sacks are almost hidden by the mass of webbing.

flour, that are bought by the housewife at her local store. Cardboard cartons and paper bags are no defense against many pests. Even plastic containers can be bitten through. Up to now the search for a lasting insect repellent has not been successful. In many cases, fortunately, there is only a short time between the packing of such foodstuffs at the factory and their consumption by the purchaser.

A number of machines have been designed for removing insect pests from stored products by mechanical means. One of the best of these consists essentially of a centrifuge. This is a drumlike device capable of revolving at high speed. A fine-grained or powdered product, such as flour, is placed in the apparatus, which is then set revolving. Any adult insects or larvae present are hurled against the wall and pillars inside the drum and are killed. The flour can then be removed from the centrifuge and stored safely in insect-proof containers.

One of the most widely used methods of dealing with stored-product pests is by fumigation with gases such as methyl bromide. This is usually done by placing a large, gasproof, plastic sheet over the product to be stored. The sheet is sealed to the floor or the ground so that no air can enter. Then the fumigating gas is pumped inside. The sheet is left in place long enough to allow the gas to penetrate the product completely.

The use of contact insecticides—those that kill if touched by the insect—in the form of dusts or sprays makes difficulties where foodstuffs are concerned. As we saw in the last chapter, some of these insecticides spoil the flavor of food crops. Others may even leave poisonous residues. Pyrethrum dust, which is not poisonous to humans or warm-blooded animals, has been widely used for mixing with grain and other products. Sometimes it produces good results, but a really foolproof insecticide for stored products has still to be developed.

The granary weevil, which is a very widespread pest, cannot survive unprotected outdoors in colder climates. Thus, in such regions, grains can be protected from the weevil by keeping them in granaries that are sufficiently ventilated for frost to form on the grain. Modern cold storage is, of course, very helpful in preventing insect damage. Deepfreezing keeps suitable products completely safe indefinitely.

Tobacco, jute, wool, leather, and many other commercial products are attacked by insects during storage and transport. In the case of such nonedible products it is often possible to apply powerful insecticides because

Below: The cigarette beetle beside a
photograph of a pyrethrum insecticide
being applied by a fogging machine
in a tobacco warehouse in South Africa.
Right: Larvae of the carpet beetle
devouring the pile of a woolen carpet.

Above: Damage caused by the biscuit beetle to a stored box of cookies. These beetles have somehow penetrated the sealed box.

There are 14 kinds of insects in the room below. Periodic inspections of these test packages by the Department of Agriculture show the effect of experimental treatments in preventing insect penetration.

the danger of poisoning the user is not so great. Two beetles, one a reddish-brown beetle, which measures only three or four millimeters in length, and the other, a larger beetle, are very troublesome pests in tobacco warehouses. They seem to be attracted most by the more expensive kinds of tobacco and attack both the tobacco leaf and the completed cigars.

Clothes moths and carpet beetles can be troublesome pests in furniture stores and textile mills as well as in the home. Since the development of inexpensive plastics, it has become fairly easy to protect clothing from attack by keeping it in mothproof bags made from these materials. Valuable furs can be protected during the summer by putting them into cold storage.

Carpets and other furnishings are often impregnated with chemicals that repel insects or make the material indigestible to them. Either way, the chemicals discourage the insects from feeding and breeding. One of these "chemical-finishing" products acts as a stomach poison to clothes-moth larvae and as a repellent to carpet beetles. Another one makes wool indigestible. A third prevents clothes moths from feeding and poisons carpet beetles. Thus, by using a combination of these or similar products, the manufacturer can keep his furnishings from being attacked by insects. Anti-moth sprays are also available for home use. Their effect is only temporary, but they are replacing the old-fashioned moth balls. Many synthetic fibers, such as nylon, are now used in the manufacture of both clothing and furnishings. They are not attractive to insects since they provide no nourishment and their wide use has brought a sharp reduction in insect damage in the home.

Protecting Buildings

As a building material and as a fuel, wood is not so important as it once was, but vast quantities are still needed for furniture, interior fittings, and paper pulp. Although enormous regions are still covered by forest in many parts of the world, the woodlands are gradually shrinking as the result of increasing populations and the need to devote more land to raising food crops. It therefore becomes more vital than ever to manage the remaining forests in such a way that they will yield the largest possible quantities of high-quality timber.

Forestry is a skilled profession and the cultivation of good timber raises many of the same kinds of problems as those with which farmers and gardeners have to contend. Timber is, in fact, simply a long-term crop. Because it takes many years to grow to maturity, timber is exposed to numerous dangers. Insect attack is serious.

In Europe the need for the care of timber forests has long been recognized, and in 1831 a special Forest Academy was founded near Berlin. In 1837 the German entomologist J. T. C. Ratzeburg began publication of his *Manual of Forest Insects,* which ran to three volumes. This was followed a few years later by two volumes dealing with these insects' parasites. This was the first work of its kind and it has become an entomological classic. Since then a great deal of writing has appeared dealing with forest pests and their control. Most of it concerns Europe and North America, where the large evergreen forests are especially apt to be attacked by insects. In tropical countries much less work has been done on this subject because there forestry is a comparatively new activity.

Growing trees are attacked by many different kinds of insects. The most important fall into two groups— those that attack the foliage, and those that burrow into the bark or the trunks. The defoliators, or leaf-strippers, are generally larvae of moths or sawflies; the wood borers are mostly beetles. Some of the worst forest pests of the leaf-eating kind are the nun moth, the gypsy moth, the forest tent caterpillar, the spruce budworm, and sawflies of the Diprion and Neodiprion groups.

Since woodlands usually cover large areas and consist of tall trees, spraying or dusting them is a much more difficult job than it is with agricultural crops or fruit trees. Very powerful machinery is necessary if spraying is to be done at ground level. The most usual method nowadays is to use aircraft when insect infestation is so heavy as to demand spraying an entire forest. The use of chemical insecticides has not proved entirely satis-

Above: Male and female forms of the pine looper moth. The antennae of the male are feathered; those of the female are threadlike. Larvae of this moth feed on pine needles. In severe infestation, trees over hundreds of acres will be completely stripped. Photograph (above) shows characteristic feeding damage done by the larvae to the needles of a young pine shoot. Right: Pinewoods in England completely defoliated by larvae.

Above: Two 19th-century engravings
by the German entomologist,
J. T. C. Ratzeburg, showing damage
done by the pine shoot moth. The female
lays her eggs close to the buds. When a
caterpillar hatches, it bores into a bud,
causing "post horn" deformation, as
shown in the pictures. When the bud
is injured, it falls over, then recovers
and curves upward again, leaving
a permanent bend in the main stem.

163

factory in dealing with forest pests. Although a high percentage of the pests may be killed, infestation sets in again usually very rapidly and the treatment must be repeated every two years. Moreover, the insecticides may also kill harmless and useful insects, as well as poisoning the fish in nearby streams and rivers. For these reasons forest entomologists are now turning more and more to sprays that contain *pathogens*. These are not insecticides in the common meaning of the word. Pathogens are disease-bearing organisms, which attack and kill only the pest that is causing trouble.

Virus sprays are particularly effective. Once a virus disease becomes established in a locality it will remain contagious and prevent large-scale outbreaks of the pest for several years. A very serious infestation of the European spruce sawfly began in North America in the 1920s and spread over thousands of square miles. The larvae of this fly defoliated the trees so completely that many trees were killed. The sawfly apparently had no serious enemies in North America. In an attempt to bring it under control, parasites were imported from Europe and soon became established. Later, it became apparent that the parasitic flies were carriers of a virus disease that is fatal to the spruce sawfly. The disease was so deadly that the sawfly infestation was very quickly reduced to a comparatively harmless level, and it has remained so ever since. Fortunately this disease still kills many sawflies, and whenever the sawfly population increases, the virus infection increases in proportion. Laboratories can now reproduce and store this virus, and it is used for dealing with outbreaks of sawflies.

One particular bacterium *(Bacillus thuringiensis)* has also been widely used against forest pests in America and Europe. In France the processionary pine caterpillar often develops into a serious nuisance, because it damages the trees and because its poisonous hairs cause severe skin rashes. Very good results have been achieved by spraying preparations containing these bacteria from aircraft. More than a hundred different kinds of caterpillar can be infected with the disease. In Canada it has been used against the jack-pine sawfly, as well as against several different kinds of budworm.

All forms of biological control are now receiving a great deal of attention from forest entomologists. Predators and parasites are encouraged in every possible way and are imported from abroad if they do not occur locally. Europeans especially have studied the value of birds in controlling forest pests. In Germany everything possible is done to protect insect-eating birds and to provide them with nesting sites. Birds are of little value once a really serious outbreak of forest pests occurs, but a large colony of birds can often help to prevent such

Left: Larvae of the jack-pine sawfly feeding on the foliage of a pine. If the tough pine needles get damaged, larvae gather, attracted by the smell. Only the five directed toward the needle tip have access to the food. Frequent attempts are made by the lower larvae to force the others out of the way.
Above: Pit props being de-barked in an English forest, to avoid infestation by the bark beetle.

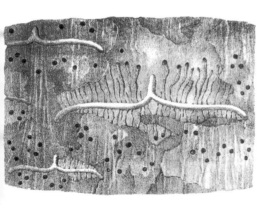

Above: Lithograph by Ratzeburg showing pupation chambers and exit holes cut by the bark beetle. The adult carves a channel in the bark, then lays its eggs. Each larva cuts a pupation chamber at right angles to the main channel. New beetles emerge between May and August. The whole cycle extends over one or two years.

outbreaks. Bats, too, are useful against night-flying moths. Some entomologists have suggested that special concrete roosts should be erected to encourage them to colonize areas in which moths cause damage. Small mammals—particularly shrews, which are greedy insect-eaters—are also of value. Many forestry experts believe that the red ant is also a valuable help in the fight against pests that defoliate trees.

The way in which a forest is planted and cared for is a very important factor in keeping down insect damage. Healthy trees, which are growing fast, resist insect attack fairly well. Thus it is desirable to plant only the kinds of trees that will thrive in the soil and climate of the particular region. Forests with different kinds of trees are often more healthy than large stands of only one kind of tree. That is why the worst insect outbreaks, especially in Europe, have usually occurred in forests planted by man rather than in those that are the result of natural growth. Evergreens are especially apt to be attacked by insects and suffer more from losing their needles than deciduous trees do if they lose their leaves.

Old and decaying trees, fallen trees, and weak trees are usually attacked first, especially by the various beetles that bore into bark and sapwood. Good forestry demands that a constant watch be kept so that all diseased or unhealthy trees are removed before they can become a source of infection. All trees eventually reach an age when they are at their best for the purpose for which they are grown, and when this time comes they should be cut down. If they are left too long they deteriorate and become a danger to the rest of the forest.

The defoliating insects always attack living trees, while the wood borers generally prefer dead or dying ones. Thus beetle damage often begins only after the trees have been felled. Once the timber has been cut, however, beetles can quickly do a lot of damage, particularly if the timber is left lying for any length of time with the bark still on the trunks. Cut timber can be protected in various ways. One of the simplest is to put the logs in water. Linnaeus, the eighteenth-century Swedish naturalist, was once consulted by the manager of the naval dockyard in Stockholm. The manager was worried about beetle damage occurring in timber stored for shipbuilding. Linnaeus recommended that the tree trunks be put into the lake during the summer, when the beetles were flying about. This simple precaution was completely effective. In Scandinavia and North America much of the felled timber is floated to the sawmills along rivers and lakes, and this prevents beetles from laying their eggs on the wood. The critical period comes later, when the logs are sawed and stacked for weathering.

Some of the most troublesome pests in lumberyards

Above: The powder-post beetle beside oak damaged by its larvae. They eat only sapwood, so infestations are discovered by the collapse of the affected wood, or by the appearance of little exit holes and small piles of wood dust. Below: Two common furniture beetles beside exit holes bored in plywood.

and sawmills are the powder-post beetles, which bore their way into the wood and gradually reduce it to a fine powder. They bore only in the sapwood—the layer of the tree trunk directly beneath the bark—and here they feed on the starch in the wood cells. They are especially numerous in Australia, where it is now required that all green wood be treated with boron compounds as soon as it comes from the mills. Lumber may be impregnated with insecticides or heated in kilns as a means of protection and to kill beetles in the wood.

The ambrosia beetles burrow deep into the trunks of many kinds of timber, especially tropical hardwoods. These beetles feed on certain mold fungi, which they themselves introduce into the burrows and which stain the wood. Thus, the damage done by these beetles is twofold and it often greatly reduces the value of decorative woods used for veneers, the outer layers of furniture. Attack can be prevented if the tree is sprayed with a chemical insecticide, benzene hexachloride, as soon as it is felled. But once the beetles have begun to burrow the only thing to do is to saw the timber and dry it as quickly as possible. These insects need quite a lot of moisture, and seasoning the wood in a heated kiln will stop the damage at once.

The common furniture beetle and the deathwatch beetle are two quite small insects that cause a great deal of damage. The furniture beetle, often called woodworm, will in fact attack all kinds of wood, both indoors and out. It lives naturally outdoors in dead trees and bushes, and often attacks fences, gateposts, and wooden farm buildings. Although the larvae feed in almost any kind of wood they prefer a rather damp atmosphere, so they are particularly common in low-lying areas or in damp buildings. The beetles lay their eggs on rough, unpolished surfaces, such as the back of furniture. From there the larvae burrow into the wood, where they feed for three years or more. Then the adult beetles emerge through the round flight holes that are so familiar in old, neglected furniture.

The deathwatch beetle is slightly larger than the furniture beetle. The deathwatch beetle attacks mainly hardwood timber, especially oak beams in old buildings such as churches. The pests seldom cause trouble while the timber is sound. But when it begins to go soft through being attacked by fungi that thrives in moisture, the beetles soon attack. In the end, the wood becomes completely riddled with their burrows and loses its strength. Under damp conditions the beetle completes its life cycle in four or five years. If the wood is dry it may feed for ten years before becoming adult.

When there is a bad infestation of furniture or deathwatch beetles, the only remedy is to remove and burn the

Above: The "deathwatch" beetle, so named because people believed the tapping sounds it makes in the mating season foretold the death of someone in the house. It is seen beside a piece of infested timber taken from a London church. In treating infested buildings, affected timbers have to be torn down, suspected timbers injected, and sound ones sprayed with insecticides.

affected wood and replace it with fresh wood impregnated with chemicals that prevent insect attack. If the beetles are not very numerous, however, the wood can be treated by painting or spraying with insecticides that have a strong penetrating action. Furniture and movable wood can also be fumigated with special chemical compounds in a sealed room or special chamber. The *Victory* was the flagship of Admiral Nelson at the Battle of Trafalgar in 1805. It now lies in the dockyard at Portsmouth, England, and has been fumigated against the deathwatch beetle. A great variety of wood preservatives are now being made commercially. One process protects timber against decay as well as insect attack by impregnating the wood under pressure. Liquefied petroleum gas is used as a solvent for the preservatives.

Another wood-boring insect that can cause considerable damage is the wood wasp, which lays its eggs in dead trees or in timber that has already been through the sawmills. The larvae are often found in wooden packaging crates, and there is great danger that the insects will be transported from one country to another. Experiments indicate that the larvae are very resistant to fumigants because they live completely enclosed in the wood. Furthermore, even unmated female wood wasps can lay fertile eggs, so that these insects can quickly increase in numbers and cause considerable damage in a short time. A special study is now under way to try to find wood-wasp parasites that could be used in a biological-control program.

The most injurious of all wood-eating insects are the termites. They are very abundant in the tropics but they occur also in more temperate regions, including some parts of the United States. They feed on cellulose, a chemical compound that they find most easily in wood. There are 1700 different species of termites, although not all of them are harmful. Many species live in underground nests, from which they make their way into buildings. Since these species always need a certain amount of moisture, they must keep in contact with the ground. They can therefore be prevented from attacking wooden buildings if these are constructed so that the termites cannot get directly to the wood from the ground. Stone, brick, concrete, or metal foundations that keep woodwork a good distance away from ground level will stop termites of this kind from entering. Woodwork can also be protected by thoroughly impregnating it with coal-tar creosote.

The dry-wood termites, which live entirely in healthy, seasoned wood, are a much more difficult problem. It is often almost impossible to detect their presence in furniture until it is too late. They can completely hollow out a chair or a table, leaving only a thin surface layer intact. The article looks perfectly solid but collapses when it is touched. The only way to prevent these attacks is by treating all woodwork with special anti-termite chemicals. The most effective of these are compounds containing arsenic, and it is best to apply them under pressure so that they penetrate deep into the wood. A few woods, including Pacific coast redwood and teak, are fairly resistant to termite attack, especially if only the solid heartwood is used. But some kind of treatment is always recommended as a safety precaution. In addition to arsenic-based compounds, zinc chloride, sodium fluoride, cupric chromate, and chlorinated phenol preparations have also proved valuable as anti-termite insecticides. All wooden furniture and other timber liable to attack from wood borers should be protected. Prevention, in this case, is obviously better than cure. Indeed cure is often impossible.

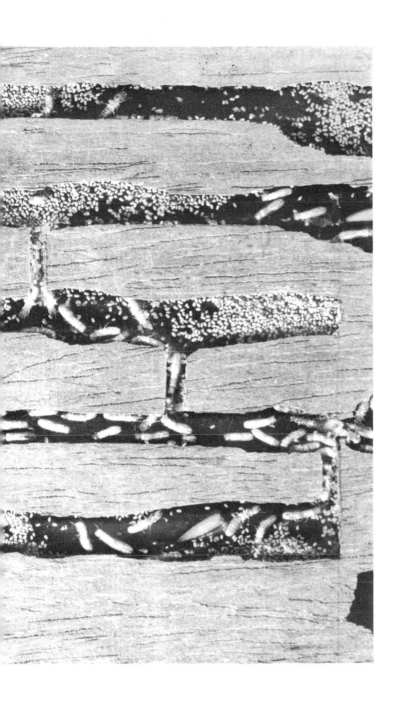

Right: Two photographs of a chair leg infested by the West Indian dry wood termite. The leg appears complete, until broken apart; then it is seen to have been hollowed out. Above: Damage done by the West African plywood termite. An outer layer of wood has been lifted in parts to show the termites living in the soft middle layer. Winged adults, nymphs, soldiers, and masses of excremental pellets can be seen.

Insects Carry Plant Diseases

ABOUT three hundred different virus diseases are known to infect plants, with more or less serious results. The diseases cause a variety of symptoms, from discoloring and crinkling of the leaves to stunted growth, deformed fruit and flowers, and inability to produce fruit. In the worst cases the plants become so unhealthy that they are not only useless for food production but may even die.

Many of these diseases, although by no means all, are spread from plant to plant by insects. At first it was thought that aphids were the only vectors, or carriers of the disease-causing viruses. It is now known that several other kinds of insects, including leaf hoppers, white flies, thrips, beetles, and even earwigs, can transmit virus infection. The aphids are, however, the most important and numerous vectors. Because they feed on only the sap of the plants, they are well adapted for transmitting viruses, which can live only inside the plant's cells. Ninety different virus diseases are so far known to be spread by aphids, and the most dangerous single species is the potato-peach aphid. This insect lives alternately on its two host plants, the potato and the peach, and is responsible for transmitting at least fifty kinds of virus infections.

Viruses can also be transmitted through the soil (particularly by eelworms). They may also be carried from one plant to another on the hands, clothes, or tools of agricultural workers and gardeners. The study and control of these diseases, most of which are crippling rather than killing, presents many difficulties.

Extremely high-powered microscopes are needed to identify the various viruses in the sap of plants, and they reveal that plants are often infected with several viruses at once. Microscopic examination also shows that the same virus may be present in several species of plants. All these plants may show different symptoms, or sometimes no visible symptom at all. The common privet, for example, is one of the host plants of the cucumber mosaic virus, which also affects delphiniums, pansies, primulas, and zucchini. But in the privet no symptoms are visible.

Viruses are also liable to mutate—that is, to undergo a very drastic chemical change. The result is that a previously fairly harmless virus disease may suddenly become dangerous. In cases where one plant is infected by several different strains of a virus, they may be present throughout the plant's tissues. Some strains may occur only in the old leaves and others only in the

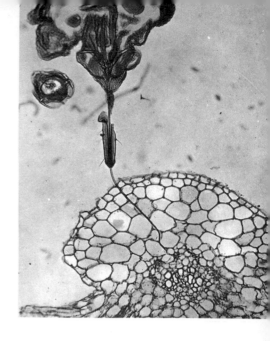

Above: Section of a potato leaf, showing the way the stylet of the aphid Myzus pseudosolani is plunged through the outer layer, so that the insect can feed on the tissue. Right: Drawing of this aphid, which transmits viruses that infect cucumbers, tobacco, and potatoes; it is fairly widely distributed in Britain and North America.

Below: Diagrams showing the progress of the tobacco mosaic virus (in black) from an inoculated leaf through a tomato plant. This experiment was made in 1934. Dwarf Champion plants were used, about 15 inches high, growing in six-inch pots in an unheated greenhouse. The results suggested that the virus travels in the phloem tissue when food is transported from the leaves.

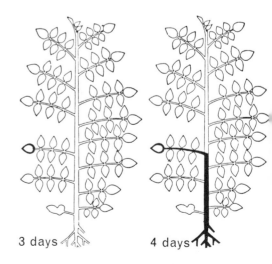

3 days   4 days

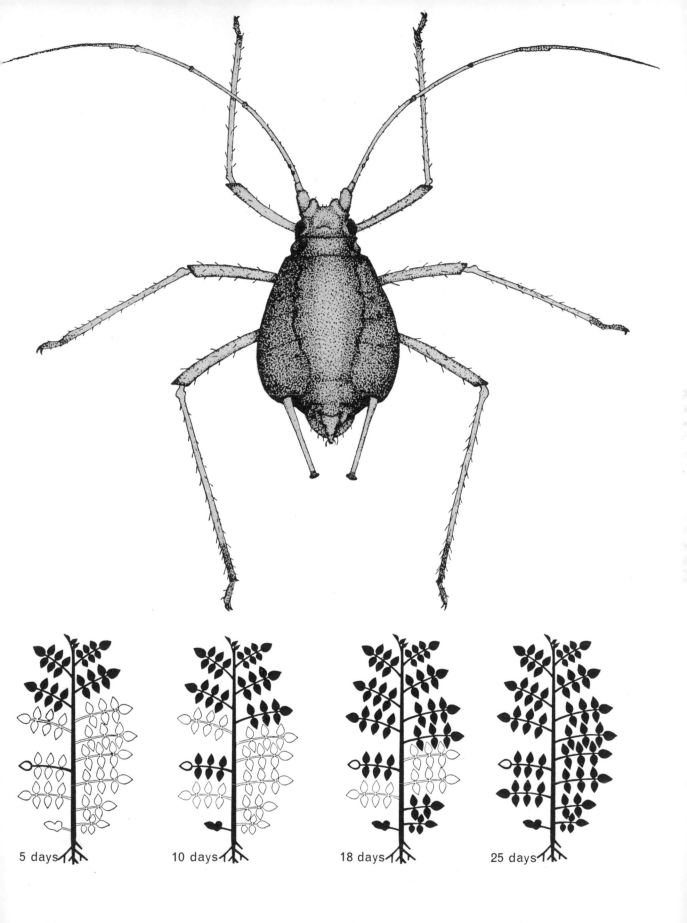

5 days   10 days   18 days   25 days

171

young ones, or some other form of distribution may apply.

Virology, or the study of viruses, is a scientific discipline in its own right. But because insects play such a large part in the transmission of virus diseases, economic entomologists must understand these diseases and the way in which they are spread.

The study of the relationship between insects and viruses has brought many interesting facts to light. It is now known, for example, that some viruses can be passed from one plant to another within half a minute after an aphid has sucked their sap. In other cases the insect must feed on an infected plant for a considerable time before it can transmit the disease. Viruses fall into two distinct categories, persistent and nonpersistent. With a nonpersistent virus the insect vector can pass on the disease only for a limited time after feeding on an infected plant. With a persistent virus, however, the insect will remain a source of infection for a long time. The insect may often be able to pass on the disease for the whole of its life, even though it may have fed on infected sap only once. Usually it takes some time—anything up to three weeks—before a persistent virus develops in the insect to a stage when it can be passed on.

Persistent viruses can also be passed on from one generation of insects to another, even though only the first generation came in contact with an infected plant. The Japanese entomologist Fukushi showed that the dwarf disease of rice could be passed through six generations of leaf hoppers. He also found that the disease was transmitted only by the female parent.

Cloverclub leaf, another plant disease transmitted by hoppers, has been passed through twenty-one generations of leaf hoppers. This experiment took five years, and even the last generation could transmit the disease to plants. This means that a persistent plant virus may remain hidden for several years among a local insect population. Then, if crops sensitive to the virus are planted in the area, they may catch the infection.

Experiments seem to indicate that the ability of an insect to pass on a persistent virus may be greatly reduced by exposing the vector to a temperature above 32°C. (90°F.) After only a short exposure to this tem-

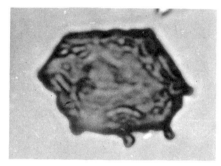

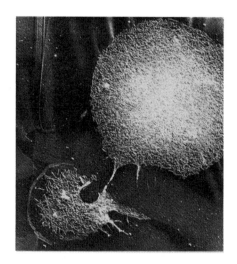

Tobacco mosaic was the first virus to be discovered. Its vector is unknown. The photographs show (top) a leaf of tobacco beside a photomicrograph of part of a single hair from the leaf, in the cells of which are embedded crystals of the virus. If a crystal is removed from the hair cell (second), then dissolved in distilled water, it is seen to be made up of numerous individual particles (third), each of which is infective. The bottom photograph is of a molecular model of a single tobacco mosaic virus particle, built of symmetrically stacked protein units; in the center of these is the infective nucleic acid.

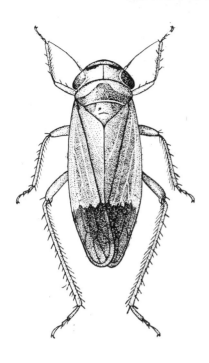

Above: A Japanese leaf hopper, the vector of a virus that causes the dwarf disease of rice. Both leaf hopper and virus appear to be confined to Japan.

Below: Drawing of the aphid that is the vector of the cabbage black-ring virus, beside an infected leaf. Black dead tissue spots develop first on the undersurface of the leaves, then spread until the whole leaf is covered. This aphid is world-wide in its distribution; it is the vector for many viruses, including those that cause leaf-drop in potatoes, and mosaic in sugar beet.

perature the infective ability returns within a few days. A longer treatment seems to completely destroy the virus in the insect. Further experiments in this field may lead to the development of important methods of controlling disease carriers. Already heat is being used in raising certain plants, such as chrysanthemums and strawberries, in an effort to produce virus-free varieties.

Although a plant may be infected with a number of virus diseases, some insects are able to transmit only one of them. Other insects can transmit several at a time. Virus diseases such as cauliflower mosaic and cabbage black ringspot often infect the same plant. The potato-peach aphid will transmit both, but a closely related aphid spreads only the mosaic virus. Some virus diseases are not transmitted by insects at all, even if they feed on the diseased plants. In the case of the hop mosaic it has been found that only the winged form of an aphid can transmit the disease. The wingless generation does not spread it even when deliberately moved from a diseased plant to a healthy one.

Researchers have used microscopes to look at the mouth parts of aphids that have been feeding on virus-infected plants. The examination has shown that the virus is carried on the tips of the stylets, the part that bores into the leaf when the aphid begins to feed. Apart from sapsuckers, it seems that the only insects capable of transmitting viruses are those that regurgitate some of their stomach contents while feeding. Caterpillars and most beetles, which do not have this habit, are not vectors of disease.

It is not yet known whether viruses cause unfavorable changes in their insect vectors. Nonpersistent viruses appear to have no such effects. The reason may be that the vector is engaged in a purely mechanical transfer of virus from sap to sap. That is, the virus is carried on the insect but does not enter into the insect's chemical

processes. Evidently, however, this is not the case with a persistent virus. We have seen that several weeks may go by before the vector can transmit such a virus. This seems to indicate that the virus undergoes some kind of change or multiplication within the insect's body. Experiments with a leaf hopper that spreads the disease known as aster yellows have shown that it is possible to infect the insect artificially by injection. Then, after an incubation period lasting four or five weeks, the insect will transmit the disease to healthy plants. Some workers claim to have discovered certain abnormalities in the body cells of insects that are carrying plant viruses. Whether this has any important effect on the insects' well-being is not yet known.

One task of the economic entomologist is to try to prevent the spread of insect-borne viruses. A vital part of his work is obviously to exterminate or control aphids and leaf hoppers by spraying, fumigating, and using systemic insecticides. However, once a virus has actually got into the cells of a plant, none of these methods can prevent it from multiplying there. Apart from heat treatment, no cure for virus diseases in plants is yet known. This means that all kinds of precautions, besides the control of insect vectors, must be taken to prevent the spread of diseases. One important method is to destroy all virus-infected plants as soon as they are noticed. Another is to keep land clean and free of weeds, since many weeds are known to act as a source of infection.

Many plants reproduce themselves through tubers,

Above: Research by the Department of Agriculture on the application of systemic insecticides. In the foreground are untreated asters that have been damaged by aster yellows, transmitted by the six-spotted leaf hopper. In the background are asters grown in soil treated with the systemic insecticide phorate, which kills many species of aphids, mites, and leaf hoppers.

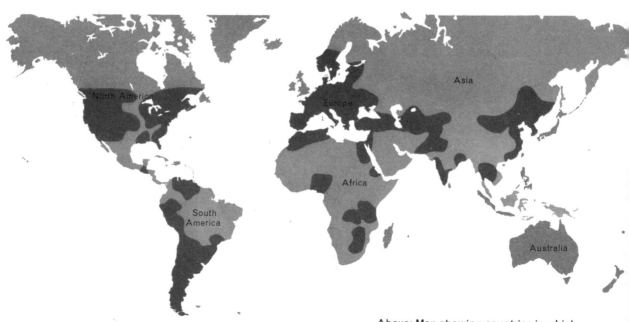

Above: Map showing countries in which the green peach aphis is known to occur. The primary host of the aphis is the peach, but it also feeds on a variety of secondary hosts. It is the vector of virus diseases of potatoes, beets, and many other cultivated plants.

bulbs, cuttings, and grafts. Such plant forms will often pass on virus diseases that cannot be transmitted through seeds. In such cases healthy crops can often be raised by starting afresh from seed. Sometimes an insect vector thrives in one region but not in a nearby region. Thus, healthy crops can be grown in the second region but not in the first. In England, for instance, the potato-peach aphid is widespread, and as a result potato crops often become rapidly poorer after two or three years. In Scotland, on the other hand, the potato-peach aphid is rare, and potato crops are seldom infected by the virus diseases that these insects transmit. So most English growers buy their seed potatoes from Scotland.

The widest and most rapid spread of plant viruses takes place during the period when the aphids are flying about. These small insects are often carried by the wind for very long distances, so a virus infection can break out hundreds of miles away from its original source. Once the aphids have settled down to the wingless stage, their importance as disease vectors diminishes. Although they are still often capable of transmitting disease, they do so much more slowly because they are much less mobile. Once aphids have begun to fly, in the spring, they are very difficult to deal with. Anti-aphid measures should ideally be carried out during the winter, when the insects are in the dormant egg stage. The notorious potato-peach aphid winters on peach trees, while other species choose plum or spindle trees. All can be controlled to some extent by spraying with egg-killing preparations in the winter.

Several times during the present century certain popular varieties of fruits, such as strawberries and raspberries, have come under attack from virus diseases. When this has happened continually over a wide area, many farmers have lost so much money that they have had to stop growing these plants. Only the most careful selection of varieties, the systematic destruction of diseased plants, and the strongest measures against insect vectors have made it possible to re-establish healthy stocks. Some growers have developed disease-free *clones*—that is, groups of a plant species reproduced by cutting from selected individuals. These growers have their stock and fields regularly examined by inspectors, and any plants showing the slightest trace of disease are at once taken up and burnt.

The fight against the vectors of virus diseases continues. Entomologists have won, and will doubtless go on winning, some notable victories against disease-carrying insects. But the main answer to the problem of plant diseases will probably be found in a quite different way—by breeding plants that are immune to virus diseases, or at least highly resistant to them.

Above: Research on virus diseases of potatoes grown in insect-proof cages. Scientific breeding of potatoes was first organized by the Department of Agriculture during 1910–1920. Calcium arsenate was among the first insecticides used.

Insects and Weed Control

IN GENERAL, man thinks of insects as enemies rather than allies. Most economic entomologists devote a great part of their time to fighting the seemingly limitless variety of insect pests. But there is another side to the picture. We have glimpsed part of it already, in the account of the ways in which certain insects have been used to control others. Another important application of biological control is the use of insects to destroy or limit the spread of troublesome weeds.

The great majority of insects feed on plants, yet no one fully understands their importance in plant ecology—that is, the relationships among all plants. Insects' effect on a natural plant community may be much greater than we realize. Their activities probably play an important part in keeping the balance between different plants, so that no one species gets too far ahead of others. Insects that feed on foliage, suck sap, destroy seeds, eat roots and flowers, or burrow into stems of plants undoubtedly have quite an influence on plant life. It is only when there is a sudden increase of such insects that the range of their activities becomes fully apparent. Entomologists have not paid much attention so far to the effect of insects on vegetation except in their role as pollen-carriers or as destroyers of plants of economic importance.

If all insects suddenly disappeared there would be vast, and possibly catastrophic, changes in the natural vegetation of the world. Exactly what these changes would be we cannot say for certain. In spite of our broad entomological knowledge, we know little about how the natural balance is established and maintained.

Man has, however, learned the danger of upsetting the natural balance within local communities by importing non-native plants or wild animals. The introduction of the rabbit into Australia is a notorious example of this. Less well known is the almost equally serious importation into Australia of prickly-pear cacti. Both rabbits and cacti had no apparent natural enemies in Australia to keep them in check. As a result they multiplied at a terrific rate and developed into very serious pests. In both cases their eventual control was due mainly to the importation of insects. A mosquito spread the disease myxomatosis among the rabbits, and a moth helped to clear the lands of cacti.

The many species of prickly-pear cacti are all natives of South and Central America. They are useful as hedging plants and their fruits are edible. For these reasons they have been introduced into many parts of the world, often with unfortunate results. In Australia the plants

Above: Admiral Arthur Phillip (1738–1814), first governor of New South Wales, Australia. On a voyage to Australia in 1787, Phillip took cochineal insects, and prickly pear plants for them to feed on, from Brazil. He wanted to produce cochineal in the new colony "in order to dye his soldiers' coats red."

Below: Map showing the extent of prickly pear infestation (colored light blue) in Australia in 1927.

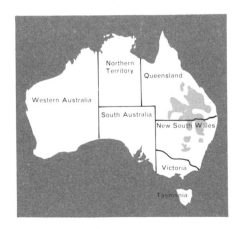

Above: Larvae of a moth within a
segment of a prickly pear. The cuticle
has been removed from the pear to
show the larvae feeding. This moth
is native to South America.

found both the climate and the soil suitable, and they quickly began to spread. Birds helped to distribute the seeds and the vigorous prickly plants took over forests and farmlands. The most seriously affected states were Queensland and New South Wales. At the peak of the invasion, in 1925, about 60 million acres of fertile land had been made useless and the cacti were estimated to be spreading at the rate of a million acres a year. The best soils were affected the most. The cacti there grew almost five feet high and formed an impenetrable barrier, especially in the acacia forests.

The danger of the prickly pear had first been realized at the beginning of this century, when entomologists had suggested using biological control to limit its spread. But more than a dozen years went by before a special commission, set up to study the problem, advised that insect enemies and, if possible, cactus diseases should be introduced from South America. In 1920 the Commonwealth Prickly Pear Board was formed by the Australian government and serious study of the cacti began. Entomologists were sent to investigate the insects connected with the prickly pear in almost all the countries where the plants were found. Soon they began to send insects to Australia for testing. Altogether 145 different insects were found, many of them unknown to entomologists before this. They included 56 moths and 50 beetles, as well as scale insects, cochineal insects, gall midges, and flies, all the insects depending for food on prickly pear or other cacti.

Another study had to be made before any of these insects could be safely released in Australia. It had to be discovered whether they would also feed on other plants and so, possibly, develop into pests of food crops. This was done by "starvation tests": the insects were not given their natural food but were supplied instead with various alternatives. Quite a number of the insects had to be rejected because it was found that they could feed themselves on tomatoes, peaches, apples, figs, and bananas. In nature none of these insects was known to be a pest of these particular crops. But the slight possibility they might become so was enough for the board to recommend that they should not be used. About 18 "safe" species were finally selected for trials. Several of these managed to establish themselves in Australia. A moth from Argentina, the Cactoblastis, quickly outnumbered the others and became the most important enemy of the prickly pear.

This moth is gray-brown in color and measures about an inch and a half across the wings. The female lays its eggs in long chains (commonly called "sticks")

Top: Dense prickly pear infestation of a woodland in Australia in 1926. Center: The same area three years later. Prickly pear has been destroyed by moths and cochineal insects.

Below: By 1931 the whole area had been planted with Rhodes grass. The Commission for the Biological Control of Prickly Pear was established in Australia in 1912.

that it attaches to the spines of the prickly pear. Each stick consists of about 75 eggs, and there are two generations a year. When the red-and-black caterpillars hatch they burrow into the cacti and feed on the sappy tissues. Their feeding quickly causes a complete breakdown of the plant and only a thin outside skin and the thickest fibers remain untouched. The damage is increased by the development of fungi and bacteria that gain entry into the half-eaten cacti. The moth larvae pupate in silky cocoons among the waste material at the base of the plants.

Originally 2750 of the moth eggs were imported, and these were raised in cages for two years. During this short time their number increased 900-fold. In 1926 more than two and a quarter million eggs were fixed to cactus plants in various localities throughout the infested areas. The eggs were either gummed on pieces of paper or put in small paper quills that were then pinned onto the cacti. The following year another six and a half million eggs were sent out. By this time the effect of the moths was beginning to show. A great many prickly pear plants had already been killed and it was clear that the moth was so well established that it was unnecessary to continue raising the moths in the laboratory. By 1929 hundreds of acres of the cactus had already been cleared and the introduction of the moth appeared to be an outstanding success.

The prickly pear is a very persistent plant, however. In many cases new growth sprang up from the roots of cacti that had been attacked. By 1933 the situation was almost as bad as it had been before the moths were introduced. Meanwhile, having destroyed most of their food plants, a large proportion of the moths had died of starvation. They therefore needed time to reproduce enough to deal effectively with the fresh cactus growth. However, they increased rapidly in numbers and prospered on the young, juicy cacti. By 1935 almost all the cacti had been destroyed, roots and all. It was estimated by entomologists that the moth population had increased 5000-fold in less than two years. Since then the moth has decreased to a mere fraction of its former numbers due to the shortage of prickly pear. But it retains its capacity for rapid increase when conditions are favorable, and so it continues to act as a natural control of the prickly pear. The lost acres have been reclaimed and are now in full use as grazing and farming lands.

Although the Australian experiment is the most outstanding example of the use of insects for weed control, similar schemes have been successful in other parts of the world and against other types of weeds. The first attempt at this kind of weed control was made in Hawaii.

Above: Plaque on the monument erected in 1958 in Humboldt County, California, in appreciation of the research that led to employing a beetle to eradicate klamath weed from the rangelands.

The economic entomology division of the Australian Council for Scientific and Industrial Research conducts many experiments on the biological control of weeds. One serious weed is klamath weed, known there as St. John's wort, which infests vast areas of New South Wales and Victoria. Leaf-eating beetles such as those, left, have successfully controlled the weed in several areas.

A shrub was spreading so rapidly over the grazing land there that the grass was being choked and the cattle starved. In 1902 a scale insect was accidentally introduced and began to attack the plants. Its success so impressed the Hawaiian cattle owners that Koebele (the entomologist who had earlier brought the Australian ladybird to California) was sent to Central America to find other species that would destroy the shrub. Eventually eight species of insects became established in Hawaii—a seed fly, a lace bug, a leaf miner, three moths, and two butterflies—and in 1950 more insects were introduced. These insects have greatly reduced the numbers of the shrubs and it is no longer such a serious problem as it once was.

Klamath weed is a serious menace in many parts of the United States, especially on lands used for sheep grazing. Biological control measures have been taken against it in the United States, Australia, and New Zealand. In California by 1940 the weed had left five million acres of land almost useless for grazing. Several insects were introduced, including a beetle. The campaign has been a complete success. Virtually all the Klamath weed has been destroyed, and it is now no

Above: Mature larvae and adults of an insect attacking black sage in Mauritius. The idea of controlling this weed biologically originated in 1939. After research, this insect was imported from Trinidad in 1948. The characteristic holing made by the adult insect is shown; the leaves then wither and fall.

longer a danger. Australia and New Zealand have also managed to bring the weed largely under control.

In Fiji a shrub, popularly known as Koster's curse, became established in the late nineteenth century. It gradually infested large areas of pasture land as well as coconut and rubber plantations. Cattle would not eat the shrub and no native insects appeared to do it any harm. The same shrub grows in Trinidad, but there it is not a serious problem. Trinidad therefore seemed a likely place to find any insect enemies the shrub might have. Several enemies were found but the only one that entomologists considered safe to introduce into Fiji was a small thrips. Hopes of success were not very high. The insects were first released in Fiji in 1930, and within eighteen months they had spread across several square miles of sea and jungle. Three years later this tiny insect was bringing the weed under control. The thrips did not kill the shrub but weakened it to such an extent that other plants—especially certain grasses— grew better and smothered it.

The black sage once caused serious trouble on the island of Mauritius. It was defeated by a leaf beetle introduced in 1948 and by a seed-eating gall fly that was brought from Trinidad the following year. Another troublesome weed, pamaki, or Crofton weed, which has been introduced into Hawaii and Australia, is now being brought under control by a Mexican gall fly. And in New Zealand, one of the native plants, manuka weed, has been kept down by a mealy bug from Australia.

The ragwort is also a very troublesome weed in both Australia and New Zealand. It invades pastures and spoils the grazing. Horses, poisoned by it, may even die; when cattle eat it there is a marked reduction in the butterfat content of their milk. Several attempts were made to bring the ragwort under control by establishing the cinnabar moth. Large quantities of the moth's pupae were imported from England. At first the moths flourished and appeared to be having some effect on the weed, but later their numbers were drastically reduced. Native birds were not stopped by the orange-and-black warning colors of the larvae and had eaten great numbers of them. The cinnabar moth experiment was a failure, but fresh attempts at control are now being made with a seed fly.

The planned control of weeds by insects is still in its infancy and undoubtedly a great deal more work will be done in this line. Most of the major campaigns have been very successful. Up to now there has been no case of an insect introduced for control purposes that has become a pest on other plants. Careful investigations are made and precautions are taken before any insects are released, so it is unlikely that this will happen.

Honeybees—Domestic Insects

MAN breeds and uses for his own purposes a variety of animals such as cattle, horses, sheep, pigs, and poultry. Among the vast range of insect species, however, only the honeybee has been exploited to a comparable extent. It is little wonder, then, that most of the research into honeybees is directed toward practical ends: the production of more and better honey and a fuller understanding of the bee's role as a plant pollinator.

Beekeeping has probably been practiced for at least four thousand years. Although sugar was known in China a very long time ago and had first reached Europe about 1000 A.D., it did not come into general use until the eighteenth century. Before then honey was the only form of sweetening known to most people and the demand for it was far greater than it is today.

The social life of the honeybee has long been a source of interest and speculation. Even the earliest beekeepers realized that these insects live and work according to certain "rules." But in spite of a great deal of modern research and observation, a complete understanding of their life and of the factors that govern their behavior has yet to be achieved.

The two most important species of honeybees are the western honeybee and the eastern honeybee. They are closely related and some entomologists consider that they are really subspecies of the same insect. The eastern honeybee retains certain primitive patterns of behavior that the western honeybee has lost. One of these is the habit of an entire colony's abandoning its hive when disturbed and flying off to make its home elsewhere. In a warm climate there may be little danger in such sudden migrations. Among the western bees, which live mainly in cooler regions, such behavior could lead to the death of the entire colony, and it hardly ever occurs. Both species build their nests under cover, in hollow trees, in rock fissures, in buildings, or in hives provided by man. The two wild honeybees—the giant honeybee and the little honeybee—are quite distinct species. They build their combs in the open, often hanging from the branches of trees or shrubs.

The western honeybee is now the most widespread of all the bees. It was brought to the American colonies in the mid-seventeenth century, probably following a winter voyage when the bees could be confined to their hive during the Atlantic crossing. Today many separate races of honeybees exist. They differ from each other in coloring, length of tongue, and, to some extent, in temperament—some being more docile and easy to

Left: The 19th-century drawings show stages in the development of the "storifying system" – the method of increasing the size of a hive to stop bees swarming from overcrowding. First: An ordinary straw hive. Second: A removable glass, which the bees fill with comb, has been added. Third: A three-story hive. The beekeeper has cut observation windows so that he can see when the hive is crowded. Fourth: Four extension glasses have been used. And finally, three hives have been fitted together. Above: A beekeeper adds an extension to a hive.

Right: Ranks of hives at a modern apiary in a Georgia pine forest. A keeper is looking for queen cells, which are either a symptom of overcrowding or mean that the existing queen is getting old and should be replaced.

handle than others. A great deal of crossbreeding has also taken place in efforts to produce bees that combine the most desirable characteristics of all the different races.

A honeybee colony consists of three distinct types of individuals. The most numerous are the workers. There may be anything up to 60,000 workers in a flourishing colony during the summer. They are all females whose reproductive organs have not fully developed. The workers build combs, feed the larvae, look after the queen, and provide the hive with food. The second type are the drones, of which there are usually a few hundred present during the summer. Drones are males that do no work but, by their presence, help to keep the temperature at the required level within the hive. A few of the drones may become the mates of future young queens either from their own hive or from others nearby. The third type is the queen, the only fully developed female in the hive. The queen lays all the eggs and is usually the mother of the whole colony. Normally there is only one queen in each colony, but new queens develop from time to time. The new queen may take the place of the old queen if she is failing through age or disease. Or the new, young queen may take the lead in swarming—that is, when groups of bees leave the parent hive to found new colonies.

Other social insects such as wasps, bumblebees, and ants have queens that can survive on their own and start nest building at the beginning of the season without any assistance. But the honeybee queen has become so specialized that she is entirely dependent on the other members of a colony and cannot live without them. The queen, for her part, is the unifying force of the community; if she is removed from the hive the workers very quickly sense her absence. After a few hours, or even less, they show unmistakable signs of "queenlessness" and begin preparations for raising a new queen to replace the one they have lost.

At one time beekeepers believed that the queen in some way gave orders to her workers and thus directed the activities of the colony in a positive way. There is no evidence to support this belief. But there can be no doubt that the queen is responsible, in a passive way, for much of the workers' behavior. In 1705 John Thorley, an English naturalist, wrote in *An Enquiry into the Nature, Order, and Government of Bees:* "They are fond of the person of their queen, whose presence is absolutely necessary to the prosperity and safety of the whole."

Apart from the word "fond," which is misleading, Thorley's statement is sound. Recent research has revealed much about the nature of the queen's attrac-

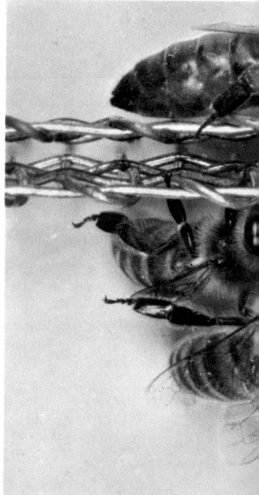

tion for the workers and her influence on behavior in the hive.

When the queen moves about the hive she is always surrounded by worker bees who feed her and con-constantly lick her body. As there is a constant turnover of individual workers attending her, the queen comes into close contact with a great many of her workers during the course of a day. Most of these are the young "household" bees, which have not yet reached the age at which they leave the hive to find food. The well-established forage bees, and especially those that are nearing the end of their life, pay much less attention to the queen. They do not seem to be attracted to her in the same way as the younger ones.

Entomologists have conducted many experiments designed to reveal the nature of the bond between queen and workers. First tested was the need for actual physical contact between them. It was found that, if the queen is removed, the bees become aware of her absence within half an hour and begin to run about restlessly as if they are searching for her. In another experiment the queen was confined within the hive in a small cage of gauze, with mesh wide enough to allow the bees to touch and feed her. They continued to behave normally even though the queen was unable to move about. Similarly, the workers behave normally if the queen is confined to one section of the hive and separated from the workers by a screen through which they can pass. But if the screen is of such fine mesh that the workers cannot get through, those bees that are outside the screen will begin to act in a "queenless" manner.

 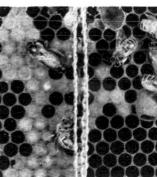

The queen bee is the controlling force of the colony. She is constantly tended by worker bees, who feed her and obtain "queen substance" from her (top left). If separated from her (bottom left) a state of "queenlessness" is induced in the workers; they become disorganized and restless. But then within 12 hours they begin rearing a new queen. Above: Normal building activity in cells. Above right: Queenless workers modify worker cells containing female larvae and prepare to rear queens from them. One will become the new queen of the colony.

The same thing happens if the queen is put with a few attendants in a double-walled mesh cage, in the center of the hive. There none of the bees outside can have direct contact with her or her attendants. Although the excluded workers can still smell the queen, this does not seem to reduce the apparent restlessness of their behavior.

These experiments showed clearly that the queen must produce some substance that attracts the workers and that can be obtained from her only by direct contact. This substance evidently stimulates the normal working behavior within the hive. This chemical messenger has been called "queen substance." Experiments have shown that the bees obtain it directly from the body of the queen and pass it on by feeding each other regurgitated food. Sometimes they cannot get a regular supply, or if the supply is insufficient for the whole hive, as happens when a queen is old and beginning to fail, a state of "queenlessness" sets in. Then the workers soon begin to raise a new queen. Young virgin queens do not appear to be able to secrete any queen substance. Not until she has mated and begun to lay eggs does a queen bee assume her full importance in the hive.

Since these discoveries, many researchers have investigated queen substance. It was found that it is secreted by glands in the lower jaw of the queen but that she spreads it all over her body when grooming herself. The substance has a very complex chemical structure, including a fatty acid. Because of its effect on the bees it is called a *pheromone*, or social hormone—that is, a substance that controls the social activity of a group of individuals. The direct effect of the queen substance on the worker bees is to prevent the development of certain glands and to keep them from building queen cells and raising new queens. If the workers do not get some queen substance, they at once begin preparations for raising a new queen and their ovaries start to develop and enlarge. If the queenless state continues for more than two weeks many of the bees become "laying workers" and produce eggs that give rise only to drones. If the hormone is fed to worker bees by artificial means it produces exactly the same effect as if they had a queen. This proves that it is not the person of the queen but the substance she produces that is the controlling factor in the behavior of the workers. If no extra queen substance is given to the bees, the queen must be present in the hive for at least seven hours each day in order to prevent the raising of new queens.

By using glass-walled observation hives and marking bees with spots of color, it has been possible to discover a great deal about behavior within the normally dark hive. The worker bees first emerge from their cells three

Above: A queen bee laying an egg. Each queen mates only when between seven and 14 days old. She stores sperm inside her body and may lay as many as 1500 eggs a day. She is able to lay both fertilized worker-producing eggs, and unfertilized drone-producing eggs, in appropriate worker or drone cells. Below: A 19th-century woodcut, compared (right) with a modern photomicrograph, of a worker egg in its cell.

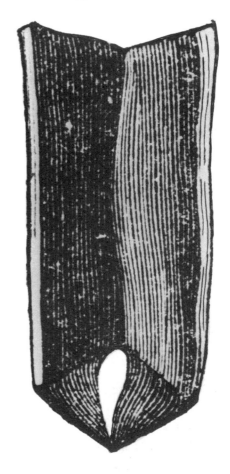

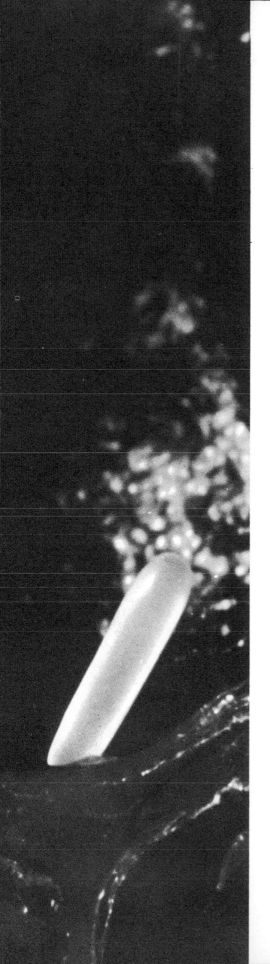

weeks after the eggs are laid. They clean and groom themselves and then begin to solicit food from other bees by stretching out their tongues and assuming what may be called a begging position. The food, which consists mainly of regurgitated honey, undoubtedly also contains traces of queen substance. After the first three days, the young workers begin to help themselves to food from the storage cells. In addition to honey, they consume a large quantity of pollen. At this age they are already carrying out tasks in the hive — mainly cleaning and polishing the cells from which more young bees have recently emerged.

Soon after they have begun to eat pollen the workers' "brood-food" glands develop and secrete a milky substance, called royal jelly, that is very rich in protein. This is fed to all the young larvae during the first three days of their life. Thereafter the worker larvae also receive honey, but any queens that are being raised continue to be fed entirely on royal jelly throughout the larval stage. While their brood-food glands are fully active, the young nurse-bees spend most of their time tending the youngest larvae. Later, when the glands are less

Above: Newly hatched worker emerging from its cell. From egg to hatching takes 21 days. During this time the developing bee passes through a larval and pupal stage. Worker bees have organs for making wax and for collecting nectar and pollen. If hatched in summer they live for four or five weeks; if in autumn, for six months or more.

active, they pay more attention to the older brood. They also undertake household duties such as building and sealing cells, and receiving and storing the loads of nectar and pollen that the forager bees bring back to the hive. In addition, they do general cleaning work, wait on the queen, and guard the entrance to the hive.

When she is about three weeks old the worker begins to take short flights from the hive and makes herself familiar with the surroundings. A few days later she joins the active forager bees and brings nectar, pollen, and water to the hive. She may still undertake a few household duties when needed, but gradually she spends more and more of her time as a forager. She continues in this way of life until she dies. During the summer, when the workers are very active, both inside and outside the hive, their average lifetime is only about four or five weeks. In other seasons, when they do not expend so much energy, they live longer. Workers that emerge in the autumn lead comparatively inactive lives throughout the winter. They die in the following spring, when the queen has again begun to lay a large number of eggs and new bees are emerging. A queen bee can live for two or three years, or even longer.

Although a worker's behavior is governed largely by her physiological development, she is also capable of responding to the particular needs of the hive at any given moment. If she cannot find enough work of one kind she will do something else instead; a worker can change from one job to a succession of others within a few minutes. If there is not enough work in the hive for a nurse-bee she will begin to forage at an earlier age than normally. Bees seem to know by instinct what is required to keep the hive in a healthy state. Without apparent direction, all the workers do whatever they find needs doing as they move about the hive.

The way in which social insects, and bees in particular, communicate with each other remained a mystery for many centuries. That bees can pass information to each other, especially about the best places in which to gather nectar, has long been known to observant bee-keepers. Thorley, writing early in the eighteenth century, noted: "Bees certainly have a language among themselves which they perfectly understand, tho' we do

Above: Trophallaxis (the process of reciprocal food exchange) between workers. The physiology and behavior of bees is largely controlled by their intake of glandular food. Left: Diagrams of three glandular stages in the worker; these correspond with different work activities. 1: Until 10 days old it feeds larvae with protein secreted from its head glands. 2: Then it builds cells from wax secreted by glands in its abdomen; the head glands shrink. 3: After the 20th day both glands contract; the bee is now a forager until it dies.

1   2   3

Above: Close-up of a bee collecting
nectar from a flower. From its 20th day
until death, the worker is a forager.
When scout bees have found a rich
source of pollen and nectar in one
species of flower, they "tell" the workers
who then collect food until the supply
fails. Between 12 and 21 days, workers
take nectar from incoming foragers,
convert it to honey, and store it away.
They also collect and store pollen.
Right: The workers on the far right
are seeking storage space for the pollen
seen on the hind legs of a forager.

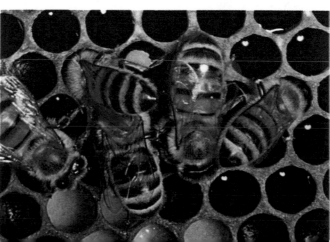

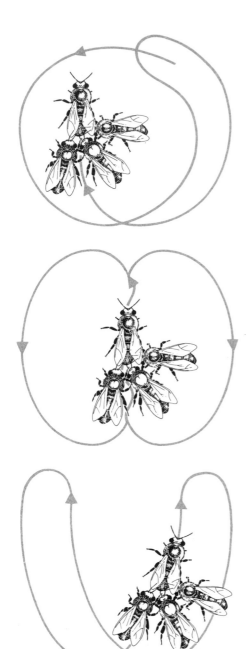

not, or at the best very imperfectly." Soon after the First World War an Austrian-born zoologist, Karl von Frisch, made a special study of the language of the honeybee. He was astonished to discover that the bees give each other detailed information by performing certain "dances" when they return to the hive after a foraging expedition. After a quarter of a century of painstaking observation and research he and other workers were at last able to interpret the language of the bees. It is now possible for a trained observer to understand what a dancing bee is communicating to the other members of the colony.

When a forager returns to the hive after finding a good source of nectar or pollen, she will perform a dance, either at the entrance to the hive or on the combs inside. The household bees, especially those that are about to become foragers themselves, follow this dance attentively. If the bee is dancing inside the hive, other bees cannot see what she is doing but have to trace her movements by touching her with their antennae. At first the younger bees find this difficult to do, because often a dancing bee moves very rapidly. With practice they soon become able to interpret the complete dance and to act upon the information it contains.

The nature of the dances varies according to the distance of the feeding places from the hive. If the food is within 50 yards or so, the bee performs what is known as a round dance. In this dance, usually done near the hive entrance, the forager moves quickly in a circle, often doubling back on her tracks. The richer and more plentiful the source of food, the more lively and animated is the dance. As soon as her audience has understood the meaning of the dance, they fly off in search of the food source. Some races of bees perform what is known as the sickle dance to convey the presence of nearby food. This dance figure is like an elongated figure-eight with the tips of the loops bent so as to point in the direction of the food. If the food source is farther away, some indication of both direction and distance is needed to help the foragers find it without wasting time and energy. In this case the bee performs what is known as a waggle dance. This usually takes place on the vertical wall of the honeycomb. The figure traced in this dance consists of a circle divided by a diameter line. The bee first moves up the diameter line, at the end of which she turns left or right and moves in a semicircle back to her starting point. Then she repeats her movement up the diameter line, and turns right or left in order to trace out the second half of the circle. Throughout this dance the bee waggles her abdomen vigorously.

If the food is not too distant the rhythm of the dance is quick and her run up the diameter line is repeated a

If the black Austrian honeybee finds foods less than 275 feet from the hive, on her return she does a round dance (top). If the food is farther away, she performs the waggle dance (middle). The number of repeats of the pattern in a given time indicates distance of the source. The Italian honeybee performs the sickle dance (bottom) for sources beyond 30 feet. The opening of the "sickle" faces the source of food; the intensity of the dance, as usual, indicates the quality of the supply.

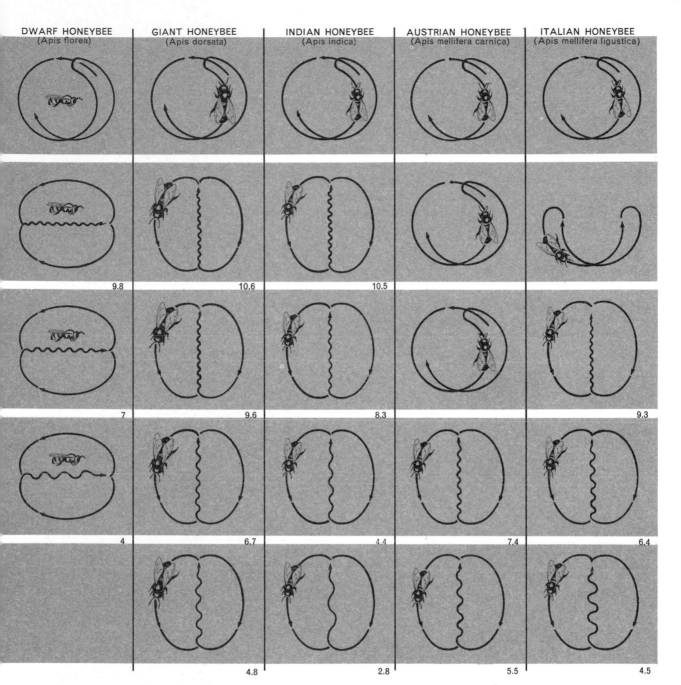

DWARF HONEYBEE (Apis florea)	GIANT HONEYBEE (Apis dorsata)	INDIAN HONEYBEE (Apis indica)	AUSTRIAN HONEYBEE (Apis mellifera carnica)	ITALIAN HONEYBEE (Apis mellifera ligustica)
9.8	10.6	10.5		
7	9.6	8.3		9.3
4	6.7	4.4	7.4	6.4
	4.8	2.8	5.5	4.5

Above: Chart showing "dialects" in the language of the dances of bees. The dwarf bee dances on a horizontal surface. All the others dance on a vertical surface. The figures (far left) give distances in feet of the food source from the hive. Speed and number of runs of the waggle dance convey distance instructions. The more rapidly the bee performs its waggle-runs, the nearer is the food supply. The figures in the squares represent the number of waggle-runs performed in 15 seconds for each distance of food source by each kind of bee.

In her waggle dance, the scout bee points out the position of the sun, as she saw it while flying to the food source, and the angle of the source in relation to the sun. Thus, if (as right) the angle of the nectar source is 60° left of the sun, the straight run of the dance shows this angle.

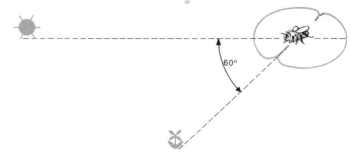

191

number of times with comparatively few abdominal waggles. The greater the distance, the longer she takes to complete the figure and the more intensively she waggles her abdomen. It has been found that a bee judges distance by the amount of energy she has expended in reaching a source of food. If she has had to fly against the wind or to some height, her dance indicates a greater distance than if she has flown with a following wind, or along level ground, or downhill, when much less energy is needed. When quite a long journey—say a mile or two—is necessary, it is important that bees making the trip for the first time should know how far they will have to go. This is because they always take with them honey to supply them with enough energy for the journey. Extremely long journeys are not economical. If a bee has found a source of food more than three miles away, she does not dance when she returns to the hive, so no other bees are recruited for that particular site. Similarly, no dance is performed if a food source is found to contain weak or watery nectar or syrup, or if the food, however good, is unusually difficult to gather.

The direction of the source of food is indicated by the diameter line in the dance figure. If the bee is dancing in sunlight on the horizontal surface of the hive's landing board or just inside its entrance, she will make the diameter line point directly toward the food source. The other bees will simply fly off in that direction for the distance indicated by the number of waggles. However, it is more usual for her to dance on a vertical comb inside the hive. There she indicates the direction of the food by the angle of the line to the horizontal angle of the sun from the hive's entrance. If the food source lies due south of the hive and the time is midday—when the sun also lies due south of the hive—she runs the diameter line straight *up* the comb. If the food lies to the north she will run straight *downward*; if it is to the west, the diameter runs horizontally from left to right; if to the east, from right to left. Thus, if it is noon and she runs up the comb at an angle of 45° to the right of the vertical, the food lies in a southwesterly direction.

Bees, like many insects and other animals, are able to allow for the change in position of the sun when they fix the direction of an object or destination at any particular time of day. Evidently the vertical surface in the darkness of the hive provides an ideal setting for the dance. When the bees dance in direct sunlight on the horizontal landing board at the hive entrance, they appear to be dazzled by the sun and often cannot indicate accurately the direction of the food source. It is not known exactly how bees are able to allow for changes in the sun's position when indicating the direction of food.

But it may have something to do with an "internal clock," which many animals have. This is some process or mechanism that takes account of the passage of time independently of external factors such as darkness and light. Birds seem to make use of a similar device to help them navigate during autumn and spring migrations.

Bees appear to be unable to indicate upward or downward direction. In practice this hardly matters. If the source of food lies uphill or downhill from the hive, the usual indications of direction and distance are enough to lead the foragers to the right place.

The workers' ability to communicate in this way is also used when a colony migrates. When the colony has left the old hive and has swarmed somewhere nearby, "scout" bees search the area for suitable nesting sites. On returning the scouts dance on the surface of the swarm in order to indicate the position of the site. At first, many different places are indicated by the various

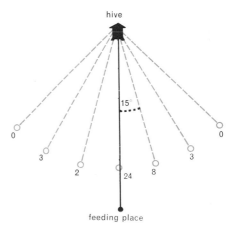

Above: An experiment that proved that foragers fly in the direction conveyed in the dances of scouts. A few numbered bees were fed on a scented bait 250 yards from the hive. They then returned to the hive to dance. Similar scented objects, this time without food, were arranged in the shape of a fan 200 yards from the hive. Figures are the numbers of bees arriving at the various points during one and a half hours.

Through code conveyed in their dances, scout bees that have found a rich source of nectar or pollen stimulate interest in other bees in the colony and give the exact location of the food supply. The film sequence (left) shows foragers moving to greet the returned scout, closing in around her to gain information as her dance gains in intensity, then dispersing when the dance ends. The scout will then move to another part of the colony and dance again. If the food supply is obviously good, the bees will visit it.

193

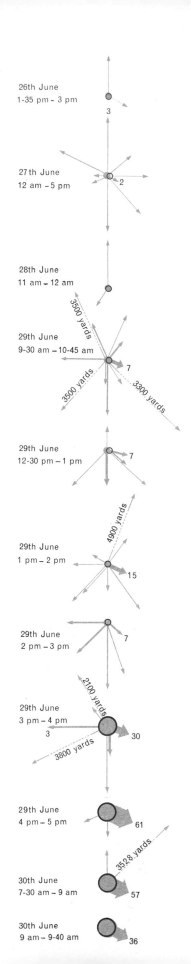

26th June
1-35 pm - 3 pm
3

27th June
12 am - 5 pm
2

28th June
11 am - 12 am

29th June
9-30 am - 10-45 am
3500 yards
3500 yards
3300 yards
7

29th June
12-30 pm - 1 pm
7

29th June
1 pm - 2 pm
4900 yards
15

29th June
2 pm - 3 pm
7

29th June
3 pm - 4 pm
2100 yards
3
30
3800 yards

29th June
4 pm - 5 pm
61

30th June
7-30 am - 9 am
3528 yards
57

30th June
9 am - 9-40 am
36

Above: Colony of bees on combs in
the open air; the scouts failed to find
a suitable nesting place. This colony
did not survive the winter.

Left: Diagrams showing how scout
bees indicate various sites to a swarm
seeking a new home. When all the
dancers agreed on one site, the swarm
departed for it. Distances and directions
indicated by new scouts are shown by
the angles and lengths of the arrows.
Numbers given are of new dancers who
agree on the location of the best site.

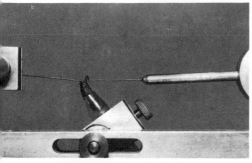

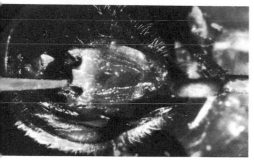

With the introduction of techniques of artificial insemination, controlled breeding of strains of bees has become possible. The photographs above and below trace the stages in the artificial insemination of a queen honeybee. Top: Semen is collected from the inverted genitalia of a drone. Second: The anesthetized queen is placed in a holder. Third: Her vagina is opened. Below: The operator is seen inserting the syringe containing semen into the vagina of the queen bee.

scouts, but some bees dance more energetically than the others. Gradually, more and more dancers appear to be "converted" and begin to adopt the movements of the more energetic dancers. Finally, agreement seems to be reached, and the swarm moves off and takes possession of its new home.

Research continues all the time on a great variety of problems connected with the behavior, physiology, and management of bees. It has been found that bees cannot see red light, which appears to them as total darkness. Thus, if a glass-roofed hive is placed in a room illuminated only by red light, the researcher can observe the ways in which the bees behave within their normally dark hive. It has also been found that bees can gradually be trained to make their way through a dark maze — even without the aid of a scent trail — merely by memorizing each turn correctly. As one might expect, some individuals can learn this much faster than others. Bees have been moved backwards and forwards across the equator or flown across the Atlantic to test their reaction to time and the position of the sun. The way in which they determine how many drones and queens to raise has also been investigated. During the last few years research on their mating habits has been done by attaching virgin queens to a leash and letting them fly about with males. Controlled breeding has now become possible with the development of special techniques of artificial insemination. However, nobody has yet succeeded in raising a queen bee artificially.

Although our knowledge of the individual and social behavior of bees has increased enormously during the present century, much work remains to be done. One line of research of particular interest to beekeepers is directed toward a more precise knowledge of the factors that trigger off swarming behavior. Bees cannot be domesticated like cows, sheep, and horses. But, by understanding their habits and the reasons why they behave in certain ways, we can learn how to use their honey-making and pollinating activities to the greatest advantage.

Collecting and Breeding Insects

THERE are many entomologists working in laboratories or museums on problems of insect classification, anatomy, physiology, and behavior. But often they find that they have little time for collecting or breeding the large numbers of insects required for tests and experiments. Insect hunters and professional insect breeders are therefore needed to supply dead or living specimens.

The study of the relationship between insects and their environment, as a step towards pest control, also requires much work by collectors. It is their task to obtain a clear picture of the relative abundance of all the insects inhabiting a certain area. This sampling of insect populations is now a regular feature of the preliminary studies necessary to work out ways and means of controlling pest species. Another stage in pest control involves testing sprays, fumigants, and systemic insecticides in the laboratory before they are tried out in the field. Again, large numbers of insects are often wanted and can usually be supplied by insect hunters or professional breeders.

Geographical variation in insects is another aspect of entomology that is of more than scientific interest. It may also be of great significance from an economic point of view. The same species may differ considerably in appearance, in habits, and in life history under different climatic conditions. It is only by collecting and breeding specimens from widely separated regions that this kind of thing can be learned. It is quite common, for example, for the same species of insect to produce only one generation a year in a cool climate and two or more generations in a warmer climate. It is vitally important that such differences are known and understood when control measures are planned.

As already mentioned, many new insects are being discovered and classified all the time, thanks mainly to the efforts of collectors. As collections become more and more complete, it becomes quicker and easier to identify any obscure insects that may be found. The great private collectors, such as the late Lord Walter Rothschild in England, have now almost disappeared. Large insect collections are now gathered and maintained chiefly by museums and other scientific institutions. These institutions obtain their specimens from both amateur and professional collectors working in all parts of the world.

The breeding of any kind of insect in captivity involves a great deal of work and a specialized knowledge of some particular branch of entomology. Large-

Above: A field research worker examines insects caught in a wind trap. He is employed by Insect Survey and Detection, a branch of the Department of Agriculture concerned with control of insect pests. Such wind traps are set in strategic places in many southern states. They indicate the degree and type of likely infestation by migrating pests.

Above: An early photograph of the author's butterfly farm, showing breeding cages. The farm was started in 1894. Initially it specialized in breeding rare butterflies for the private collector; now large quantities of comparatively common species are bred to be sold in many countries for demonstration and experiment in colleges and laboratories.

scale insect breeding is comparatively new. Before economic entomology gained its present importance the demand for huge numbers of insects did not really exist. Until the end of the nineteenth century insect breeding was limited mainly to people who raised a few insects — usually butterflies and moths — more or less as a hobby or to study the details of their life history.

One of the more unusual cases of an insect breeder is that of the Englishman L. W. Newman. His regular work was in the tobacco trade but he devoted all his spare time to collecting and breeding moths and butterflies. Then in 1894 Newman was encouraged by several wealthy English collectors to become a full-time butter-

Early entomologists were mainly interested in discovering and classifying new species. Such work has to precede that of the professional insect breeder. Above is a page from Insectorium . . . Theatrum (1634), by Moffett. Apparently Miss Muffet of the nursery rhyme was Moffett's daughter, who was afraid of spiders because her father's house was full of huge insects.

fly farmer. At that time this was an almost completely new venture. Although quite a number of professional collectors were already at work, very few men had yet tried their hand at professional insect breeding. During these years many wealthy Englishmen were interested in insects but they could not devote much time to their hobby.

The new butterfly farm very quickly began to supply a demand. Eggs, larvae, chrysalises, and mounted specimens of native British insects were much sought after, and especially those of rare varieties and color forms. Because L. W. Newman was already a clever and experienced collector, he was able to find rare specimens to serve as breeding stock when other breeders failed to do so. He also worked out and perfected breeding methods that we still use today, and what had once been his hobby soon became a well-established business.

Since that day many changes have taken place. Wealthy private collectors are far fewer, and people who still take an interest in rare insects usually prefer to collect specimens themselves. What is more, since the invention of the mercury vapor lamp—which we shall discuss later—collecting moths has become so easy that even busy people can find time for it. So the range of insects that a breeding farm supplies is now much narrower than it used to be, and rarities are seldom offered at all.

Nevertheless, the over-all demand for insects has increased, with schools, colleges, and science laboratories taking the place of private clients. Instead of breeding rarities for special customers, a butterfly farm now concentrates on producing large quantities of comparatively common and showy species. Because of their large size, such insects as Cecropia moths are much in demand for experimental and demonstration purposes. Selective breeding for varieties has almost come to an end. Instead, the emphasis is now on raising masses of healthy strains of insects that can be fed on easily obtainable plants and that will provide suitable teaching material for biology and zoology classes. Today the demand for insects comes first and foremost from educational institutions and economic entomologists. Butterfly farming has changed to suit the times.

Lime hawk moths are easily bred in large quantities. They are sold for research purposes to schools and colleges. These moths are easily raised in normal temperatures and need no artificial heat. Their larvae overwinter as pupae in soil at the bottom of the breeding cage. In May they emerge and climb up the twigs to dry their wings.

The Insect Hunter

ENTOMOLOGY would never have become a science without the enthusiasm of entomologists and naturalists who have collected insects all over the world. The study of insects, their distribution and classification, covers a tremendous field, and each year the number of known species increases. Vast numbers of previously unknown insects were brought to the big museums in Europe and elsewhere during the latter part of the nineteenth century and the early years of the twentieth by collectors who risked their lives in tropical jungles and among savage tribes for the sake of new knowledge. For although some insects—usually those that like man's blood, food, or homes—come to our notice far too much for comfort, the majority must be sought out, often in difficult and inhospitable country.

Two famous collectors were Alfred Russel Wallace and Henry Walter Bates, both of whom spent many years in South America, especially in the Amazon country. They left England in 1848, and at first traveled together. Wallace returned after four years, leaving Bates to continue his work in South America until 1857. In 1854 Wallace left England again, this time to spend eight years in the Malay Archipelago. Both men published accounts of their travels and collected and described innumerable animals, birds, and insects unknown until then. During his eight years in the Malay Archipelago Wallace collected no less than 13,100 different species of moths and butterflies alone. It was he who discovered those two wonderful birdwing butterflies that are among the most beautiful insects in the world. His vivid descriptions of the tremendous excitement of the chase and the triumph of capture are as fresh when read today as when they were written more than ninety years ago.

Since the days of Wallace and Bates many other entomologists have followed their example. William Gerhard went to Bolivia in 1898 and hunted insects for Andrew Weeks of Boston, a wealthy entomologist and collector. Gerhard was away for over a year, crossed great mountain ranges, hacked his way through tangled forests, survived a revolution in La Paz, Bolivia, and desertion by his Indian guide, to return in the end with some 13,000 butterflies, 1200 moths, 1000 dragonflies, 1000 beetles, and several thousand other insects. Among his collection were 80 butterflies that had not been seen or named before. Only a few years later, at the request of Lord Walter Rothschild, A. S. Meek went out to the Solomon Islands to collect birds and butterflies. He was

Right: An 18th-century engraving from *Papillons d'Europe* by Marie Dominique Engramelle. A butterfly is being caught with a forceps net, an old-fashioned hinged net used mainly to catch stinging insects. It is heavier than a normal net and is about three feet long. The cage is made of wire netting.

Above: Alfred Russel Wallace (1823–1913), British naturalist and entomologist, and a contemporary of Darwin. In 1848 Wallace set off with Henry Walter Bates on an expedition to the Amazon. Without proper equipment they had to contend with an environment similar to that depicted in the engraving (right) from *Flora Braziliensis*, by the zoologist von Spix and the botanist von Martius.

away for more than two years and lived through many hardships and adventures such as hurricanes and encounters with head-hunters. He sent back more than 20,000 specimens to England, including several previously unknown insects. One of his most notable captures was a female birdwing butterfly that had black forewings instead of the normal brown.

A well-known insect hunter of the present day is the fearless Miss Evelyn Cheesman, famed for her collecting trips to tropical islands. Except for her first journey with the St. George Expedition to the Pacific in 1925, she had always traveled alone and collected insects in remote and dangerous places with the aid of only a few native helpers. In 1934 a party of British botanists and entomologists explored the Ruwenzori Mountains in central Africa. In 1952 the Northern Insect Survey, organized by the Department of Agriculture in Ottawa, spent many months in the Canadian Arctic, collecting and studying the insect life there. In 1963 a Japanese Expedition was organized to study the high altitude insects in the Himalayas. There are still many regions that are unexplored.

Many economic entomologists have also spent a good deal of their time as insect hunters. Their work has often been more difficult than any other kind of collecting because they have deliberately confined themselves to hunting parasites and predators that could be introduced elsewhere to control insect pests. One of the first and most skillful hunters of this kind was Albert

This butterfly with black forewings was discovered in the Solomon Islands early in this century by the naturalist A. S. Meed. Below: Part of a mass of two million hibernating ladybirds. They were found in May 1953, on a sheltered snowfield in the Himalayas at a height of about 14,000 feet, by members of an entomological expedition.

Koebele. The story of how he introduced the Australian ladybird to California has already been told (page 147). He also did a great deal of work of the same kind in Hawaii, where he collected suitable insects both for pest and weed control, often working under very difficult conditions in fever-infested areas. Collectors are still at work in many places, for the insect population of the world is still far from being fully explored.

In dense forests, where the thick canopy of leaves makes the forest floor dark and sunless, many more insects live among the higher branches than at ground level. Many of them in fact, spend their entire lives some hundred feet or more above the ground, where they feed on flowers and leaves in the sunlight. There is still much to be done in the study of the insect life of the jungle treetops, because exploring the forest roof requires a special technique. Platforms have to be built in the tall trees and the collectors have to be hoisted up with block and tackle. The difficulties of this kind of insect hunting have been well described by R. W. G. Hingston in his book, *A Naturalist in the Guiana Forest*.

In spite of special techniques, very few creatures are captured in virgin forest, simply because it is much too dense. Insect hunters in the tropics find that their hunting becomes really profitable only when they make a clearing or come upon a place where fallen trees have allowed the sunlight to penetrate. Wallace described tantalizing glimpses of many colorful butterflies fluttering round the treetops. He was unable to catch any until, one day, he came to part of the forest that had been burnt. Here flowering creepers were once again beginning to climb up the trees at the edge, and the butterflies were coming down from the heights to feed.

The popular idea of an insect collector is that of a man chasing after a butterfly with a net. In reality a skilled insect hunter seldom does much chasing because he knows the insect nearly always wins the race. The experienced collector stalks his prey calmly and carefully. If possible, he waits by some inviting patch of flowers or even by a bait that he has put down himself. Then he quickly nets the insect when it settles to feed.

In the tropics especially, the thick and spiny vegetation often makes it impossible to follow an insect off the beaten track. Collectors there try to attract butterflies by a lure. Ripe or overripe fruit, animal dung, or sometimes even a decaying carcass can be useful. A felled tree oozing sap from the severed trunk, or a long gash in the bark of a tree still standing, will often attract many other insects as well as butterflies. Sometimes a glittering or light-colored object, such as a piece of bright metal or a white cloth or garment, will bring a few high-flying butterflies down to ground level. Arti-

The tree roof of a forest is a distinct entomological zone. Above: A tree lift, or platform, used to hoist the insect collector or observer. In the zone are found flying insects (such as moths and butterflies, bees and wasps) that need lighter, drier conditions than those lower down in the dense forest. Ants and beetles are also abundant.

ficial decoys of suitable shape and coloring have also been successful. Water—particularly rather dirty and smelly water—is very attractive to butterflies. Insect hunters like to station themselves by stagnant pools or stretches of wet, foul-smelling mud, where insects settle in large swarms to drink. Watercourses through the forest are nearly always good places for finding insects, especially in regions that have a dry season.

Above all, an insect collector must be an alert observer. Insects, except for certain large and colorful species, are not particularly conspicuous against their natural background. Often their presence can be detected only by various signs of their activities. To be able to recognize these the hunter must have a working knowledge of entomology. A bitten or curled leaf, dust trickling from a tiny hole, an oddly shaped gall, a bare twig on a leafy branch, a patch of dead grass in the green turf—any one of these could mean the presence of some insect or other. And when the sign has been detected the clue must be followed up in the right way. The chances of capture are increased for the observant collector who knows, for example, the habits of a particular insect, such as where its eggs are usually laid or the times of day when it flies and rests.

Some excellent examples of what Evelyn Cheesman calls insect idiosyncrasies, which are a great help to the insect hunters, are given in her book, *Time Well Spent*. She noticed, for example, that cicadas and grasshoppers that came into her hut seemed to prefer to settle in a

Knowing the habits of particular insects simplifies their capture. Butterflies drink from muddy water (above); burying beetles (below left) feed on dead animals. The insect hunter looks for natural lures like these. He also sets his own lures; the tree trunk (below right) is smeared with molasses and rum; feeding from it are some intoxicated heart-and-dart moths and some common yellow underwings. Both these species fly by night.

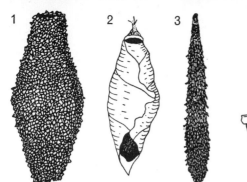

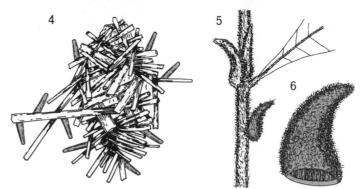

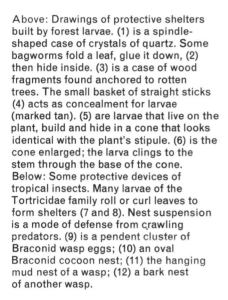

Above: Drawings of protective shelters built by forest larvae. (1) is a spindle-shaped case of crystals of quartz. Some bagworms fold a leaf, glue it down, (2) then hide inside. (3) is a case of wood fragments found anchored to rotten trees. The small basket of straight sticks (4) acts as concealment for larvae (marked tan). (5) are larvae that live on the plant, build and hide in a cone that looks identical with the plant's stipule. (6) is the cone enlarged; the larva clings to the stem through the base of the cone.
Below: Some protective devices of tropical insects. Many larvae of the Tortricidae family roll or curl leaves to form shelters (7 and 8). Nest suspension is a mode of defense from crawling predators. (9) is a pendent cluster of Braconid wasp eggs; (10) an oval Braconid cocoon nest; (11) the hanging mud nest of a wasp; (12) a bark nest of another wasp.

Below: A spiral gall, formed by the larva of an aphis developing inside the tissues of the stem of a poplar leaf.

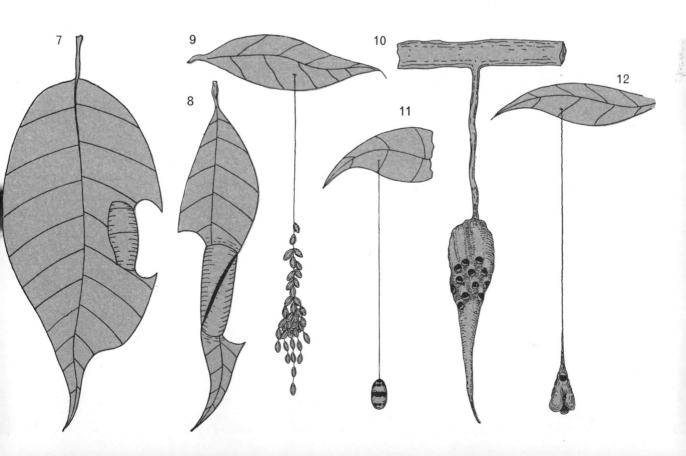

certain shaded spot on a screen. By making sure that the screen was always in the right position, she secured many specimens of these insects. Certain butterflies, she found, rested during the heat of the day in limestone caves or in shady places along the jungle paths. They came out regularly every day at the same time and followed the same set route, where they could easily be intercepted. There are many similar insect habits that can help the collector once he knows them. Some butterflies, for instance, regularly take up a position on some prominent leaf or twig and behave as if they were defending it. They fly out to attack any moving object that approaches and then return again to their perch. The small copper butterfly in England behaves like this, and so does the beautiful royal butterfly found in Indonesia.

It is comparatively easy to collect many moths by using a strong light, which will attract them either into a trap or towards a white sheet where the collector waits ready with a net. The mercury vapor lamp, mentioned earlier, revolutionized moth hunting. Wherever a vehicle can penetrate, the mercury vapor lamp can be used, because it can be run off a generator connected to any car. If the collector has to work in an area that a car cannot reach, he can use the old-fashioned acetylene lamp.

Weather conditions play an important part in catching moths. If the weather is just right, and scent spreads quickly through the air, moths can be lured to a bait consisting of some sweet liquid such as molasses, mixed with beer or rum. Once they find the bait, usually smeared on a tree trunk or a wooden post, the moths become so intent on feeding that they scarcely notice the careful approach of the moth hunter. The alcohol in the mixture dulls their senses so that they are easily caught.

Dragonflies, flies, mosquitoes, wasps, and bees are usually caught in a net. However, stalking and waiting,

The experienced insect hunter knows that many insects lay their eggs on the underside of leaves. Above: The eggs of a moth on the underside of a leaf of wild black cherry.

Right: Diagram of a chloroform light-trap—a simple trap used mainly by amateurs. Here it is being held against a tree trunk. Night-flying insects attracted by the light swoop into the net and are stupefied by the chloroform.

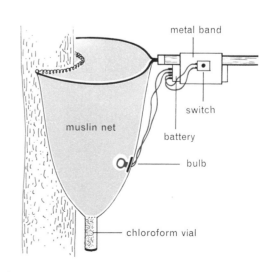

metal band

switch

battery

muslin net

bulb

chloroform vial

Right: Diagram showing the construction of a mercury-vapor lamp trap, which is more efficient and complex than the chloroform trap (left). A bulb (a) containing mercury vapor attracts insects by giving light with a high content of ultra-violet. This bulb is connected to the outlet through a unit (c) that regulates current. Insects swoop down to the light, are dazzled by it, and spiral helplessly between the deflection plates (b) into the metal container. Above: One of these traps in use. A moth by-passing the lamp is netted.

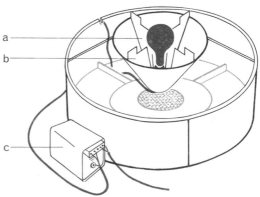

a
b

c

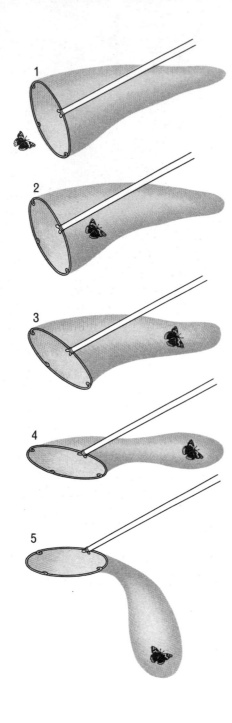

rather than chasing, is always the best method. All these insects have their favorite feeding and resting places. It is there that the hunter, dressed in clothes that blend with the background and as motionless as he can be, waits for them to approach. Mosquitoes and flies often dance above some small shrub or stump, or hover along the edge of shrubbery or a group of trees. Dragonflies frequently dart up and down a pathway along a river bank or lake shore. Many bees and wasps return again and again to the same group of flowers when they are gathering food. Newly felled timber is nearly always attractive to many different kinds of beetles. Large flower heads, such as those of hogweed or wild parsnip, are excellent places to look for insects that feed on nectar and pollen.

Insects that do not fly must be hunted in different ways. For those that crawl about among shrubs and the lower branches of trees, "beating" is an old and effective method. Either a sheet is spread on the ground beneath the bush or tree, or a "beating tray" is held beneath the boughs. (The beating tray is simply a piece of strong material, usually black cotton, attached to a frame constructed so that it can be folded like an umbrella when not in use.) With the sheet or tray in position, the bush or branch is beaten with a stick so that the twigs are suddenly jarred. Any insect that is not clinging very tightly is dislodged and falls. Winged insects, suddenly knocked down, often pretend to be dead for a moment or two before they recover from the shock. They too can often be caught and put into boxes. It is surprising how many insects can be taken by beating from even quite a small bush.

Insects living among grass and other low-growing plants—including many kinds of beetles, leaf hoppers, and grasshoppers—are usually caught with a sweep net. This has a wide opening, and is made with an especially strong frame so that it can be swept along the ground and scoop up all insects that happen to be in its path. A rich and varied haul of insects in all stages of development can also result from searching under stones, under loose bark, in grass tufts, among dead leaves or shallow roots, under moss, ivy, and fallen logs, in the holes and burrows in sunny banks, in dead tree stumps, in hedge bottoms, and among rubbish and debris of all sorts. Sometimes, when the insects are in an early stage of development, it is difficult to tell what species they are. If kept in a box or breeding cage with a top of glass or fine gauze, many will continue their development and eventually emerge as adults, when they can be more easily identified.

An interesting branch of insect hunting is the collecting of galls, the swellings on plants. If they are cut off

Diagrams illustrating the correct method of netting a flying insect. The net is held sideways and the insect swept into it. The wrist is turned to bring the mouth of the net horizontal. A fold of material then closes the neck of the net, so the specimen cannot escape.

from plants in the proper way, they can be kept fresh in water or standing on damp sand. Then it is often possible to breed large numbers of insects from them. The insects that actually cause the galls, their parasites, hyperparasites, and the lodgers (or *inquilines*) in the galls, form a complicated and fascinating insect relationship. There is still much to learn about them. Small insects, especially ants and others that scurry about quickly, are difficult to pick up unhurt, and many people use an aspirator for this delicate operation. An aspirator may be either a glass bottle or a wide glass tube

Right: A beating-tray made of canvas stretched on a frame. The collector taps the foliage, and insects drop onto the tray. Below right: Equipment for catching and carrying insects. In the center is an aspirator (2). The collector poises the pick-up tube over small insects (such as the ants and their eggs in the photograph below), then draws them into the bottle by the rubber suction tube. Specimens are poisoned in the killing bottle (1). Tubes (3) are used to carry live insects. If glass-bottomed pill-boxes (4) are put upside down over insects, they make for the light; the lid is then slid under the box.

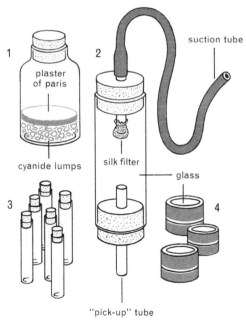

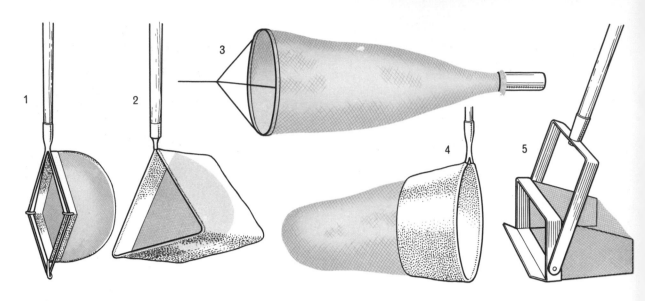

Aquatic insects near the bottom of streams and ponds can be caught with the reinforced diamond-shaped net (1). The dip net (2) with the protecting apron is used in shallow water. Minute insects collect in the detachable glass tube of the plankton net (3). (4) is a sweep-net strengthened with canvas. (5) is a strong dredge used for collecting from the bed of a pond or stream; the container is made of wire, the bottom edge is reinforced with a scraper.

fitted with two narrower tubes. By sucking hard on one of the tubes the collector draws into the bottle a stream of air strong enough to lift small insects from their perches or the ground and pull them into the aspirator.

Hunting for aquatic insects is usually done with a net. A small net with a strong square or diamond-shaped frame, which can be pushed against gravel and stones or through mud, is usually the best. Dredging nets, which can also be used, should be flat and should have the front edge reinforced or fitted with a scraper. If it is to be used on the bottom, the net itself should be made of some kind of fine metal screen. For merely sweeping through the water, any fairly strong material will do, provided it allows the water to run through quickly. Plankton nets, used for collecting very small water creatures, have a plastic or glass tube fitted at the end of the funnel of netting. It is here that the creatures are trapped, still floating in water. A net of this kind can simply be fixed in a stream to gather anything that comes floating down. It can also be towed behind a boat or even by somebody wading or swimming.

Useful traps for collecting insects that wander about from place to place are simple glass jars sunk into the ground. Unwary insects fall into the jars and are unable to get out again. Many insects hide away in dark places during the day. Collectors can take advantage of this habit by providing suitable hiding places that can easily be removed once the insects have moved into them. Old sacks and pieces of dark material, boards, corrugated

Below: Larvae of the leopard moth feed and pupate inside twigs. The only way of deducing the presence of these larvae is by the entry holes they cut into twigs. Some insects blend with their environment and are thus concealed from the hunter. Right: The North American pine sphinx closely resembles shoots of the white pine on which it feeds.

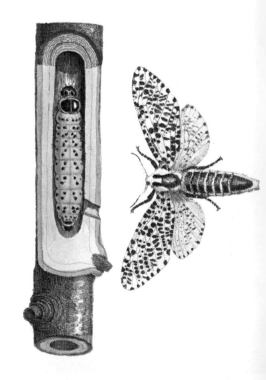

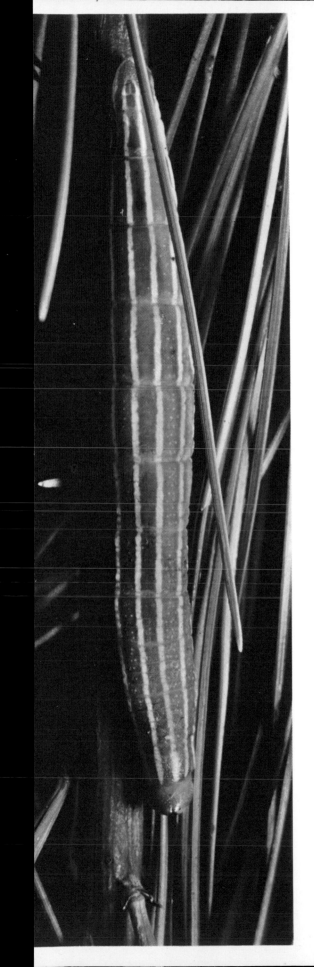

asbestos sheets, wooden boxes, hollow pipes, flower pots filled with hay—all these make hiding places and profitable traps with little trouble. By arranging such traps at different levels—on the ground, in bushes, or higher up among the branches of trees—the collector can vary the kinds of insects he catches.

Soil insects are perhaps the most difficult to collect because of the work involved. When surveys of soil pests have to be made, samples of soil are taken from different parts of the field. These samples have to be carefully sifted and examined for any living creatures. Sometimes the soil is even washed to float out any very small insects. Many soil insects feed in the roots of plants, and it often possible to locate them by noticing the unhealthy look of a plant. Yellow leaves, stunted growth, or wilting are signs to look for.

Insects that live inside their host plant are also very difficult to find. A single dying shoot, a wilting twig, a swelling, or an unnatural kink in a stem may be the sign that some insect is burrowing in the plant tissues. The many different species of clearwing moths all have larvae that burrow inside the stems of plants and shrubs. One species, the currant clearwing, is sometimes a pest in fields of black currants, where its mining activities kill the young shoots. Another species attacks the guelder rose. Many years ago, the English collector, L. W. Newman, was collecting caterpillars in the hedges in the early spring. He noticed that certain twigs of guelder rose were abnormally swollen or showed small round holes covered with a sunken "cap" of bark. He gathered about two hundred twigs and kept them standing in damp sand. In June that year a number of moths emerged—the orange-tailed clearwing, whose life history had not previously been known.

Insects that eat a great many green leaves during their larval stage are usually fairly easy to find, if you look for them in the right places. Here it is not a case of looking for the insects themselves, but rather of keeping an eye open for the damage they have done. This usually takes the form of holes in leaves, entire twigs bare of foliage, leaves that have been skeletonized with only the veins intact, buds that have failed to open, or fruits that have been scarred. All these signs indicate that some creature is, or has been, feeding and may still be hiding among the leaves. Few caterpillars feed in such a way that they are fully exposed to view. During the day, at least, they nearly always hide on the undersides of leaves, or lie along the edge, or on a prominent vein, or along the leaf stalk. Some stop feeding altogether during daylight. Supported by a fine silken thread, they take up a position that makes them look like twigs, standing out at an angle from the branch. Many moths' caterpillars use this type of camouflage. Others are patterned and marked in such a way that they blend in among the shadows, or resemble a bird dropping, or a piece of lichen. Some, like the Essex emerald moth, even hide themselves under a covering of small pieces of their food plant. Certain larvae feed inside a folded leaf or spin themselves a kind of feeding tunnel.

Sharp eyes and a knowledge of where to look are needed to find such hiding places as the nests of solitary bees and wasps, the burrows of tiger beetles and dung beetles, the conical traps of ant lions, the holes of field crickets, the underground galleries of different kinds of ants, and the hide-outs of earwigs. Each locality has its own distinctive insect population. In every locality with which he is familiar the successful insect hunter knows, at a glance, more or less what kinds of insects he can expect to find at different seasons of the year. It is in entirely new surroundings that collecting becomes at once more difficult and more exciting. A really keen hunter is prepared to try his luck almost anywhere. There is always the chance of finding something rare or new, even in places that may seem most unpromising. Not so very many years ago a damp London cellar near the Thames River yielded a previously unknown moth, which was feeding on the fungus on the rotting beams.

Above: The stick caterpillar stands supported by a fine silken thread from the twig it closely resembles.

Left: An adult tiger beetle. Its larvae live in vertical burrows in sandy soil (below) and keep their heads level with the surface. They snap and seize any victim of less than three or four millimeters that comes within reach of their mandibles.

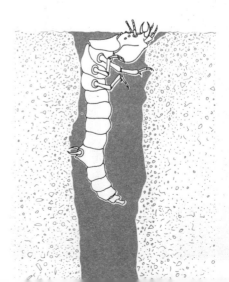

214

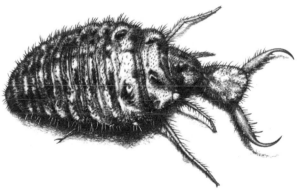

Above: Only the head of the ant lion is exposed as it awaits its prey. The vicious-looking "horns" are really its curved jaws, each bearing three teeth and many hairs. Left: The complete larva; it is 7 millimeters long. Its slender front and middle legs are used to pile sand on a captured insect's head. Drawings (below) show how the ant lion constructs funnel-shaped pits in sand or fine soil. An approaching ant slips over the pit rim; the ant lion, hiding at the bottom, pelts sand upward, causing its victim to slide down to be devoured.

The Insect Farmer

IN THEIR natural surroundings different insects demand different breeding conditions, and if a species is to breed successfully in captivity the breeder must try to provide the conditions it needs. Some insects are comparatively easy to breed, while others are extremely difficult because they require conditions that are not easy to provide. For example, insects that can tolerate a wide range of temperature and humidity and perhaps also feed on many different foods are easier to raise than those that can tolerate only a limited range of temperature and feed only on one food plant.

Success in breeding depends on other factors as well. One problem is to obtain perfectly healthy stock to begin with; another is to decide on the ideal scale of breeding. Breeding in small numbers is usually easier than breeding on a large scale, but some gregarious insects will not thrive unless they have a number of their own species around them.

Many moths and butterflies are quite simple to breed, but others are almost impossible — and entomologists are not always sure why. The European giant peacock moth, for example, never completes its metamorphosis when raised in a cage. The large blue butterfly can only be bred in association with certain ants in whose nests the larvae spend part of their life. Some moths and butterflies absolutely refuse to mate in captivity, and others are so wild that they will not settle down to feed. Various theories have been put forward to explain why certain species are so difficult to breed. One idea is that they need direct sunlight or wind, which they can obtain sufficiently only in the open air. None of the theories is yet proved.

The swallowtail butterfly is reasonably easy to raise artificially, and it is bred on a considerable scale at the butterfly farm. This insect lives through the winter in chrysalid form. Early in May the chrysalises are put into mosquito-net cages in a sun-warmed greenhouse. If possible the chrysalises are still attached to the twigs on which they fixed themselves when the caterpillars pupated the previous year. The cages are shaded with brown paper so that the chrysalises will not become too hot, and in warm weather they are dampened several times a day with a fine spray of water.

Toward the end of the month, the adult butterflies begin to form and the wing pattern can be seen through the shell. Dampening is increased to make sure that the young butterflies will be able to emerge easily without sticking to their pupal cases because of lack of moisture.

Swallowtail butterflies can be bred artificially in great numbers. A large cage with overhead sunlight is needed for the adults. They lay eggs on only a few plants, one being fennel (below). Females begin laying eggs a day after mating.

When the butterflies do emerge, they usually manage to crawl up the mosquito-net sides of the cage or on to twigs provided for the purpose. In this way they can stretch and dry their wings, although now and then an insect needs some assistance.

Once the butterflies have emerged, the shading is removed from one end of the cage. As the insects become ready to fly they congregate at the top of the cage, near the sunny end. There they have to be fed. Swallowtails hesitate to feed from anything but real flowers, so bunches of valerian, sweet rocket, lilac, and other nectar-rich flowers are placed daily in the cage. The actual position of the flowers is important. They must be in the sun and within four to six inches of the top of the cage. If the flowers actually touch the netting there is no room for the butterflies to sit comfortably while feeding. If they are too low down the butterflies ignore them and soon begin to grow weak from lack of nourishment. With swallowtails, as with all butterflies, feeding is important. Without nectar or sugar syrup the females will be very short-lived and the eggs will be mostly infertile.

For successful mating the swallowtails must also have sun and warmth. It has been noticed that these insects mate best on hot days when the sun is covered at intervals by small clouds, thus giving alternate periods of sun and shade. The right conditions for mating can then be achieved by dampening the floor to the greenhouse to increase the humidity, raising the temperature to between 79 and 86 degrees F., and yet allowing a certain amount of fresh air to circulate.

At this time the butterflies have to be constantly watched. As soon as a pairing is seen, the two butterflies are removed very carefully by hand to a separate cage. There they will not be disturbed by the constant fluttering of the other, unmated insects. When they part, in anything from half an hour to two hours, the males are either killed for use as display specimens or are returned to the emerging cage where they will very often mate again. The now fertile females are put in a cage by themselves.

The European swallowtail will lay its eggs on many

Left: Sequence of photographs showing the emergence of the swallowtail from its pupal case. This insect passes the winter in pupa form, attached to a twig (top). In late May, the wing pattern of the adult butterfly is seen through the shell (second). To ensure that the young butterflies will be able to emerge easily, the breeder dampens each pupal case. In early June the butterfly breaks free (third), then crawls up the twig to stretch and dry its wings (bottom).

Above left: A single swallowtail butterfly's egg on the leaf of a fennel plant. In its natural environment the butterfly lays each egg on a separate leaf to ensure sufficient food for each larva. When bred in captivity, butterflies tend to lay their eggs in three's and four's because they are confined in a cage. To avoid congestion, the breeder repeatedly puts fresh plants in the cage during egg-laying. Eggs hatch within two or three weeks, and the larvae feed initially on potted plants (above right).

different plants belonging to the family Umbelliferae. (Dill, parsley, and carrots are members of this plant family.) The British subspecies will deposit its eggs freely only on very few plants, while each American species has its own particular preference. To raise swallowtails a good supply of the preferred plant must always be kept in readiness. When the fertile females are placed in the laying cage they must be given two or three of the plants, together with fresh flowers. Here again it is essential that the pots should be raised to the correct level, near the top of the cage.

The day after mating, the females will begin to lay, but if too many eggs are laid on one plant the caterpillars will be overcrowded in the early stages. This must be avoided at all costs. As soon as a fair number of eggs are seen, the plants are taken out of the cage and fresh pots put in to replace them.

Three days after they have been laid, the eggs—if they are fertile—will turn light brown. Hatching takes place between two and three weeks later, depending on the temperature. The young larvae are allowed to feed at first on the potted plants, and a constant watch is kept to see that they have enough to eat. When they have eaten most of their initial food supply, they are moved over to fresh plants of the same kind or to young fennel plants, growing in cages or on seed trays. The larvae themselves are handled as little as possible. If practicable, the piece of leaf to which they are clinging is cut off from the old food plant with a small pair of scissors. This piece of leaf is then placed on the new food plant so that the larvae can crawl on to the fresh leaves by themselves.

The larvae are kept as long as possible on growing plants. If supplies run out, they can be fed in the later stages on cut fennel that is placed in jars of water. The water must be changed daily, for if it is allowed to become stale and yellow the caterpillars will die. Warmth and good ventilation are both very important at this stage, to keep the larvae healthy and growing steadily. Any disturbance caused by a sudden drop in temperature may be fatal. If conditions are right and the stock is healthy, the larvae reach maturity in about a month. They then pupate, attaching themselves to the stems of the food plant.

This is a critical time, for parasites must be guarded against. As soon as a caterpillar has spun its girdle and silken pad on the stem, this part of the food plant is cut off and the larva is placed in a tightly closed cardboard box. Here it can pupate in safety, without the risk of being stung by parasitic chalcid wasps, so small that they can easily pass through mosquito netting. When the chrysalises are hard and firm they are put away in boxes in a cool place. There they are examined every few days to see whether any are changing color. Those that do are removed to emerging cages. The rest will spend the following winter as chrysalises before emerging, so they must be stored away in large tins with well-fitting lids.

Methods of raising insects vary from species to species. Many hardy insects, especially moths, are raised during the caterpillar stage entirely outdoors, on growing shrubs and trees. This is done, for example, with the big hawk moths. After mating has taken place in the emerging cages, the females are confined in cardboard boxes or in round wooden tubs lined with muslin

Above: The larva of a swallowtail butterfly preparing to pupate on the stem of a fennel plant. It spins a silken pad and thread with which it attaches itself to the stem. The pupae stay inert throughout the winter. The breeder keeps them stored in tins, safe from predators.

Left: Diagrams showing the sequence in breeding the swallowtail butterfly. The larvae turn to pupae (1). Still attached to the twigs on which they pupated, they are placed in shaded cages and sprayed with water to keep them moist (2). At the end of May, dampening is increased to aid emerging butterflies. Shading is removed from one end of the cage, and nectar-rich flowers placed on a raised stand in the sunlight (3). Humidity and temperature are increased to provide conditions suitable for mating. As they mate, couples are transferred to a separate cage; afterwards, some of the males may be killed as specimens (4). The fertilized females are put in a cage with a fennel plant on which to lay their eggs and flowers on which to feed (5). The young larvae are placed on feeding trays of fennel (6); they pass through four instars (7). Pupae are kept in a closed box to protect them from parasites such as the chalcid wasp and the caterpillar of the clothes moth (8); these parasites will attack unprotected pupae. Above: An ichneumon wasp newly emerged from a swallowtail pupa that it has killed.

and supplied with flowers. Here they lay their eggs. Each box or tub is labeled with the date when laying begins. A few days before the eggs are due to hatch, the boxes (or the muslin from the tubs) can be put outside on the branch of the appropriate tree or shrub. A *sleeve*—a cheesecloth bag open at both ends—is tied firmly around a branch. Inside it, unable to escape, the young larvae will begin to feed on the leaves as soon as they hatch.

They are left undisturbed in the sleeve for some time. When the daily inspection shows that the amount of food left is no longer enough or when the leaves shrivel or become coated with dirt, the larvae must be transferred to another branch. The twigs or small pieces of leaf on which the larvae are sitting are snipped off and carefully placed among the foliage in a new sleeve. There they go on feeding until another change becomes necessary. As they grow they eat more and more leaves. When a number of large larvae are feeding in one sleeve, it may have to be changed every day.

When the caterpillars are almost ready to pupate they stop feeding, usually undergo a change in color, and often shrink slightly in size. When this happens they are taken out of the sleeve and put into wooden

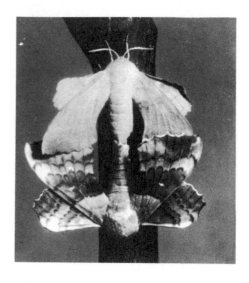

Above: Two poplar hawk moths mating. When eggs are due to hatch, they are transferred to poplar trees. Eggs and foliage are then encased in muslin "sleeves" (below). There the larvae stay, safe from predators, until ready to pupate. The breeder inspects them regularly to make sure they have enough food.

cases filled with peat or with old pieces of clean cloth. There they hide away or burrow down out of sight until they eventually pupate. They are left undisturbed for two or three weeks and then removed for storing in airtight tins.

Whether raised in sleeves or in cages, caterpillars must always be kept perfectly clean. Dead leaves and larvae, old skins, and excrement must never be allowed to collect in the sleeve or at the bottom of the cage. Otherwise conditions will become unhealthy and any diseases that may be present will spread rapidly. Overcrowding, too, must be avoided, and the larvae must never be allowed to go hungry, even for a single day. Stale, waterlogged food or food that is dirty, shriveled, or contaminated in any way should never be used. Cages must be well ventilated and light, but not too hot and sunny. After a breeding cycle is completed, cages must be thoroughly scrubbed with hot water and disinfectant. As well as guarding against specific parasites, the breeder must also take precautions against such creatures as spiders, ants, earwigs, predatory beetles, and hover fly larvae. All these insects can do a great deal of harm and can very easily be introduced accidentally when fresh food is put in the cages. Mice can also be a nuisance. Outdoors, tits often peck holes in the sleeves and drag out the caterpillars. Wasps, too, sometimes bite their way into the sleeves and carry away the caterpillars bit by bit. Clothes-moth larvae often attack pupae while they are being kept in storage.

Larvae can often be successfully raised in small numbers in glass jars or in plastic boxes. Especially useful for raising very young larvae are sandwich boxes. They keep food fresh without the need for standing it in water, they allow the breeder to see at a glance when they need cleaning out, and they are convenient to stack in a limited space. These boxes also make excellent egg containers. If a piece of damp blotter is put in the box, the atmosphere can be kept slightly moist to assist hatching. This is important, because most insect eggs are small and can very easily dry up when they are kept indoors, especially in a heated room.

The refrigerator, too, is a great help to insect breeders, since it enables them to prolong the diapause—a delay in development—in all stages. This means that insects from warmer countries, which under natural conditions would hatch before their food plants are in leaf, can be timed to emerge at the most convenient moment. The refrigerator is useful in another way, too. Hibernating butterflies come through the winter better when the temperature is low but steady. When it is necessary to hasten the development, a previous period of chilling in a refrigerator makes it possible. Heating devices, from

Above: Close-up of the interior of a "sleeve." Hawk moth larvae are disguised among the foliage; arrows indicate two just visible. Below: Small plastic hatching box. Damp cotton wool (b) keeps the air moist; eggs rest on squares of cardboard (a). Hatched larvae will develop in the breeding jar. The perforated lid (c) enables them to breathe. The stems of the food plant (d) are in water; a cotton wool plug (e) stops larvae drowning. The larvae pupate in soil and granulated peat (f).

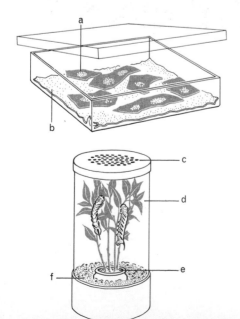

the simple lightbulb to more elaborate thermostatically controlled heating elements, are also a great help to breeders, particularly those working in an unreliable climate such as that of England. Artificially grown insects are much easier to deal with if temperatures can be kept fairly steady instead of being allowed to fluctuate with every change of weather.

Breeders sometimes find difficulty in obtaining a good supply of the right kind of food. There have been many experiments, some of them entirely successful, in making artificial food mixtures. However, most breeders have found that unless larvae are fed on the artificial diet

Above: Silkworms in boxes feeding on mulberry leaves. In the loose straw in the background, larvae spin cocoons. To do this, each larva secretes a protein-like substance through its spinneret, a small opening under the jaw. It spins a filament around itself in the form of a figure of eight. In three days the cocoon is complete. The breeder then heats the cocoons to suffocate the larvae, while taking care not to harm the delicate silk filament. The cocoons are finally sent to a factory where the silk is unwound and collected into skeins.

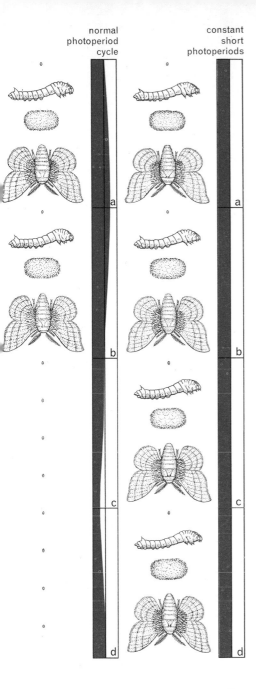

normal
photoperiod
cycle

constant
short
photoperiods

Above: A comparative study of the effect
on Japanese silkworms' breeding habits
of regular short photo- (or light) periods.
Under natural conditions, the fluctuating
photoperiod stimulates production of the
diapause hormone in the first generation
(a). The hormone is passed on to the
eggs of the second generation (b) and
makes these stay dormant throughout
winter (c). Silkworms reared artificially
under constant short photoperiods breed
continually without entering diapause.
Such photoperiods thus arrest
production of the diapause hormone.

from the moment they hatch, they will not take to it.
Even when they have had the artificial diet since hatching, they will always change over at once to their natural
food if it is offered. Silkworms are in great demand for
laboratory work and for teaching, but the breeder may
have difficulty in feeding them. They will normally eat
only fresh mulberry leaves, and in some places these are
often hard to get, partly because the mulberry tree
comes into leaf very late in the year. But the situation
now shows signs of improving. Experiments carried out
in Japan have shown that it is possible to raise silkworms successfully on a food consisting mainly of a
dried powder prepared from mulberry leaves. Trials
have also been made with a preparation consisting of
cellulose powder, potato starch, sucrose, vitamins, and
water; but unless the mulberry leaf powder is added,
most silkworms refuse to eat the mixture. Of those
which do eat it only a few reach maturity, and then they
produce only a very low yield of silk. Other experimental diets are being made with agar-agar (the product
of certain seaweeds) instead of potato starch. Although
the formula is improving with experience it has not yet
been possible to produce a synthetic mixture that is in
every way as satisfactory as the fresh mulberry leaves.

The cabbage looper moth has been bred for as many
as twelve generations on an artificial food consisting of
soaked lima beans, brewer's yeast, agar-agar, and water,
together with small quantities of vitamin C and a chemical substance introduced to prevent the growth of
mold. All the ingredients are mixed in a blender, heated,
and then poured into glass jars to set in a one-inch-
thick layer at the bottom. Twenty-five larvae can be
raised in a one-pint jar on this artificial diet. They will
feed and pupate without further attention in fourteen
to fifteen days if they are kept at a steady temperature
of 80° F. Other mixtures containing casein and wheat
embryo instead of lima beans, together with small
quantities of several vitamins and various anti-microbial
agents, have also been found satisfactory for feeding
certain insects, especially the larvae of the Lepidoptera
group.

Large-scale insect breeding can easily become labori-
ous and time-wasting unless the right techniques are
developed. W. A. L. David and B. O. C. Gardiner have
described the techniques used in Cambridge, England,
for breeding large cabbage whites. The butterflies are
kept in a specially built greenhouse, in cages that admit
light and air. The temperature in the building is never
allowed to drop below 77° F. To prevent diapause and
to enable the butterflies to breed continuously throughout the year, artificial light is used to assure sixteen
hours of "daylight" every day. To simulate sunshine

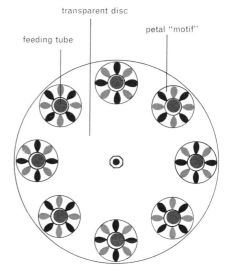

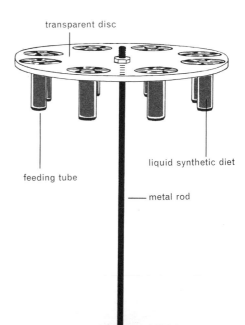

Left: A general view of the inside of a cage used by David and Gardiner to breed large or small cabbage white butterflies. A heating tube maintains the temperature at 24°–30° C. The 500-watt tungsten (daylight) lamp is kept on 16 hours a day; the muslin net gives ventilation. The artificial feeding disc is raised to the light on a stand; the cabbage plant for egg-laying is placed on the floor. Below: Two views of the feeding disc. In the center of each "flower" is inset a cup containing a sugary liquid. Butterflies feed more readily from the "flowers" than from unadorned cups.

transparent disc

feeding tube

petal "motif"

transparent disc

feeding tube

liquid synthetic diet

metal rod

and encourage the adult butterflies to feed and mate, 500-watt tungsten lamps are fixed above the mating cages.

The adult butterflies are fed on honey or sugar solutions, which are offered to them in plastic and glass flowers, painted bright blue and yellow. When these were first tried out on wild stock newly introduced into the cages, the butterflies almost completely ignored the artificial flowers and would take nectar only from real flowers. Then gradually they began to get used to artificial feeding. After a few generations they became so adapted to this method that it was possible to stop giving them real flowers altogether. This, of course, saved a great deal of work. At first the adult butterflies were very wild, constantly trying to escape from the

cages and battering themselves against the sides, but this behavior also changed in time. The laboratory-bred race is now much quieter and easier to deal with. The butterflies will mate without difficulty in the cages if the tungsten lights are on and the temperature is raised to 86° F. or a little above.

Potted cabbage plants are provided for the butterflies to lay their eggs on. These are changed each day, or even every few hours if the females are laying very heavily. In this way the larvae can begin feeding as soon as they are hatched, with no need for humans to handle them. As the young larvae finish eating one plant, other plants are placed around it so that the leaves touch and the larvae can move over by themselves to their new supply. Later on, when they begin to eat large amounts of leaves, cut cabbage is put into the cages. Finally the caterpillars crawl up the sides of the cage and pupate on the walls. The cages are cleaned out regularly and well scrubbed and disinfected between each batch of larvae. In this way something like 15,000 adult cabbage white butterflies are produced every year, as well as numerous larvae that are used in various ways before they reach the adult stage.

Butterfly farms have several times raised very large numbers of the cinnabar moth for shipping to Australia and New Zealand. The caterpillars have always been collected in the field, when about two-thirds grown, and are then reared in large cages on cut flowering stems of ragwort. A four-inch layer of peat is placed in the bottom of each cage. Fresh food is supplied when needed—usually every other day, but sometimes daily if there are a large number of larvae in a cage. As the caterpillars become ready to pupate, they crawl down from the flowers and burrow into the peat. To enable them to do this, someone must clear away from time to time the surface layer of dirt that accumulates on the peat and forms a hard crust. When all the caterpillars have disappeared, the jars of food are taken out of the cage and it is left untouched for two weeks. By then all the pupae are firm enough to handle without causing them any harm, so the peat can be carefully removed from the cage and sifted. The pupae are sorted by hand and all those that are in any way malformed are rejected. Finally they are packed in flat metal cans, 200 pupae to each can, neatly placed in rows between layers of cotton wool. Each pupa is gently felt, before packing, to make certain that it is firm and healthy. Those that are affected

Left: Cabbage white butterflies in various stages of activity. From top to bottom are shown: A general view of the top surface of a feeding disc; a close-up view of a butterfly drinking from the cups; butterflies mating on the floor of the cage; mating and egg-laying on the cabbage plant; a close-up of a female laying eggs on a cabbage leaf; a close-up of clusters of eggs on a leaf.

by any bacterial disease are easily noticed since they will crush at a touch. They are also usually darker in color than the healthy ones, and often have an unpleasant smell. The individual cans of perfect pupae are packed in larger cartons with plenty of shock absorbent material for the trip to their faraway destination.

The codling moth is a pest of apples, and it is much used for the testing of insecticides. Normally the moth has only one generation a year, but under artificial breeding conditions it is possible to bring about continuous breeding. The adult moths are put into cylindrical laying cages lined with waxed paper and supplied with a moistened pad of cotton wool. In these cages the pairs will mate, and a little later the females begin to lay — always at twilight. It has been found that natural twilight is better than any artificial substitute. Each female lays only about twenty eggs. The larvae are raised on small apples, which are gathered during the late summer and which, at freezing point, can be kept more or less indefinitely. The apples, separated by strips of corrugated cardboard, are placed in metal boxes lined with waxed paper. Each box contains about 130 small apples, and 600 eggs are distributed among them still attached to the paper on which they were laid. When the larvae hatch they burrow into the apples and begin to feed. The boxes are kept at a temperature of between 84° and 86° F., and under these conditions the larvae complete their feeding in eighteen days. They then leave the apples and spin their cocoons in the corrugated cardboard. At this stage the apple boxes, with their lids off, are placed in large cages. There is a muslin sleeve at the top so that when the moths emerge they collect at the top of each cage. The whole life cycle, from moth to moth, takes twenty-eight days.

All daylight is excluded from the breeding room. Instead, tungsten filament lamps are kept burning all the time. This constant, steady light prevents the moths from going into diapause. Unfortunately, mortality among the larvae is high, partly due to the fact that they tend to eat each other as well as the apples. (The oriental fruit moth gives the breeder much better results for two reasons: the females lay a larger number of eggs, and the larvae are not cannibalistic.)

Another small moth, the spruce budworm, is a serious forest pest, especially in North America. A great deal of laboratory work has been done in efforts to find the best ways of controlling it. In its natural surroundings this moth has only one generation a year. The larvae feed only on the young shoots of fir and spruce trees, and spend ten months in hibernation immediately after their first molt. It is not an easy insect to breed in captivity. But after much experiment a satisfactory

Above: A codling moth on an apple. Below: A segment of apple shows a larva feeding. These moths can be bred continually under artificial conditions. They can thus be produced in quantity, for the cycle from moth to moth takes only 28 days.

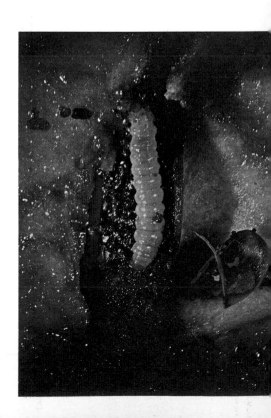

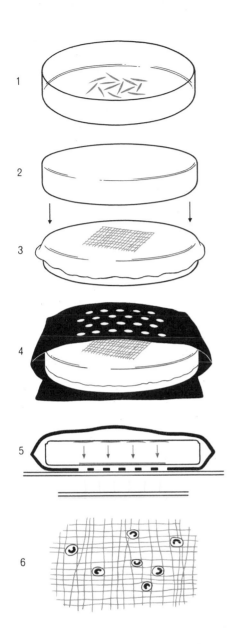

method was worked out a few years ago, and the insect can now be raised in large numbers.

In captivity, the insects are kept during their active stages in a rearing room at a temperature of 71° F. with a relative humidity of between 68 and 75 per cent. As far as is possible they are never touched by hand. To obtain eggs, a male and female moth are placed in a glass jar lined with paper and provided with a small fir twig of the previous year's growth. The jar is then closed with a screwtop lid that has a wire screen in the center to provide ventilation. The moths usually mate within two or three days. A day or so later the female will begin to lay her eggs on the needles of the twig. The eggs are deposited in clusters, and any needles that have eggs on them are removed from the twig each day and put into petri dishes labeled with the date. (Petri dishes are flat, covered plates used mainly for the culture of bacteria.) Hatching begins six or eight days later, and twenty-four hours beforehand the black heads of the baby larvae can be seen through the eggshells.

At this stage the egg-bearing spruce needles, about a dozen at a time, are glued to the bottom of a petri dish with a little rubber cement. Each dish is sealed with a plastic cover bearing a square of double gauze fixed to the inside. It is then slipped into an envelope of black paper with some holes perforated in one side. The gauze in the petri dish is placed nearest the perforated side. All the envelopes are now placed on a glass table, holes downwards, and light is directed from below the table into the petri dishes through the holes in the envelopes. When the eggs hatch, the young larvae are attracted by the light and drop from the glued spruce needles down onto the gauze. There, between the threads, they spin their tiny hibernation webs and undergo their first molt.

The petri dishes containing the hibernating larvae are left in the breeding room for another two or three weeks and then removed to a room where the temperature is kept at freezing point. There they stay for twelve weeks. Then they are brought back again into the breeding room, a supply of spruce buds is put into each dish, and they are again placed on the light table. When the larvae wake from hibernation they are attracted to the light as before. They drop down onto their food in the bottom of the dish. The larvae prefer to feed only on young unfolding buds, so it is necessary to have a supply of these throughout the year. To assure this supply, large quantities are gathered in the spring, packed into special containers that can be sealed to make them airtight, and then deepfrozen at 94° below zero F. for several hours. After this they can be stored indefinitely at 23°F., and thawed as required.

Overcrowding must be avoided, so a constant watch

Above: A laboratory method for rearing the spruce budworm. Spruce needles bearing clusters of eggs that are about to hatch are glued to the bottom of a petri dish (1). The dish is then sealed with a layer of plastic, to the inside of which is fixed a square of gauze (3). The lid (2) is placed on the petri dish. A black envelope with light holes cut in it is pulled over the dish, with the holes next to the gauze (4). The dish is then placed upside down on an illuminated table (5). Larvae hatching from the egg clusters are attracted by the diffuse light; they drop down and spin their winter cases between the threads of the gauze mesh.

is kept on the dishes while the larvae are waking from hibernation. When about a dozen have begun to feed, the gauze is removed and put over another dish. Fresh food need not be given for a week or so, but the dishes must be opened regularly to dry out excessive moisture. As the larvae grow they are split up again, leaving only six in each dish. Food is added as needed and the old. stale food is removed. The larvae become fully fed in three to four weeks and then pupate. The pupae are carefully removed from the dishes and placed, singly, in glass tubes. Each pupa lies on a piece of filter paper. Here the moths emerge after seven days, and they can be paired for mating a few hours later. Despite all the precautions there is a fairly high death rate among the young larvae, especially during hibernation. Nevertheless, the number increases six-fold every generation.

Vast numbers of locusts are raised in captivity, not only for studies connected with locust control but also for feeding many animals and birds in zoological gardens. They are not difficult to breed, but like all laboratory-bred insects they need constant attention. If neglected they will become diseased and die. Most breeders use the standard locust cage, which is a box measuring 15 inches square and 20 inches high. It is made from hardboard fixed on an aluminum frame and has a glass panel at the front. The roof, which has a small trap door for cleaning purposes, can be removed and there is a false floor of perforated zinc raised four inches above the real floor. A flap door in front provides access to the space between the two floors. This door is normally kept open when the cage is in use, to assist ventilation. Near the front of the cage four circular holes ($1\frac{1}{2}$ inches in diameter) are cut into the false floor to hold the egg-laying tubes.

Warmth is essential for locust rearing and cages are usually heated by electric light bulbs—two 25-watt bulbs near the back of the cage under the false floor, and one 60-watt bulb at the top of the cage. These bulbs make it possible to keep a daytime temperature of about 93°F. and a night temperature of about 82°F. simply by switching off the stronger bulb in the evening. Beyond keeping the cages as dry as possible, there is no need to control the humidity. Locusts do not mind crowded conditions, and up to 300 adults can be raised in a cage of standard size. They must, however, have plenty of perches to sit on when they are changing their skins. The best way of providing these is simply to put plenty of natural twigs in the cage.

Locusts are fed on green grass and dry wheat bran. They should have a good handful of fresh grass in one corner of the cage every day, after the old withered grass has been taken out. If fresh grass is not available,

Above: Cages for rearing locusts. The locusts molt and rest on the dry twigs near the heat-giving bulb. Containers of moist sand are provided for the egg-laying adults. Small groups of locusts are reared in jars. Below: Diagram of the construction of a cage. Zinc gauze (a) provides ventilation; the cage opens at the roof (b); the false floor (c) has holes for the oviposition tubes, three of which are in place; an empty tube (d) stands beside the cage.

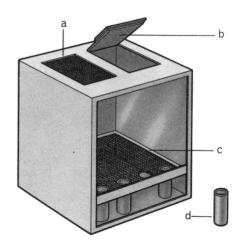

Above: Adult locusts are kept in large breeding cages. A 60-watt light bulb keeps the temperature at about 93°F.; it is kept on 12 hours a day. Food of fresh grass and wheat bran is changed daily. A cage of two cubic feet can house 300 adult locusts. The tops of the sand-filled oviposition tubes are visible; they lie flush with the false floor.

breeders often use wheat, grown in seed trays. The wheat bran is put in a shallow dish at the bottom of the cage and must be changed at intervals. Adult locusts also need some water, although the young do not. The cages are cleaned out daily and any rubbish that falls down between the floors is removed.

Locusts lay their eggs in damp sand. When these have reached the adult stage and begin to mate, the egg-laying tubes, which are flat-bottomed and made of glass or metal, are put into position in the circular holes in the false floor. Their rims must be level with the false floor and the bottoms must rest on the lower floor, so

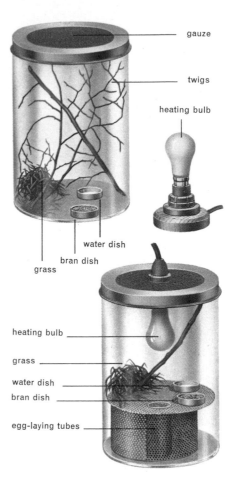

gauze

twigs

heating bulb

water dish

bran dish

grass

heating bulb

grass

water dish

bran dish

egg-laying tubes

Top: A cylindrical plastic cage showing the quantity of twigs necessary for rearing locusts. This cage is heated by an outside electric bulb; a ring of five cages can be heated by the same bulb. The other cage is equipped for keeping adult locusts; only one twig is needed. The false floor is supported by a ring of zinc gauze. An inside electric bulb heats this cage.

Left: An adult desert locust emerging from the final moult. Locusts moult five times in all. The newly fledged adults are mainly pink, but later males become bright yellow and females become dull yellow. When reared artificially, they start to lay eggs after six weeks; a complete generation takes three months.

they are just four inches deep. A female locust lays her elongated egg pods in the sand-filled tubes, which must be changed daily. If more than two egg pods are laid in each, they will not hatch properly. After they have been removed the tubes must not be disturbed. They are covered with glass or metal caps to prevent them from drying out and are then stored in the same temperature as that of the breeding cage. Depending on the type of locust, the eggs take anywhere from eleven to twenty-five days to hatch. The lids are taken off the tubes just before hatching and the young locusts are allowed to crawl out and spread around in a cage of their own to find their food. An average of forty to fifty hoppers hatch from each egg pod. As many as 1000 can be allowed in one cage, where they will normally produce about 300 adults.

The number and variety of insects bred by man for different purposes is astonishing. Fruit flies, because of their rapid breeding, are popular insects for laboratory work. They can easily be reared on a diet of ripe fruit, especially bananas. Meal worms, which are the larvae of a slim brownish-black beetle, are reared in boxes of grain for sale as bird food. Houseflies are often wanted for testing sprays and may be raised in a mixture of wheat bran and alfalfa meal, moistened with a yeast suspension and a solution of malt extract. Or, more simply, they are raised in a mixture of wheat bran, alfalfa, and brewer's grains, moistened with water. This mixture is put in glass jars, the fly eggs are introduced, and the jars are then kept at a temperature of 87°F. Development is completed in nine days.

Mosquitoes, too, are often needed in large numbers, and this is how they are raised. A steady temperature of 82°F. and a humidity of 70 per cent is required and the air in the breeding room must be kept in constant motion with an electric fan. The adult mosquitoes are kept in cages containing about 100 females and a varying number of males. There they are fed every third day by allowing them to suck blood from the arm of the person in charge of the rearing. Petri dishes filled with water are placed at the bottom of each cage on pieces of black paper, which contrast with the cream colored floor of the cage. The females come down and lay their eggs in the water. This is filtered each day, and the eggs thus collected are stored for four days on damp filter paper in glass jars.

On the fifth day the eggs, still on the filter papers, are put into clean bowls. An especially-prepared feeding mixture (brown bread crumbs, water, and common salt) is mixed with cold water and poured over them. The shock of the cold water makes the eggs hatch, and the next day the paper is removed and more of the mixture

Above: Photograph of the way a desert locust lays her eggs in sand. She digs down with her ovipositor and leaves her eggs well buried, in pods of 30 to 100. Below: Drawings showing the normal position of the ovipositor and how it is bent under the abdomen during oviposition. A secretion from the accessory glands determines the structure of the egg pod. That of the desert locust is simple (a); it has no proper wall. That of the Moroccan locust (b) has a thick outer wall and a lid (c).

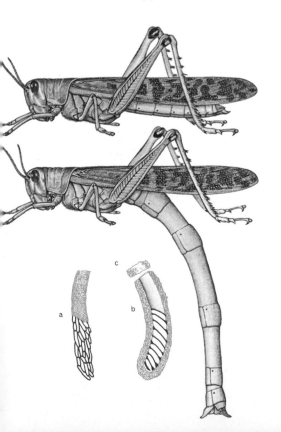

is added. On the third day the larvae are filtered out and divided. About 1000 are put into each bowl, which contains a half-and-half mixture of water and the feeding mixture. Each day the water is changed and the strength of the mixture increased. On the sixth day the larvae, which have by now nearly all pupated, are living in a 100 per cent solution of the feeding mixture only. On the seventh day the mosquitoes begin to emerge and the bowls are placed in cages so that the adults can fly up and settle at the top. When they have all emerged, the bowls are removed. Mosquitoes that are not needed at once for various tests can be kept alive for some time by feeding them on sugar, raisins, and water. They are not given a meal of blood unless needed for breeding.

Quite apart from breeding insects for study and test purposes, many people nowadays are interested in making photographic records, both in color and in black-and-white, of all the stages in the life history of insects. Such photographs, especially when taken at a high magnification and while the insects are alive, can be extremely valuable. They show details that are not visible to the unaided eye and stages in processes that are normally difficult to observe. Preserved specimens of insects always deteriorate in some way or another over the years, but a good photograph can be kept as fresh as on the day it was taken. It is often a much better and clearer aid to teaching than is a preserved specimen, which may have lost its color and can give little impression of what the insect looked like while it was alive. Films showing insects in action are most valuable for behavior studies. Slow-motion films have revealed many interesting things about the movements of insects that had formerly been almost impossible to observe. The

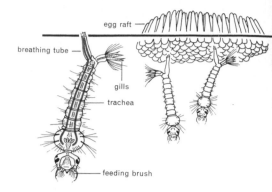

Above: A drawing of a floating egg raft of an anopheles mosquito. About 300 spindle-shaped eggs form this raft. Young larvae hatch into the water. Mature larvae swim freely and come to the surface of the water to breathe through their respiratory siphons.

Below left: Diagram of the anopheles pupa. It swims by flicking its abdomen; it breathes air through the breathing trumpet above the thorax. Certain structures of the adult mosquito, such as the compound eyes, wings, and mouthparts, show through the pupal skin. The photographs below, from left to right, show part of a film sequence of the emergence of an adult. The pupal case splits above the head and thorax. The mosquito pushes its way out head first. The broken case floats like a raft on the surface of the water; the adult rests on this raft while its wings enlarge and harden; then it flies away.

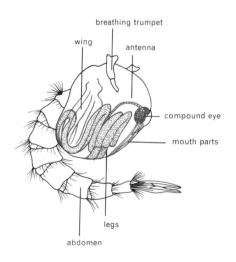

dances of bees, for example, could not really be interpreted properly until they had been filmed in this way.

Many moths and butterflies are also bred for the purpose of producing display specimens of certain varieties that differ from the normal in their coloring or wing patterns. Some insects are naturally very variable, and many different forms occur in the wild. The garden tiger moth and the lime hawk moth are two common moths that show this kind of natural variation. If they are bred in captivity and the parents of each generation are carefully selected, it is possible to establish strains that show a remarkable development of certain characteristics. The lime hawk, for instance, normally has two irregular dark green marks on the forewing. By selective breeding it is possible to make these two spots fuse into a single thick band. The proportion of brown and cream in the markings of the garden tiger varies very much, and after some generations of intensive breeding in captivity it is possible to produce individuals with forewings that lack most of the cream pattern and are almost entirely brown. By selective breeding the magpie moth can be made to produce adults that differ so much in appearance that it is difficult to believe they are the same species. Some may be almost entirely black while others are deep orange-yellow or milky-white, with varying numbers of dark spots or streaks.

Some entomologists are particularly interested in obtaining hybrids—that is, the offspring of two different species of insects. This can be done only when two species are closely related, and even so the resulting hybrids are nearly always incapable of having offspring of their own. In some cases these hybrids are very difficult to raise, but others show what is known as

Above: Testing insecticides on mosquitoes at the Ross Institute of Tropical Hygiene in London. The experimenter uses an aspirator to transfer mosquitoes from a cage to glass containers. These are fitted over jars filled with insecticides and left overnight. Next day, the percentage of dead mosquitoes is measured against the type of insecticide used.

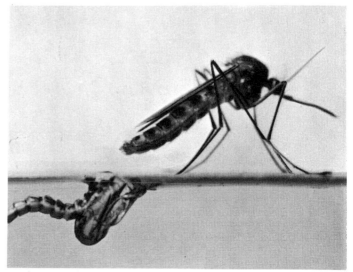

"hybrid vigor" and are exceptionally strong and healthy. Many of the silk moths can be hybridized, and so can some of the swallowtail butterflies. The European and the British race of swallowtail, which are two subspecies of the same insect and very similar in appearance, will hybridize and produce fertile offspring. However, a mating between the British species and an American "black" swallowtail produces a sterile hybrid that differs in appearance from both parents, although it is superficially more like the American insect. It is sometimes possible to obtain a pairing between the eyed hawk moth and the poplar hawk moth, which do not even belong to the same genus. But the eggs will hatch only if the female parent is an eyed hawk, and the larvae are always difficult to raise. The resulting moth resembles the poplar hawk, but unlike it the hybrid has a small "eye" on the hindwing.

Butterflies are often released in an attempt to establish new colonies, to re-establish them in places from which they have disappeared, or simply to strengthen local colonies that already exist. For these purposes the butterflies are reared in captivity, out of reach of all their natural enemies. When they are released, they are usually adults. Large numbers of wild insects are not needed to start a breeding program like this. Usually a few females, if taken at the right time and properly managed, will lay enough eggs to raise a very large number of larvae. In nature the wastage of eggs is very high, and few of them ever get as far as pupating. But with all the precautions and protections of breeding in captivity, losses are often slight. From half a dozen females, enough butterflies can be reared to increase a local insect population tremendously in a short space of time. It is in this way

Above: A Dutch large copper butterfly being released from its breeding cage at a nature reserve in England. The cages are built in the nature reserve: butterflies then stay in this habitat when released. Below: By crossbreeding the poplar hawk moth (left) with the eyed hawk moth (right), the hybrid species (center) results. It resembles the poplar hawk in coloring but has a diffused "eye" on the hindwing.

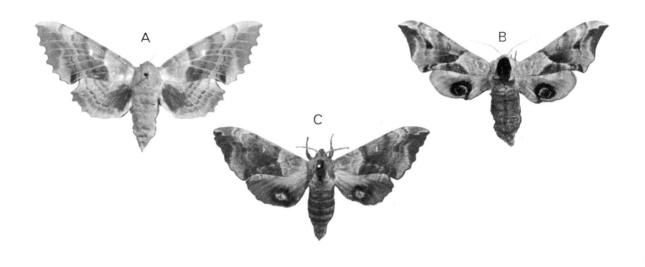

that the stock of swallowtails and the Dutch large copper butterfly is kept up at Wicken Fen nature reserve in Cambridgeshire in England. This is also the way that many keen amateurs are able to release common butterflies each year to beautify their gardens.

Far more difficult is the establishment of new colonies or the re-establishment of colonies when a butterfly has disappeared. The black-veined white butterfly vanished from England early in this century. It was last seen in the county of Kent. All attempts to bring it back there, by releasing adults or by planting out nests of young larvae, have failed. Attempts to establish the Camberwell beauty butterfly in England have also met with no success. However, there have been success stories. The Dutch large copper has been introduced in eastern England and several colonies of marsh fritillaries have been started in suitable localities of Britain.

Insect breeding is carried on not only by professionals but also by amateurs all over the world. It can be a most interesting and absorbing hobby, and many valuable discoveries have been made through breeding experiments. Only in this way can the heredity of insects be studied and a great many other problems investigated under controlled conditions. In many countries big insect breeding houses are now being set up in connection with research stations, and new breeding techniques are constantly being tried out. By making full use of many modern inventions, insect breeders are finding ways of making their work easier. A real interest and a continuing enthusiasm for the work is perhaps the most important factor of all.

Above: A photograph illustrating methods of testing the effects on Drosophila flies of insecticidal residues taken from various crops. The residue is mixed with raspberry pulp in petri dishes; insects are placed on the mixture and left to feed. Later they are transferred to containers. Then (below) the number that die within 24 hours are counted. Such mortality indicates how toxic the various residues are.

Insects in a Changing World

ONLY a few generations ago most people thought of insects as little more than an unavoidable nuisance. The few people who collected and studied them were regarded as harmless eccentrics. Today the situation is vastly different. Throughout the world much time, effort, and money is willingly spent on the study of various problems: insect anatomy and physiology, the comparison of different species, the investigation of the habits of insects in nature and in the laboratory, the influence of climate and weather on their abundance and distribution, and the far-reaching problems of insect control. We are becoming more and more aware of the tremendously important part that insects play in the world of nature and in our own lives. As a result we want to learn as much as we can about them.

Yet the interdependence of living things—from the lowest form of microscopic life through plants and the animal kingdom to man—is a vast and complex subject. The more we know of it the more we realize how much remains to be discovered. In attempting to control one species of plant or animal that we do understand, it is all too easy to disturb the whole balance of nature, of which our understanding is only partial and imperfect. During man's rise from primitive hunting and foraging to his present stage of civilization, he has learned to control and utilize many of the forces of nature. But his struggle against insect enemies, despite some successes, has been full of setbacks, defeats, and blunders. The old warning, "Know your enemy," has too often been ignored. In economic entomology, the urgency of the situation has often called for immediate and desperate measures against pests and disease carriers. The nonselective use of poison sprays has sometimes had unfortunate results on birds, animals, and even humans. Rachel Carson, in her book *Silent Spring,* made an eloquent plea for more care and forethought in the

Above: The male (top) and female of screwworm flies and a pupa. The female lays her eggs, about 250 at a time, on cut or wounded livestock. Hatching larvae eat the undamaged flesh, often killing untreated animals. Grown larvae drop to the ground to pupate. The cycle from egg to adult fly is 21 days.

At the converted airstrip and buildings at Mission, Texas (below), radioactive cobalt-60 is used to make sexually sterile 75 million screwworm flies each week. The flies are reared at this unit, the center of the Southwest Screwworm Eradication Program.

Stages in rearing screwworms for sterilization at the Texas farm. Top: Piping a mixture of ground meat, beef blood, and water into vats containing screwworm larvae. Second: Placing an aluminum canister containing 18,000 pupae onto a hoist. This is transferred mechanically to a chamber where the insects will be sterilized by gamma rays from radioactive cobalt-60. Bottom: Loading planes with crates of sterile flies for release in infested areas.

handling and use of such poisonous sprays. Although they are now commonplace we still do not really understand what their long-term effects on humans may be.

Before planning drastic measures against one specific pest, modern entomologists now realize how important it is to make a thorough study not only of individual insects but also of the entire insect and animal population of a district. The old idea of trying to exterminate some particular harmful insect completely is now becoming rejected. Biological control aims instead at establishing a balance through the interaction of many forces. In this way no single insect species in a community will increase sufficiently to become a serious pest. However, a great proportion of the human race lives precariously on the borderline of famine. We cannot allow food wastage through insects to go unchecked, and insecticides are therefore still essential. For this reason a tremendous amount of research must go on to find substances that are effective against specific insects but not dangerous to plant and animal life.

There are obvious practical difficulties in observing the behavior of insects in their natural surroundings over a period of time. These difficulties have long made the study of their habits and distribution a major problem. Scientific discoveries are now leading to new methods. With the help of radioactive substances and Geiger counters, entomologists can now trace the movements of insects far more efficiently than they could a few years ago. Mosquitoes raised in water containing radioactive phosphorus remain radioactive for thirteen days. By treating them in this way entomologists have been able to find and follow them when they are released and discover how far and where they normally fly. Radioactive cobalt has also been used for sterilizing male insects before releasing them over an area where a campaign is being carried out against a particular species. This means that a great many of the females will lay only infertile eggs. Where this method has been used along with insecticides, results have been very encouraging. This modern technique has been used against melon flies on the Pacific island of Rota. It has also been used in a concentrated effort to wipe out the cattle pest known in the United States as screwworm.

The modern practical entomologist can no longer rely on only his specialized knowledge of insects. So many new methods are now being used for insect control that chemists, electrical engineers, and physicists must be called in to assist. For example, in recent years there has been a great increase in the use of aerosols and various electrically controlled vaporizing smoke generators for dealing with insects in greenhouses and other buildings. These devices raise technical problems that

Above: An Insect-O-Cutor installed in a bakery. It consists of a metal framework and an electrically charged grid. Very little electricity is required. Contact or near-contact with the grid kills insects immediately. To attract night-flying insects, the device is fitted with "black light" fluorescent tubes emitting short-wave light. To attract day-flying insects, the grid is strategically placed in situations of light, heat, or smell that attract insect pests. A drawback of this device is that it kills all insects indiscriminately.

the entomologist may not be equipped to deal with. Again, the veterinary entomologist may have to call on practical engineers to construct special apparatus for spraying sheep and cattle. Indeed, the whole question of how best to apply insecticides—both in a confined space and over large areas—is one that calls for research not only by entomologists but also by chemists, physicists, and economists. Here the problem is not merely to find the most effective method. It should also be an economical one, because pest control programs must not become so expensive that they are hardly worthwhile to the grower or breeder.

The many drawbacks of poison sprays have encouraged a great deal of research on other methods of killing undesirable insects—among them the use of electricity. Wood-boring insects are already being killed by the use of microwaves. Both in Europe and America a special electrical installation is being employed to deal with flying insects. This is an electrified grid that attracts insects by means of a so-called black-light short-wave lure and then electrocutes them as soon as they touch the wires. It has proved highly effective at many food factories and also near sewage works. It can be kept running night and day at a very low cost, and can cause no harm to any creature that does not actually come into contact with the screen. It is certain that as research goes on many more anti-insect devices of this kind will appear. A great deal more work will be done on the use of ultrasonic sound waves for insect control.

In today's world rapidly increasing human populations are making ever increasing demands on food producers. Entomologists and technicians are thus giving more and more attention to the problem of grain storage. One of the latest ideas in this field is an inflatable warehouse made of pest-proof nylon fabric. After the container is filled with air, grain is pumped into it from the top; once filled, it is deflated. It then collapses over the grain and is sealed. What little oxygen remains inside with the grain is soon used up and from then on no insects can live in the grain. The first experiments with these new granaries are just beginning in India. If they prove successful, the storage of grain and vegetables in tropical countries will be completely revolutionized and a major victory will have been won over insects without the use of poisons.

It is little more than half a century since the first international entomological congress was held in Brussels. In that comparatively short span of years, the exchange of knowledge and co-operation between entomologists in different countries has increased enormously. Economic entomology has developed from a somewhat neglected offshoot of pure science into a

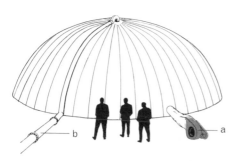

Above: Inside a huge inflatable nylon warehouse used for storing grain. It is 66 feet in diameter, 22 feet high, and can hold 500 tons of wheat. The grain is blown through a pneumatic conveyor (the pipeline shown below) and falls vertically from the top center of the dome. When full, the warehouse is collapsed and is then airtight, so that trapped insects soon die from lack of oxygen. Scientists believe such warehouses may be the solution to the problem of huge losses caused by insect pests when grain is stored in the tropics.

subject whose importance is recognized throughout the world. It is no surprise that a science that has developed at such speed has run into difficulties from time to time and made its share of mistakes. What is surprising is that it has achieved so many resounding successes. During fifty years entomologists around the world have scored great triumphs over insect-borne diseases and lessened the damage of economic pests. Through research entomologists have thrown new light on age-old mysteries of the natural world.

Some of the most outstanding of these successes have been made possible only by international co-operation. The encouraging results of international locust control and the world-wide campaign against malaria have shown how rapidly progress can be made when entomologists of many lands pool their knowledge and resources. Co-operation means not only teamwork among entomologists of all lands but teamwork among entomologists of all kinds. In the control of insect pests, for instance, basic research in the laboratory and practical measures in the field are of equal importance. Detailed knowledge is not a weapon in itself, but without it practical efforts are wasted. It is in teamwork among field workers, laboratory workers, and the scientists engaged in basic research that the future of entomology lies.

Short Classification of Insects

Insects belong to the Phylum ARTHROPODA, which contain animals with the body divided into segments and with an external skeleton that can be shed periodically so that the animal can grow. The following table gives the principal orders of the class HEXOPODA. They have the body divided into three main parts: head, thorax, and abdomen. The thorax has three pairs of legs and usually one or two pairs of wings. The abdomen has no legs. Typical specimens of each of the principal orders are illustrated. The first sentence of each classification gives those details which can most easily be identified with no more than a hand lens. Details in subsequent sentences are more difficult to observe and require experience; they are included for the benefit of the serious student. The number below each order shows the number of known species, but many more are discovered each year.

SUBCLASS	**APTERYGOTA**	
Wingless insects.	Metamorphosis slight or absent. Adult with one or more pairs of vestigial abdominal appendages located ahead of the external reproductive organs.	
PROTURA 70	Minute, up to 2mm; head markedly tapered; abdomen long with no long appendages at end; fore-legs not used for walking but held like antennae; no eyes or antennae. Piercing mouthparts, withdrawn into head; abdomen with three appendages. The attitude of the forelegs indicates how the antennae may have been derived; the abdominal appendages (a) are the relics of past limbs.	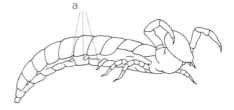
THYSANURA Bristletails Silverfish Firebrats 400	Small to medium size, elongate; often covered with scales; long appendages at end of abdomen; long antennae. Biting mouthparts; eyes present or absent. Live concealed in soil or rotting wood, dense vegetation, or the nests of ants and termites. The most primitive order of insects; unique in becoming sexually mature before fully grown; may alternately moult and mate through 50 instars. Lepisma lives in buildings and destroys starchy goods.	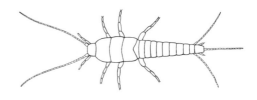
COLLEMBOLA Springtails 1500	Minute, up to 5mm, of variable shape; usually hairy; a forked jumping organ at end of abdomen. Biting, concealed mouthparts; no eyes. Very abundant, up to 250 million springtails in one acre of English meadow; lives in soil, dense vegetation, nests of termites and ants, and on the surface of water; one species lives on the surface of the sea and is submerged at high tide.	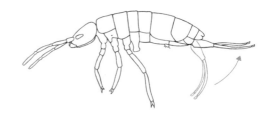

SUBCLASS   PTERYGOTA

Insects usually with wings. Adults usually without pregenital abdominal appendages. Two groups: 1. Hemimetabola, rarely with a pupal stage; wing buds visible externally in young stages; young stages look like adults. 2. Holometabola, metamorphosis with larva, pupa and adult, which all have different structures. Wings develop externally.

PLECOPTERA

Stone flies

1500

Moderate to fairly large size; wings folded back flat over abdomen, hind pair usually largest; flattened, broad, square head; front segment of thorax (a) large and mobile; long antennae; usually with long appendages (b) at end of abdomen.

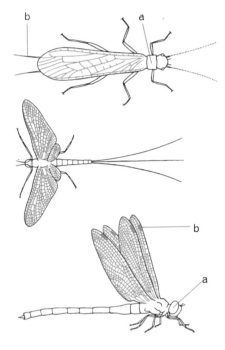

EPHEMEROPTERA

Mayflies

1500

Medium size; wings held vertically when at rest; front wings triangular, hind ones reduced or absent; three long appendages at end of abdomen; short antennae. Reduced mouthparts. After a larval life span of up to three years the adult life span lasts only a few hours. Unique in producing a winged "subimago" which then moults into the true adult.

ODONATA

Dragonflies
Damselflies

5000

Fairly large to large; legs placed well forward and the wings backward on the thorax; long abdomen; antennae short; prominent eyes (a); wings usually with stigma (b). Biting mouthparts; often found near water; catch insects on the wing. Two suborders: Zygoptera, wings of similar size, held vertically over abdomen; eyes project laterally. Anisoptera, wings of different size, held horizontally; eyes close together.

ORTHOPTERA

Grasshoppers
Locusts
Crickets

10,000

Medium to large size; front part of thorax large (a); hind-legs swollen; wings present or absent, fore-wings hard. Biting mouthparts; eyes usually large; sound-producing organs. Two suborders: Acridiids (Short-horned Grasshoppers and Locusts), with short antennae. Tettigoniids (Long-horned Grasshoppers and Crickets), with long antennae.

Stick and
Leaf Insects

2000

Medium to large size; front segment of thorax short, rear segments long (a); legs similar to each other. With or without wings; biting mouthparts. Sit on twigs (Stick insects) or leaves (Leaf insects) which they strongly resemble.

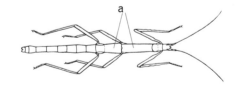

Cockroaches
and Mantids

5800

Fairly large to large; antennae long; wings held flat over abdomen; hind-wings pleated like a fan under fore-wings, sometimes reduced. Biting mouthparts. Two groups: Cockroaches, with a shield-like extension of the thorax nearly covering the head and fore-legs unmodified. Mantids, predators, head not covered, and fore-legs raised in a prayer-like attitude. They do not usually fly. No sound-producing organs.

ISOPTERA	Medium size, of variable shape; skin thin and flexible; front segment of thorax very distinct (a); appendages at end of abdomen short. Fore-wings similar to hind, held horizontally over abdomen, but are soon shed; biting mouthparts; antennae fairly long; intricate social life. Large numbers of different castes in one society.

Termites or "White Ants"

1900

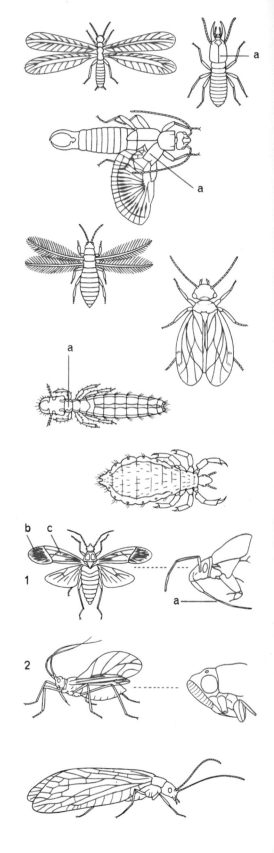

DERMAPTERA	Medium size, elongate; fore-wings hard and short (a); hind-wings semicircular when extended; may be wingless; long antennae; forceps at end of abdomen; broad, horizontal head. Biting mouthparts; unusual in brooding over eggs and caring for the young.

Earwigs

1000

THYSANOPTERA	Small to minute; wings, if present, very narrow, with long hairs at edge; head square. Piercing mouthparts; antennae fairly long; no abdominal appendages. On hot days they swarm in large numbers.

Thrips

3100

PSOCOPTERA	Small or minute; wings, if present, very narrow, with long hairs at edge; head square. Piercing mouthparts; antennae fairly long; no abdominal appendages. On hot days they swarm in large numbers.

Booklice

1100

MALLOPHAGA	Small (0.5-6.0mm); body and head flattened horizontally; front segment of thorax distinct (a); no wings. Biting mouthparts; reduced eyes; short antennae; parasites in feathers of birds and on a few mammals.

Biting lice or Bird lice

2800

ANOPLURA	Small, flattened horizontally; conical, pointed head; no wings; thoracic segments fused. Sucking, piercing mouthparts; eyes reduced or absent; feed on the blood of mammals; antennae fairly short. The human louse transmits typhus.

Sucking lice

300

HEMIPTERA	Small to large, very variable in shape; mouthparts for piercing and sucking, usually plant juices, and lie in a clearly visible snout. Two pairs of wings usually present, front pair hardest; no appendages at end of abdomen; antennae fairly long. Two suborders: Heteroptera (Shield bugs, Bed bugs, Assassin bugs, Squash bugs (1), Water-boatmen), tip of fore-wings membranous (b), basal part hard (c); snout (a) not lying between base of legs; Homoptera (Cicadas, leaf-hoppers, Aphids (2), Scale insects), front wings uniformly hardened, or membranous; snout lies between base of fore-legs.

Bugs

55,000

NEUROPTERA	Small to fairly large, of variable shape; soft bodied; fore-wings similar to hind, held roof-like over abdomen; long antennae. No appendages at end of abdomen; well-developed biting or sucking mouthparts; predators, often found on vegetation at the side of streams; the ant lions dig pits into which unwary insects fall.

Alder Flies
Lacewings
Ant Lions

5000

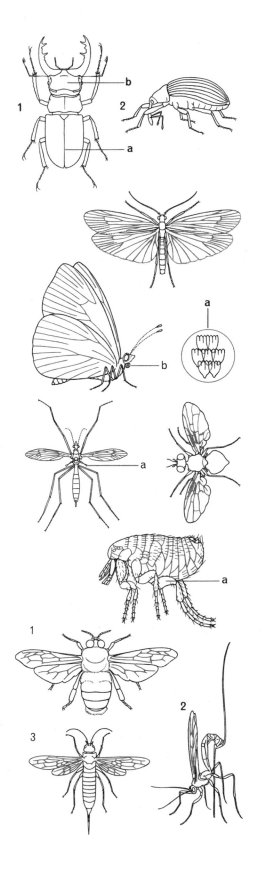

COLEOPTERA

Beetles

275,000

Minute to large, (0.5-155mm); heavily armoured insects; fore-wings hard, usually cover the abdomen, and meet in midline to form a straight line (a); front part of thorax large (b). Biting mouthparts; hind-wings folded under fore-wings, often reduced. Concealed under stones, in the earth, under bark, etc.; the largest order of all animals. Divided into two main sub-orders: Adephaga (Carabids (1), Water beetles); Polyphaga (Weevils (2)), include many extremely destructive types.

TRICHOPTERA

Caddis flies

4500

Small to moderate size; moth-like in appearance; wings usually densely matted with hairs, held roof-like over abdomen, the fore-wings narrower than the hind; legs long and slender. Mouthparts reduced, for licking; long antennae; live near water.

LEPIDOPTERA

Butterflies
and Moths

200,000

Medium to large size; wings with few veins and covered with microscopic scales (a); proboscis (b) usually coiled like a spring under head; long antennae; large eyes. Two suborders: Homoneura, veins of fore- and hind-wings identical and no coiled proboscis; Heteroneura, veins not identical in fore- and hind-wings and coiled proboscis; sub-divided into Butterflies, usually with clubbed antennae, and Moths, usually with pointed antennae.

DIPTERA

True flies

85,000

Minute to fairly large; one pair of visible wings, the hind-wings reduced to small club-like organs (a). Mouthparts for piercing or sucking; large head and eyes. Divided into three suborders: Nematocera, Crane-flies, Mosquitoes, Midges; Brachycera, Horse flies, etc.; Cyclorrhapha, House flies, etc. Includes many disease carriers.

SIPHONAPTERA

Fleas

1100

Small, flattened from side to side; no wings; thoracic segments not fused; base of legs very swollen (a). No eyes; mouthparts for piercing and sucking; short antennae; parasites in fur and feathers, mainly on mammals, feeding on blood. Carries the plague from rats to man.

HYMENOPTERA

Ants, Bees
Ichneumon flies
Wasps, etc.

107,000

Size ranges from microscopic to fairly large; hind-wings smaller than fore-wings and articulated to fore-wings; abdomen usually constricted at base to form a "waist." Mouthparts for biting, sucking or lapping; head large and mobile, with large eyes. A very specialized order: some bees and wasps and all ants live a complex social life; many can reproduce without a male and the group shows many examples of parasitism. Divided into two suborders: Symphyta (Sawflies (3), Wood wasps), with "no waist" to abdomen; Apocrita, abdomen usually with a visible "waist"; subdivided into the Aculeata (bees (1), ants and wasps) which sting, and the Parasitica (Ichneumon flies (2), Gall wasps and Chalcids) which are parasitic.

Index

Numbers in *italics* refer to illustrations and captions to illustrations.

Credits

LHN denotes that these photographs were supplied or taken by L. Hugh Newman

Key to illustration position
(T) top (C) centre
(B) bottom (L) left
(R) right etc.

6 LHN/Photo Stephen Dalton
10 LHN/Photo Laurence Perkins
11 (L) LHN/Photo Stephen Dalton
   (R) LHN/Photo Shephen Dalton
13 (T) FAO Photograph
14 (T) British Museum
15 LHN/Photo Stephen Dalton
17 British Museum
18 F. M. Hull, *Robber Flies of the World*, Smithsonian Institution, 1962
19 (T) Photo LHN
20 Courtesy of London Entomological Society
21 Photos Frank W. Lane
22 A Shell photo
23 Shell photos
24-5 LHN/Photos Stephen Dalton
26 (T) Taken from A. D. Imms, *General Textbook of Entomology*, Methuen & Co. Ltd., London, 1957
   (CL) Aldus archives
   (CR) LHN/Photo Stephen Dalton
27 (T) LHN/Stephen Dalton
   (B) Taken from A. D. Imms, *General Textbook of Entomology*, Methuen & Co. Ltd., London, 1957
28 (T) LHN/Photo Stephen Dalton
   (B) Frank W. Lane/Photo Lynwood Chace
29 (T) LHN/Photo Stephen Dalton
30 (T) John Curtis, *British Entomology*, 1832
   (B) LHN/Photo Stephen Dalton
31 LHN/Photo Andrew E. Carr
32 British Museum
33 (T) Borradaile et al, *Envertebrata*
   (B) From A. D. Imms, *Outline of Entomology*, Methuen & Co. Ltd., London, 1961
34 (T) LHN/Photo Stephen Dalton
   (B) Photo LHN
35 (T) Frank W. Lane/Photo H. Lou Gibson
   (B) LHN/Photo Stephen Dalton
36 (T) LHN/Stephen Dalton
   (B) Photo J. Carayon
37 Photo Alexander B. Klots
38 Photo from *Vie et Moeurs des Papillons*, Horizons de France, Paris
39 (T) LHN/Photo M. W. F. Tweedie
   (B) LHN/Photo Stephen Dalton
40 LHN/Photo Stephen Dalton
42 LHN/Photo M. W. F. Tweedie
43 LHN/Photo Stephen Dalton
44 (T) LHN/Photo Ray Palmer
   (B) LHN/Photo Stephen Dalton
45 LHN/Photo Stephen Dalton
46 A. E. Shipley, *Zoology of the Invertebrata*, 1893
47 (TL) LHN/Photo Ray Palmer
   (BL) From V. B. Wigglesworth, *Principles of Insect Physiology*, Methuen & Co. Ltd., London, 1953
   (TR) LHN/Photo Gavin Grant
48 LHN/Photo Laurence Perkins
49 LHN/Photo Stephen Dalton
50 LHN/Photo Stephen Dalton
51 A. E. Shipley, *Zoology of the Invertebrata*, 1893
52 LHN/Photo Andrew E. Carr
52-3 After G. P. Baerends
53 LHN/Photo Stephen Dalton
54 (B) Aldus archives
55 (T) LHN/Photo Stephen Dalton
   (B) LHN/Photo D. Ashwell
56 (T) Photo Uni-Dia-Verlag
   (B) LHN/Photo L. F. Linssen
56-7 LHN/Photo Stephen Dalton
57 (B) LHN/Photo A. E. Carr
58 LHN/Photo Stephen Dalton
59 LHN/Photo Stephen Dalton
60 Frank W. Lane/Photos Georg Schützenhofer
61 *Die Forst-Insecten*, Ratzeburg, 1839
62-3 LHN/Photos Stephen Dalton
64 (T) LHN/Photo Stephen Dalton
   (B) Taken from A. D. Imms,

General Textbook of Entomology, Methuen & Co. Ltd., London, 1957
65 Frank W. Lane /Photo Lynwood Chace
66 (B) Paul Popper Ltd.
67 Reproduced by permission of Dr. N. E. Hickin, Rentokil Laboratories Limited
68 Taken from F. M. Hull, *Robber Flies of the World*, Smithsonian Institution, 1962
69 Frank W. Lane
70 (T) From Pierce, *U.S. Nat. Museum Bulletin 66*, 1909
   (B) From Grandi, *Bull. Lab. Zoo., portici 14*, 1920
71 (L) Science Museum, London/ Photo Lucien Bull, 1907
   (B) Taken from A. D. Imms, *Insect Natural History*, Wm. Collins & Sons Ltd., London, 1947
72 (T) Taken from A. D. Imms, *Insect Natural History*, Wm. Collins & Sons Ltd., London, 1947
   (B) Taken from J. W. S. Pringle, *Insect Flight*, Cambridge University Press, London, 1957
73 (T) Rothamsted Experimental Station/Photo V. Stansfield
   (B) Photo LHN
74 (B) Rothamsted Experimental Station/Photo V. Stansfield
75 (L) Photo Paul Popper Ltd.
   (R) Photo C. B. Williams
76 (T) Taken from C. B. Williams *Insect Migration*, Wm. Collins & Sons Ltd., London, 1958
   (C) A Shell photo
   (B) British Museum
77 Taken from C. B. Williams, *Insect Migration*, Wm. Collins & Sons Ltd., London, 1958
78 From Ento. Rundschan, 49(7), 1927
79 (T) Taken from C. B. Williams, *Insect Migration*, Wm. Collins, & Sons Ltd., London, 1958
   (B) LHN/Photo Stephen Dalton
80-1 Dragonfly: British Museum (Natural History)
   Chicken: Aldus archives
81 (T) From C. B. Williams, *Insect Migration*, Wm. Collins & Sons Ltd., London, 1958
82 From John Smart, *Insects of Medical Importance*, British Museum, 1956
83 LHN/Photos Stephen Dalton
86 LHN/Photos Stephen Dalton
87 LHN/Photos Stephen Dalton
88 National Audubon Society/ Photo Hugh M. Halliday
89 (T) Photo George E. Hyde
   (B) Swains (Photographers) Ltd., Norwich
90 Anti-Locust Research Centre/ Photos C. Ashall
91 (T) Imperial War Museum, London
   (B) LHN/Photo Stephen Dalton
92 From Paul Pesson, *The World of Insects*, George G. Harrap & Company Limited, London, and Horizons de France, Paris/Photo Pesson
93 LHN/Photo G. F. Woods
94 LHN/Photo Stephen Dalton
   (B) Mansell Collection; From Ferris, *Monograph on Sucking Lice*, Stanford University Press, Stanford
95 (T) Taken from H. G. Andrewartha & L. C. Birch, *Distribution and Abundance of Animals*, University of Chicago Press, Chicago, 1954
   (B) Sir Aldo Castellani & A. J. Chalmers, *Manual of Tropical Medicine*, Cassell & Co. Ltd., London
96 Aldus archives
97 Taken from H. G. Andrewartha & L. C. Birch, *Distribution and Abundance of Animals*, University of Chicago Press, Chicago, 1954
98 LHN/Photo M. W. F. Tweedie
99 LHN/Photo Stephen Dalton
100 (T) LHN/Photo H. Bastin
   (B) A Shell photo
101 (T) Taken from E. B. Ford,

Butterflies, Wm. Collins & Sons Ltd., London, 1945
   (B) Aerofilms & Aero Pictorial Ltd.
103 (T) From Sir Aldo Castellani & A. J. Chalmers, *Manual of Tropical Medicine*, Bailliere, Tindall & Cox Ltd., London, 4th edition, 1933
104 From Farmer's Bulletin No. 2151, U.S. Department of Agriculture
105 (T) From Farmer's Bulletin No. 2151, U.S. Department of Agriculture
   (B) Photo U.S. Department of Agriculture
106 (T) *Le Journal Illustré*, 1874
   (B) Photo Hubert Coulon
107 Taken from Elton, *The Ecology of Invasion*, Methuen & Co. Ltd., London, and Trouvelot, *Ann. Epiphyt. N.S.I.* 1936, and European and Mediterranean Plant Protection Organisation
108 Photo National Film Board of Canada
109 Photo Keystone
110 (T) Rentokil Laboratories Ltd.
   (B) Taken from A. D. Imms, *General Textbook of Entomology*, Methuen & Co. Ltd., London, 1957
111 John Curtis, *Farm Insects*, 1860
114 Photo Almasy
115 (T) A Shell photo
   (B) A Shell photo
116 (T) WHO/Photo Almasy
   (B) FAO photo
117 (T) A Shell photo
   (B) USDA photo
118-9 (T) Duhamel du Monceau and Tillet, *Histoire d'un Insecte equi dévore les grains de l'Angoumois*, 1762
   (B) British Museum (Natural History)
120 (T) Ciba Pictorial Archives, Basle
   (B) Institut Pasteur, Paris
121 (T) British Museum/Photo Michael Holford
   (B) The Wellcome Historical Medical Museum and Library
123 (T) N. V. Nederlandsche Combinatie voor Chemische Industrie, Amsterdam
   (B) WHO Photo
124 (T) Radio Times Hulton Picture Library
   (B) London News and Feature Services
125 A Shell photo
126 (T) Redrawn from World Health Magazine, Feb. 1964
   (B) A Shell photo
127 (T) The Wellcome Historical Medical Museum and Library
   (B) WHO Photo
128 (T) A Shell photo
   (B) L. Dudley Stamp, *The Geography of Life and Death*, Fontana Library, 1964
129 (T) Lino Pelligrini
   (B) Paul Popper Ltd.
130 (T) Wellcome Historical Medical Museum and Library
   (B) Photo Almasy
131 (T) Rentokil Laboratories Ltd.
   (B) WHO Photo
132 *Annales de Service des Antiquites de l'Egypte*, Vol. 33, 1933, Egyptian Museum, Cairo
133 Uni-Dia-Verlag
134-5 (B) A Shell photo
136-7 (T) Anti-Locust Research Centre
   (B) A Shell photo
138 A Shell photo
139 (T) Anti-Locust Research Centre
   (B) A Shell photo
140 Anti-Locust Research Centre, Reprint 77 from British Agricultural Bulletin, 1953, Vol. 6, No. 26, *International War on Locusts*, by Uvarov
141 Anti-Locust Research Centre
142 (T) Paul Popper, Ltd.
   (B) A Shell photo
143 Shell photos
144 British Museum/Photo Michael Holford
145 (T) *Le Journal Illustré*, 1878 British Museum
   (B) *Les Insectes de la Vigne*,

146 1890, British Museum
(T) Supplied by the Pyrethrum Bureau
(B) Science Service
147 (T) Department of Biological Control., University of California, Riverside
(B) Courtesy of Gunther and Jeppson, *Modern Insecticides in World Food Production,* Chapman & Hall Ltd., London, 1960, and the American Chemical Society. Reprinted from the *Journal of Agricultural and Food Chemistry,* Vol. 2, No. 1, page 13, January 6, 1954, © 1954 by the American Chemical Society and reprinted by permission of the copyright owner, and the author, C. P. Clausen.
148 USDA photos
149 (T) From Trouvelet, 1931, *Entomophagus Insects,* by C. P. Clausen, McGraw Hill Book Company, New York, 1940
(B) USDA photos
150 (T&B) USDA photos
151 USDA photos
152-4 USDA photos
155 (TL&TR) USDA photos
(c) Herbert Bayer, *World Geographic Atlas,* Container Corporation of America, 1953
(B) Auburn University, Auburn, Alabama
156 (T) Institut de Recherches du Togo
(B) USDA photo
157 (T) Paul Popper Ltd.
(B) USDA Photo
158 By permission of Her Britannic Majesty's Stationery Office. British Crown Copyright
159 USDA photos
160 (L) Supplied by the Pyrethrum Bureau
(c&R) USDA photos
161 (T) From Ministry of Agriculture, Fisheries and Food, *Insect Pests in Food Stores,* AL 483. By permission of the Controller of Her Britannic Majesty's Stationery Office
(B) USDA photo
162 From Forestry Commission Leaflet, No. 32. By permission of the Controller of Her Britannic Majesty's Stationery Office
164 Photo Arthur W. Ghent
165 (T) Central Office of Information
166 (T) From Forest Products Research Laboratory Leaflet No. 3. By permission of the Controller of Her Britannic Majesty's Stationery Office
(c) British Museum (Natural History)
(B) A Shell photo
167 (T) Rentokil Laboratories Limited
(B) From Forest Products Research Laboratory Leaflet No. 4. Revised April 1963. By permission of the Controller of Her Britannic Majesty's Stationery Office
168-9 British Museum (Natural History)
170 (T) USDA photo
(B) From F. C. Bawden, *Plant Viruses and Virus Diseases,* 3rd ed. The Ronald Press Company, New York, 1951, and from G. G. Samuel, *Annals of Applied Biology*
171 (T) M. Pseudosolain. From Kenneth Smith, *Textbook of Plant Virus Diseases,* J. & A. Churchill Ltd., London, 1937
172 (TL&CB) Courtesy of the Virus Laboratory, University of Berkeley, California
(TR) Agricultural Research Council, Virus Research Unit, Cambridge
(B) Photo Richard Fowler, Vista Productions, Inc., San Francisco
173 (T) From Kenneth Smith, *Textbook of Plant Virus Disease,* J. & A. Churchill Ltd., London, 1937 (After Fukushi)
(B) Agricultural Research Council, Cambridge
(L) From Kenneth Smith, *Textbook*

of Plant Virus Diseases. J. & A. Churchill Ltd., London, 1937
174 (T) USDA photo
(B) Commonwealth Institute of Entomology. Distribution Map of Myzus Persicae, Series A. No. 45
175 USDA photo
176 (T) Radio Times Hulton Picture Library
(B) Commonwealth Scientific and Industrial Research Organisation (formerly C.S.I.R.) Bulletin No. 34, Melbourne, 1927
177 Biological Section, Queensland Department of Lands
178-9 Biological Section, Queensland Department of Lands
180 (L) USDA photo
(R) By permission of Division of Entomology, C.S.I.R.O., Australia
181 Photo from J. R. Williams (1951). The control of the Black Sage in Mauritius by Schematiza cordiae Barb. (Col., Gaterucidae). *Bull. Ent. Res. 42:* pp. 455-463. Reproduced by permission of the Commonwealth Institute of Entomology
183 (B) Photo Treat Davidson/ Frank W. Lane Agency
184-5 Photos Coleman & Hayward Agency
186 (T) Harald Doering/Frank W. Lane Agency
187 (L) Harald Doering/Frank W. Lane Agency
(R) LHN/Photo Stephen Dalton
188 (T) Photo Coleman & Hayward Agency
(B) K. von Frisch, *The Dancing Bees,* Methuen & Co. Ltd., London, 1954
189 (T) Photo Treat Davidson/ Frank W. Lane Agency
(B) Photo Coleman & Hayward Agency
190 (T) Redrawn with permission. © 1962 by Scientific American, Inc., all rights reserved
192-3 (c) Photo Treat Davidson/ Frank W. Lane Agency
193 (R) K. von Frisch, *The Dancing Bees,* Methuen & Co. Ltd., London, 1954
194 (L) From C. R. Ribbands, *The Behaviour and Social Life of Honeybees,* Bee Research Association, 1953. (After Lindauer 1951)
(R) Photo Coleman & Hayward Agency
195 Photos Coleman & Hayward Agency
197 Photo L. Hugh Newman
198 USDA photo
199 Photo L. Hugh Newman
200 (L) British Museum
200-1 (c) Photo Stephen Dalton
202 Mansell Collection
203 (T) The Linnean Society of London
(B) British Museum
204 (T) Photo Conzett & Huber, Zurich
(B) Photo/Dr. M. S. Mani, Zoological Survey of India
205 Photo Nicholas Guppy
206 (T) Bates, *The Naturalist on the River Amazon,* 1863
(BL) Photo L. Hugh Newman
(BR) Photo M. W. F. Tweedie/ Photo Researchers
207 (T&B) From Major B. W. G. Hingston, *A Naturalist in the Guiana Forest,* Edward Arnold (Publishers) Ltd., London, 1932
(c) LHN/Photo Stephen Dalton
208 (T) Photo Alexander B. Klots, City University of New York
209 (T) Photo L. Hugh Newman
210 (T) From C. V. A. Adams, *Nature is My Hobby,* A. Wheaton & Co. Ltd., 1959
211 (T&BL) Photos L. Hugh Newman
212 (B) From Ratzeburg *Die Forst-Insecten*
213 Photo Alexander B. Klots, City University of New York
214 (T) Photo L. Hugh Newman
(BL) Photo Bayard, Paris
215 (T) Photo BPS
(B) From Natural History Magazine
216 (T) Photo L. Hugh Newman
217 (BL) Photo S. Beaufoy

(BR) From F. W. Frohawk, *Complete Book of British Butterflies,* Ward Lock & Co. Limited, London, 1934
218 Photos George M. Bradt/ Frank W. Lane Agency
219 (L) Photo S. Beaufoy
(R) Photo L. Hugh Newman
220 Photo L. Hugh Newman
221 (R) Photo L. Hugh Newman
222 (T & B) Photos L. Hugh Newman
223 (T) Photo L. Hugh Newman
224 Photo Stephen Dalton
226 Photos Chris Ridley. Courtesy W. A. L. David and B. O. C. Gardiner, A.R.C., Unit of Insect Physiology
227 Photos Chris Ridley. Courtesy W. A. L. David and B. O. C. Gardiner, A.R.C., Unit of Insect Physiology
228 (T & B) Shell photo
229 From G. Stehr, *The Canadian Entomologist,* 86 (A). The Runge Press Limited, Ottawa, 1954
230 (T) A Shell photo
(B) Anti-Locust Research Centre
231 Anti-Locust Research Centre
232 (L) A Shell photo
(R) Anti-Locust Research Centre
233 (T) Photo Stephen Dalton
234 (BL) From D. G. Mackean, *Introduction to Biology,* John Murray (Publishers) Ltd., London, 1962
(BR) Photo A. Bayard, Paris
235 (T) Photo Chris Ridley. Courtesy The Ross Institute of Tropical Hygiene
(B) Photo A. Bayard, Paris
236 (T) Photo L. Hugh Newman
(B) Photo Eric Duffey
237 (T & B) Shell photo
238 (T & B) USDA photos
239 USDA photo
240 Photo Henry Simon Limited
241 Manufactured by The Gourock Ropework Company Ltd.

ARTISTS' CREDITS
David Cox: 208, 211, 214, 215(B), 223, 226, 234
Gordon Cramp: 27(BR), 41, 95(T)
Ian Kestle: 66(T)
Brian Lee: 209, 241
Shirley Parfitt: 188(B), 190, 191, 193(BR), 194(L)
Edward Poulton: 29, 64, 68, 71, 72, 76, 77, 84-5, 97, 107
Victor Shreeve: 33(T), 52-3, 54(T), 67(T), 101, 102, 105(T)
Graham Wall: 122, 126, 128(B), 134(LCR), 140, 149(T), 152(B), 155(c), 157(T), 174(B), 176(B)
Sidney Woods: 210, 212, 215(c), 221, 225, 229, 230, 232, 233, 242, 243, 244, 245

All pictures credited to the British Museum, British Museum (Natural History), Imperial War Museum and Science Museum, London, are reproduced by courtesy of their Trustees.

Art assistants working on this book have included Edward Poulton, David Parry, John Dobson and Jill Mackley. Glossary text written by Keith Reid.